Mushrooms

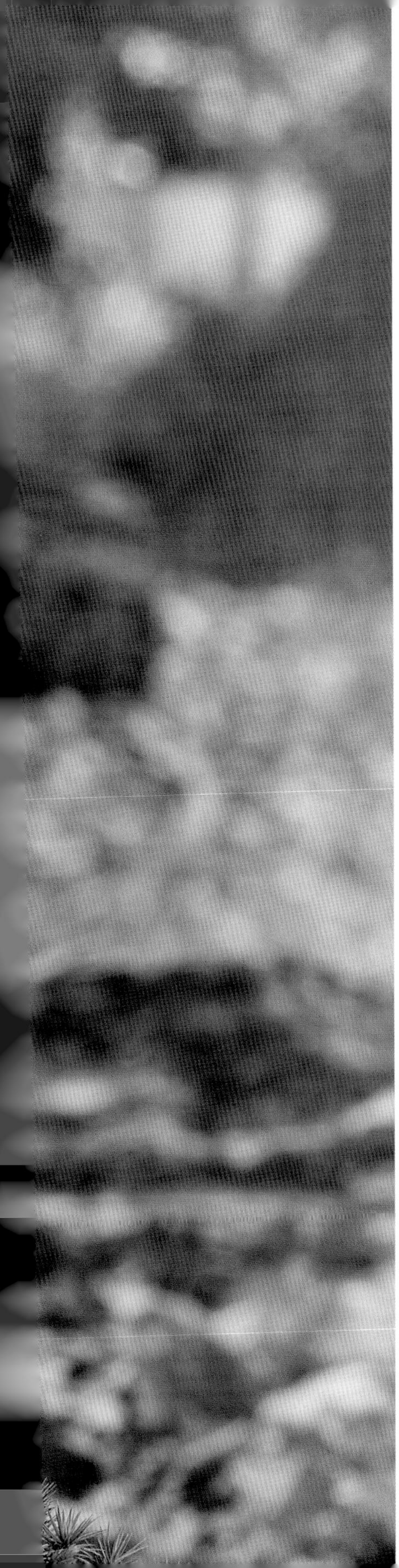

British Wildlife Collection 1

Mushrooms

The natural and human world of British fungi

Peter Marren

British Wildlife Publishing

The British Wildlife Collection

For almost a quarter of a century, *British Wildlife* has published in-depth articles on all aspects of our natural history and its conservation. Many of these have become classic sources of information. As an natural extension of this legacy, we have commissioned this series of beautifully presented books, written by some of Britain's finest writers and leading experts, whom we feel have something important and innovative to say about their chosen field. We are delighted that Peter Marren, one of our most eloquent and accessible natural history writers, has provided the first book in the series on a subject for which he has had a life-long passion.
Andrew and Anne Branson, British Wildlife Publishing, 2012

Dedication

To my mentors in field mycology:
Roy Watling, Malcolm Storey and Ted Green.
Peter Marren

Design: James Hughes

Jacket artwork: Carry Akroyd

Previous spread: Honey Fungus in the New Forest *Bob Gibbons*

First published 2012 by
British Wildlife Publishing Ltd
The Old Dairy
Milton on Stour
Gillingham
Dorset, SP8 5PX

ISBN 978-0-9564902-3-0

Printed by Gorenjski Tisk, Slovenia

Contents

	Foreword	6
1	A fungal autobiography	8
2	Meet the mushrooms	20
3	What's in a name?	44
4	Mushrooms on parade	64
5	What mushroom is that?	82
6	Natural habitats	100
7	In our midst: our fungal neighbours	120
8	Earthtongues, waxcaps and hedgehogs: what fungi tell us about the natural environment	140
9	Scarcity and plenty: why some mushrooms are common and others are rare	160
10	Forays amongst the funguses	182
11	The good, the bad and the crazy	196
12	Picking for the pot	220
13	Saving mushrooms	234
	References and further reading	264
	Photographic credits	266
	Index	267

Foreword

Mushrooms have never been more popular than they are today. Fungus forays are firmly on the autumn agenda – not just for specialists but for anyone with the slightest interest in mushrooms. Mine attract people of all ages, from wide-eyed young children to their parents and grandparents. Conservation organisations now talk about their plans and research programmes for fungi, while restaurateurs routinely serve 'wild mushrooms' which, at least in some cases, are genuinely wild and not cultivated. We have also become much more conscious of the dark world of fungi, even if we notice them only for a few weeks in the autumn when they push their bald heads through the lawn, or sprout in tiers and fans from wood piles and logs. There is, in my experience at least, an eager audience for tales of mushroom magic, whether factual or fable, whether impersonally biological or concerned mainly with the kitchen. There are, indeed, two ways of looking at fungi. One is through scientific inquiry, aimed at establishing the truth about how they grow and reproduce, the habitats they exploit and the means by which they compete for resources. The other is concerned with what might be called their cultural value, from the different perspectives of the gardener, the walker, the cook, the land manager, in fact, anyone with a view.

In this book, I have tried to combine both the cultural and scientific approaches in a narrative that takes us from what fungi are, and what they do, to the ways in which we use or take delight in them. This is not a field guide. There are several excellent guides to identification in print and it is not my intention to add to them. Nor is it a textbook on the science of mycology. I have aimed instead at writing a personal account of the wonderful world of fungi in which I have been sometimes a bystander, sometimes a participant, since my boyhood half a century ago. Hence, I begin unconventionally with my own fungal autobiography. From there, the narrative introduces the fungi in all their glorious diversity, the often unexpected ways in which they survive in a deeply competitive world, and the pleasure they give to so many of us. There is no glossary. I have avoided technical terms except where they are absolutely necessary, and in such instances have explained them on the spot. Nor are there any keys, graphs or tables of data. I have used

English names and scientific names together. And, above all, I have done my best to make use of my own resources and experience as a natural-history writer. I hope this book will be a pleasure to browse through and read, and that it may even make you smile from time to time.

It is a pleasure to thank the many friends and colleagues who have helped me with this book. The following have found intriguing items in the press or have donated ideas and images: Jill Butler, Bryan Edwards, Sandy Coppins, Sue Everett, Liz Holden, Ted Green, Bruce Ing, Geoffrey Kibby, David Mitchel, George Peterken, Dave Shorten, Brian Spooner, Fred Stevens, Malcolm Storey, Des Thompson, John Wright, Mark Wright and the image libraries of Plantlife and the Royal Botanic Gardens, Kew. I thank the contributors to Wikimedia Commons for their selfless policy of allowing their images to be used free of charge. Scottish Natural Heritage generously allowed us to make use of the excellent images taken by David Genney. Similarly, my old friend Bob Gibbons came to our aid with his own marvellous images, many of them taken on our field trips together. The publisher would also like to thank Paul Sterry and Barry Hughes of Nature Photographers Ltd for allowing access to their wide ranging collection of excellent images.

I am very grateful to Peter Roberts for reading and commenting on the entire text, and to Martyn Ainsworth for his perspective on two of the chapters. And I must express my warm appreciation of the contribution of Victoria Chester and Plantlife International, a body that helped to establish fungi in the conservation agenda, not least by bringing all the main players together in a forum.

For this book I had the advantage of working with publishers who are also old friends. Thank you, Andrew and Anne Branson for producing a beautiful book.

The responsibility for any mistakes is, of course, solely my own.

Peter Marren
Ramsbury, 2012

chapter one

A fungal autobiography

For as long as I can remember, fungi, especially mushrooms and toadstools, have been part of the landscape of my life. They were rarely centre-stage, and the passion has taken different forms over the years. To begin with, it was just a wide-eyed fascination for the strange growths with smudgy gills that appeared towards the end of the school holidays, along with the rain and the fallen leaves. I liked the way they seemed to come from nowhere, as though they were not so much living things as upheavals of the earth. I tried to identify them with my *Observer's Book of Common Fungi*, and later (and with more success) with the first Collins field guide, universally known as Lange & Hora. My passion for fungi has never been particularly academic. Rather, I love them for their own sake, intellectually engaging in their difficulty, of course, but also delighting in their myriad colours, shapes and scents. They brighten up the autumn in every sense, just when the natural world seems to be going to sleep.

◄ Dreaming of Fly Agarics.

My first awareness that there were such things as fungi probably took place in the kitchen. My father enjoyed field mushrooms for breakfast – not the soppy little supermarket buttons but flat, black-gilled wild 'mushies' picked from the airfield, with their scents of ink, earth and decay. I remember the fleshy discs sizzling in the pan, and thought to my six-year-old self that they were a funny thing to want to eat. Even odder was my father's queer taste for baker's yeast (another fungus, although very unlike a mushroom), which he kept in a paper packet and swallowed by the spoonful after a brush with nephritis. He never ate any other kind, although my mother vaguely remembered blewits, or 'blue-tails' as she knew them, sold at the market in Leicestershire when she was a girl.

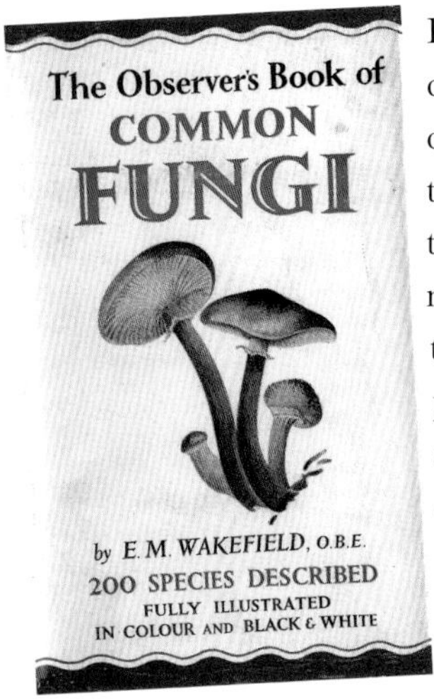

▲ ***The Observer's Book of Common Fungi***, the beginner's mushroom book for the generation born in the 1950s and 1960s.

Dad's breakfast aside, my grand inaugural meeting with wild fungi came when we lived in the Peak District at a bleak and terrible place called Harpur Hill. We inhabited an RAF married quarter near the top of the hill, where the bitter wind flapped the washing lines and the trees grew straggly and partly horizontal. Beyond the stone wall that marked the end of the bit of hillside which we called a garden lay a further rise to a rocky hilltop. We called it Barker's Hill. It was a wonderful place to roam, high above the village with views over quarries, crags and vales. In September, the sheep-cropped grass suddenly sprouted colourful mushrooms the consistency of candle wax, red, yellow and orange, some shaped like umbrellas, others like little yellow rockets. They were waxcaps, not that I knew it at the time. But I thought them pretty cool, with their strange waxen skins, like fungal sweets.

My Observer's Book, by Elsie Wakefield (a real auntie name), failed on the waxcaps, but it did unfold a wonderful parade of puffballs, stinkhorns and all sorts of other mushies, some 'edible and good', others 'not edible' or even downright 'poisonous'. There was one of those right at the beginning of the book, clearly a top fungus, called the Death Cap. If you ate it you died in horrible agony over several days, and *there was no known cure*. Wow! I longed to find a Death Cap, and even more so its red, spotty neighbour, the Fly Agaric (it became a family joke, this name, which my father insisted was pronounced *argh-grick*). At the age of six you have had little experience of life outside the home, and no ability to contextualise knowledge. What you do have in spades is curiosity and its helpmate, imagination. What naturalists have in common, I think, is the eagerness, or stubbornness, to hang on to these precious things in later life. We retain a child's eye for wonder, we bug-hunters and bird-spotters. One day, I told the hidden companion inside my little head, I would find a stately troop of phantasmagoric Fly Agarics in some magic woodland dell, perhaps with toads squatting on top, and would feel like a conjurer.

My relationship with fungi did not develop much further until my early teens. My family lived peripatetically, usually based somewhere near an airfield, and moving on every two years or so with each RAF posting. Although most of our homes were more comfortable than the wretched Harpur Hill, none of them were as productive for fungi. Eventually, like most RAF officers' boys of the day, I was sent to boarding school. Cut off from nature for most of the time, I could only daydream about it. There was school biology, of course, but, apart from a few trips to ponds and streams, it was of the indoor kind. And there was no mycology at all. 'I can tell you the names of about 500 species of fungi,' I boasted to the biology teacher. I don't think he asked me to prove it.

▲ **John Webster**, first of my mentors, Professor of Biological Sciences at Exeter University from 1969 to 1990, and author and illustrator of *Introduction to Fungi*.

Then, as a fresher at Exeter University in the autumn of 1969, I suddenly found myself in a mycological environment. That first weekend, the department had organised a fungus foray. By happy chance, the new Professor of Biological Sciences was that rare and now practically extinct being, an academic mycologist. John Webster (always Professor Webster then) was a plain-speaking Yorkshireman, an upright man who all too clearly disapproved of all the long hair and late 1960s licentiousness around him. To add to his frustrations, only three of our year's intake of scruffy student biologists opted for the botany course, which included mycology. I was one of them. I had gone to Exeter to read zoology and geology, but Webster's course on fungi turned my head. It was a ray of light in a course that seemed to have been hijacked by maths freaks and biochemistry nutters. Webster was different. He was interested in living things and the way they worked. He studied the way fungi projected their spores into the air, lassoed tiny worms for dinner, and ate their way through plant tissue and heartwood. Admittedly, he seemed to be more interested in mildews and moulds than proper fungi with caps, gills and pores, but he possessed a genuine artistic talent and drew his tiny subjects with great technical skill, using a mapping pen on white artists' paper. His book, *Introduction to Fungi*, is crammed with them. Webster was the man for me. Besides, I had grown tired of doing unkind things to frogs.

Professor Webster's abiding passion was for certain microscopic mildews that live in streams, known as aquatic hyphomycetes. They had been discovered 30 years earlier by his friend and academic hero, C Terence Ingold. He fished for them in the foam left behind by bubbling brooks, and under the microscope the fungi would reveal their amazing spores, shaped like bananas, anchors, sputniks or crescent moons. A few, notably the ones named *Ingoldia* in honour of Webster's mentor (and trust him to bag the best one), even looked like little animals. Webster wanted to know how and why these fungi produced such odd-looking spores. In my final year he offered me a research project, working alongside a PhD student, which meant, in effect, acting as his lab assistant. The work was fiddly and, to be honest, not a lot of fun, consisting mainly of isolating and measuring spores – an authentic

▲ **Friends of fungi**: Roy Watling, *mycologiste extraordinaire*, and Jane Smart, then chair of the Fungus Conservation Forum.

glimpse into the tedium of academic research. My proudest moment came when the Prof, eying my latest batch of measurements, pencilled the single word 'significant'. I think they suggested to him that the faster the current, the longer were the anchor-lines of the spores. They suggested to me that I should stick to stuff I found on forays.

In 1977, I joined the Nature Conservancy Council in Scotland as their man in Aberdeen. One of the perks of the job was an annual, all-expenses-paid trip to Kindrogan Field Centre, in Perthshire, to study a subject of one's own choosing. I naturally chose fungi, and there I met Roy Watling. Like John Webster, Roy is a Yorkshire polymath. But his main interest lies in the larger fungi, and above all agarics and boletes, in other words, the sort of things you find on forays. Roy is a great forayer. He has followed the fungal trail from the arctic to the tropics, and closer to home has explored the fungi of the Scottish mountains and glens, and many of the islands too, including the Hebrides, Orkney and Shetland. He identifies poisonous fungi for the medical profession, including the one that nearly killed the author of *The Horse Whisperer*. He has written lots of books. He has championed the fungal art of Beatrix Potter. And he has run a famous field course at Kindrogan since the 1960s. Quite rightly, there are fungi named in his honour, such as *Conocybe watlingii*, a fungus collected 'on discarded household material mixed with pony dung'. Roy was the first person I had ever met who could put a name to pretty well any fungus one found, peering at it with intense interest, and tending to address it, rather than you, and loudly, too. Unlike Webster, who says 'fung-i', Watling says 'funge-aye'.

I attended one course at Kindrogan where Roy put on a double act with the photographer, Heather Angel. While Roy told us what the fungi were, and all about them, and, as I say, loudly, Heather showed us how to take their picture. We learned how to hold a muslin sheet over the mushroom to soften the harsh sunlight and create a warm, soap-ad glow around it. We used Kit Kat wrappers as mirrors to illuminate the parts where the sun rarely shone. *Don't* use flash, implored Heather, be imaginative, use natural light, and always carry a good tripod. Hers was a cast-iron Benbo weighing as much as a set of golf clubs, but that week at least, there was always someone willing to carry it for her. In some ways, mushrooms are ideal subjects for photography. Unlike animals, they do not run away, and unlike plants they do not sway in the wind. But, given their awkward shape, it is hard to pack all the diagnostic features into a single snap. A proper mycologist will therefore show several specimens, laid out at different angles. Admittedly, that ruins any attempt at naturalness, which is perhaps why mycologists rarely win photo competitions.

We saw some wonderful fungi that week, including one or two that Roy said might be new to Scotland. There was, for instance, *Lactarius repraesentaneus*, a big, shaggy, yellow milkcap that bleeds violet juice, *Cortinarius violaceus*, deep purple and scaly, like an exotic lizard, and *Russula illota*, a fawn-coloured brittlecap with curiously dotted gills and a strong whiff of Cherry Laurel. There is a good case for placing scrubby Highland glens near the top of the list of the best places for fungi. Roy addressed each specimen gravely, through hooded eyes. It is good to witness a great naturalist at work, in his element.

Back home in Aberdeen, I helped to organise fungus forays for the parent-teacher association, for local schools and for natural history outings. One quickly learnt that this kind of popular foraying is a very different thing from those organised by the British Mycological Society. The smiling parents and their scampering children know nothing about fungi (why should they?). They are looking forward to nothing more than a nice walk with a purpose, in other words, to some wildlife entertainment. They do not expect you to bombard them with Latin names, nor do they care about the subtle distinctions between various little brown jobs which are obviously all the same. But they appreciate amusing tales from the backwoods, are interested in the fungi you can eat and concerned to avoid those which are thrillingly deadly. Hence, our gatherings tended to end up not in the herbarium but on the plate. For a few years I did a double act with Neil Bayfield, a Morris-dancing ecologist. I would put on a slide show while Neil, being the better cook, conjured up a medley of wild fungi, served in a sauce on fingers of

▼ **A tooth fungus**, probably a species of *Phellodon*, top-shaped, with spines in place of gills, taken by the author under the supervision of Heather Angel.

▼ **Ted Green** displaying the war-zones of fungi inside a slice of timber.

toast. I like to think we were ambassadors for the fungal tribe, planting little sparks of interest and affection among those whose lives had been blighted by golf, gardening and television.

One soon discovers that children are the real stars on these 'people's forays'. For a start, they are better at finding things, maybe because they are closer to the ground. They are also more willing to experiment with fungal smells and flavours than their stolid, head-shaking parents. When you see their eager little faces fill with wonder or amusement, you feel, just for a moment, that a teacher's life might not be entirely, irredeemably awful. But then some cheeky lad, urged on by his mates, dumps a slimy, rotting bolete in your lap, and you come back to your senses.

Better field guides and colour printing meant that, by the 1980s and 1990s, you stood a much better chance of naming your mushroom than before. Until then, if you wanted to get on in the fungal world, one was reduced to collecting off-print keys, or Roy's price-shattering fungus flora, or, if the passion took you that far, spending hard-earned money on expensive foreign tomes. It helped that, by then, the hitherto fluid taxonomy of larger fungi was settling down. Today, practically every group of larger fungi has an expert among the fraternity of field mycologists. My own reluctance to use a microscope prevents me, alas, from ever becoming one of them. When something starts turning into hard work and ceases to be fun, I find you might as well do something else.

There have, indeed, been long periods in my life when I hardly looked at a fungus. Such was the mid-1980s, after I had moved from my lovely pristine Scotland to the polluted hell of Peterborough, with its dead-end streets and boring toadstools. I began to recover after meeting another grand mycological personality, Ted Green. Ted was then a ranger of some kind at Windsor Great Park, with one foot in the Crown Estate and the other in the Nature Conservancy Council. Like Roy, Ted has a tendency to pronounce, loudly and with absolute conviction, on every fungal topic under the sun. He is a man of certainties, without in-built doubt or the nervous qualifying of a lesser naturalist. He is a man of a different sort, a visionary, an autodidact tub-thumper, a kind of mycological preacher. He knows his fungi, of course – it was Ted who supplied Roger Phillips with many of the specimens for his groundbreaking book. But he is equally immersed in the role of fungi in woodland, how they assist trees to feed and grow, and recycle waste into soil. One of Ted's great ideas is that fungi go on 'helping' trees in old age by reducing their weight and vulnerability to wind and drought. He has helped to turn such once wacky notions into mainstream orthodoxy by sheer persistence. And so, after an entertaining, thought-provoking, and slightly exhausting day out with Ted at Windsor, and another in the New Forest with him and the late Derek Reid of Kew, fungi entered my life again. Indeed, inspired by Ted's gastronomic adventures, I started a new and secret little hobby, sampling as many edible (or at least non-poisonous) kinds as I could, cooking them in various unimaginative ways.

After a wandering youth and a maturity spent in the north, south and middle of Britain, I have washed up in the Kennet valley of Wiltshire. I continue to lead forays, when asked to, in the local woods, downs and heaths, with occasional long-distance excursions into Berkshire, Dorset and the New Forest. For a while I was a member of the Cotswold Fungus Group, ably led by Dave Shorten (another keen mycological gastrophile). But mostly I foray with a few friends, or with a local group such as the Wiltshire Botany Group, which I take to the woods once a year with a real expert, Malcolm Storey (he does most of the names, I do the stories). Among our regular beats are Savernake Forest, much of which is dull but with little nodes of diversity inside, like nuts in a choc-bar, certain churchyards noted for coral fungi and waxcaps, and the woods around Greenham Common which, being full of damp hollows and corners, tend to produce something of note even on a dry day. In recent years the uncertain weather has been a problem. September, formerly the second-best month (and in Scotland, it was *early* September), is now often barren (although not in 2010, when it was the *best* month). In some seasons we have to wait until November, when low light hinders visibility.

In the 1990s, my mycological life took a new direction. As I will explore in a later chapter, the idea of conserving fungi is new, and mycologists are not very good at it. Conservation bodies would probably ignore fungi, even now, were it not for pressure from European bodies. The 'Earth Summit' at Rio, in 1992, came to the rescue of mushrooms and toadstools by obliging governments to do something. Specifically, it set us on the course of conserving declining species and habitats through 'action plans'. The British Mycological Society, with a bit of prompting, provided a short list of fungi. As a fairly experienced and now freelance conservationist who had dabbled in mycology, I was in a position to contribute. Through the charity Plantlife (which includes fungi in its remit as 'honorary' plants), I was commissioned to find out as much as I could about an exotic mushroom called the Devil's Bolete *Boletus satanas*, which was being considered for protection. Boletes are among my favourite fungi. I love their stumpy, homely shapes and rich colours, and they don't come any more colourful than the Devil's Bolete which is red, white, orange and yellow, and turns pale blue when cut (it feels intriguingly heavy, too, when weighed in the hand). Fortunately, that year, 1997, was a good one for Devil's Boletes, which is to say, it turned up in a few places in numbers greater than double figures. After due investigation, I felt I had enough evidence to suggest that the bolete was not rare at all, nor necessarily declining, but just badly recorded. I felt rather smug, I admit, at being able to recommend no particular 'action' at all. But pride goes before a fall, and soon afterwards I was caught with my pants down. The Post Office asked me, as the notional expert on Devil's Boletes, to endorse a picture of the bolete for use in a presentation pack of a set of stamps on endangered species. It was a poor photograph, and I said I wasn't sure, but that was as good as a thumbs-up so far as the Post Office was concerned. It turned out to be the wrong bolete. The only thing to do on these occasions is to keep your head down and pretend ignorance.

► **The Devil's Bolete** *Boletus satanas*, in its habitat of Beech woodland on chalk or limestone, often among snaggling roots.

On the heels of *Boletus satanas* I was involved in another project on another bolete, this time an actual protected species, Royal Bolete *B. regius*. The problem here was different, in that many of the records for this stately crimson and yellow mushroom were doubtful. Nearly all the preserved material turned out to belong to a recently discovered look-alike, *B. pseudoregius*, which I christened The Pretender. The latter, too, is quite rare, but not rare enough to warrant any special conservation action, even if we had a better idea of its requirements. I will return to this interesting case towards the end of this book in the chapter on conservation.

My third and last project of this kind was largely a desk job. This was a survey of the status of the 'stipitate hydnoids', or hedgehog fungi. There was special interest in these curious fungi, which have spines instead of gills, and they had been added to the Biodiversity Action Plan *in toto*, largely on evidence from the Continent, where they are

declining. I was able, mainly through the contributions of others, and especially Gordon Dickson, the British authority on the group, to suggest that they too were vastly under-recorded, but that there was good evidence that they were confined mainly to old woodland on undisturbed soil. After that, I moved on to other things. The coming man in conservation was Martyn Ainsworth, who worked on a variety of projects for English Nature before becoming our first full-time conservation mycologist in 2010.

Conservation depends on adequate data about distribution, habitats and threats. Without it, the planners, who tend not to be mycologists, and sometimes not even naturalists, are building castles in the air. I cannot pretend that I added much original research in my three reports. We know as much as we do because there are experts out there beavering away, collecting records, sorting out the entangled taxonomy, and investigating promising habitats. For boletes, the top man is Alan Hills, a one-man industry, who maintains meticulous records, pays proper respect to microscopic work, and keeps in touch with experts on the Continent. He has been rewarded by the discovery of several new species in Britain. For hedgehog fungi, it is Gordon Dickson, who I met for the first time on that distant day on Roy's course at Kindrogan. For *Inocybe*, it is Alan Outen, for *Mycena*, Ernest Emmet, for cup fungi, Brian Spooner. All-rounders such as Geoffrey Kibby, Alick Henrici and Malcolm Storey seem to know everything. There are many more. These are the quiet men who make it possible for conservation to be a practical reality, and, on behalf of the conservation industry, I pay them tribute.

My last big mushroom job with Plantlife was 'Important Fungus Areas': a review of the best sites for fungi in Britain. This was my idea, based partly on Plantlife's ongoing work to identify the best areas for plants in Britain and Europe, and partly on the old Nature Conservation Review of 1977, which identified the best examples of natural habitats in Britain. Of course, one could not attempt anything remotely comparable for fungi because the data simply was not there, but I thought it would be a good idea to see just how far we could go using the existing information. The result was inevitably patchy. With the help of Shelley Evans from the British Mycological Society and Martin Harper at Plantlife, we came up with some basic criteria for top sites (500+ species, 5+ scheduled species, or simply the best example of its kind in the area). We depended heavily on work by the local fungus groups, augmented by BMS forays and data from habitat surveys of dunes, grasslands and churchyards. In the end (the exercise took quite a long time), we were able to list about 500 sites that met our criteria, and we had a shot at grading their relative importance. It was a start, but it still tends to advertise the places that are forayed most regularly and so have built up long lists of species (on the other hand, there must be some link between objectively the best sites and the most often visited ones). Like the provisional Red List, it provides something to build on. Or, as my colleagues expressed it in their best official language, it can 'support, inform and underpin existing protected area mechanisms designed to conserve biodiversity in the UK'.

Perhaps my best-known contribution to field mycology are my articles on British fungi and regular news column in *British Wildlife*, which went on for 18 years, with between two and four contributions per year. It began as a one-off piece about bracket fungi in 1991, inspired in part by my wanderings with Ted. Andrew Branson, *British Wildlife*'s founder and editor, liked it and asked for more. So, over the years I added a series of mini-monographs about boletes, Amanitas, gasteromycetes, hedgehog fungi, *Agaricus* mushrooms, waxcaps and other topics, usually with the assistance of a real expert (my role was more that of a jobbing journalist). I had no illusions that I was necessarily the best man for the job, but, try as I might, I could not persuade anyone else to take it on. It was regarded, I believe, as my patch (although Graham Mattock, James Merryweather, Ted Green and others did help out with pieces of their own from time to time). In 2008, a real mycologist, Peter Roberts, just retired from Kew, agreed to relieve me.

I also, for reasons lost in the mists of time, write answers to questions about fungi sent in by the readers of *BBC Wildlife*. They used to describe me as 'a mycologist', which I found embarrassing, especially when a reader pointed out that I was *not* a professional mycologist (in the sense of thinking and working on fungi and nothing but fungi). I agree. I am a naturalist, and by extension a natural-history writer. Nature is too full, too interesting, to spend one's days peering at only one small part of it. But, still, I'm fond of mushrooms, and have managed to learn something about them over half a century or so. I only hope I can communicate something of their charm and mystery, and the pleasure I find in them, in this book.

There, by way of introduction, are my credentials. There is one more excuse to make and I am done. I am an inveterate communicator. I lead forays for the same reason that I write stories and books (this is my 20th), because I like nothing more than finding out about things, giving them shape and then writing about them. This will be a conversational book, full of stories that interested me, and I hope will interest you. Until recently, books about fungi tended to be rather technical or dedicated narrowly to the process of identification. I doubt you could identify anything from this book. On the other hand, I hope that it will stimulate, refresh and even amuse anyone who finds fungi even faintly intriguing.

And that is enough about me. It is time to meet the mushrooms.

chapter two

Meet the mushrooms

Open any book about fungi and you will find yourself pitched straight into a strange world. We are used to plants that grow in an ordered way, with trunks and stems, branches and leaves, roots and flowers. But fungi do not segregate their various functions like that. Since they do not manufacture food by photosynthesis, like green plants, they do not need leaves or chlorophyll. Nor, since fungi simply absorb what they need through the walls of their tissues, do they have roots. They are, on the face of it at least, much more simple organisms. For much of their lives, fungi consist of no more than webs of matter we commonly know as 'mould'. When free of obstructions, they tend to grow outwards in a circular manner, as with mould in a Petri dish or a neglected jar of jam. It is only when it is about to fruit that the fungus takes on a more individual and recognisable form. At this point, it puts on a spurt of growth. The webs coalesce, swell and seem to solidify, finally morphing into shapes like balls, cups or trumpets, or even more fantastical forms. The most familiar fungi are, of course, the mushrooms, with their broad, gilled caps surmounted on a stalk (or, strictly speaking, since it isn't really a stalk, a 'stipe').

We associate mushrooms and other large fungi with damp and often shady places, but they all require light to stimulate the production of their fruit bodies. Many of them feed on rotting matter, which is most abundant in late summer and autumn as fallen leaves accumulate. The mushroom fruit bodies appear suddenly, and disappear just as quickly, within days, or in the case of smaller ones in just hours. Yet, we must remember, these fruit bodies are no more than apples on an invisible, underground 'tree'. Many fungi live in the soil all year round, and in some cases for many years. We think of them as seasonal because that is when we see their fruits, just as plants seem to be seasonal because we notice them by their flowers.

◀ **Red-belted Bracket**
Fomitopsis pinicola, a distinctive, tough, hoof-shaped bracket of conifers and, less often, broadleaves. Although widely distributed and common throughout the northern hemisphere, it is comparatively rare in Britain.

Mankind came to an understanding of fungi not from casual encounters in the field but from the instruments of science: from studies using microscopes, stains and experimental cultures. It was biochemistry that revealed their true nature, the discovery that fungi are made not from cellulose, like plants, but mainly from chitin, like insects. That did not, of course, mean that fungi are insects, or even animals (although it does probably mean that fungi and invertebrates shared a distant common ancestor). Nor are fungi lowly forms of vegetable matter, as 19th-century botanists had assumed. They are not plants at all. Formerly herded together with mosses, liverworts and algae as spore-forming plants, or 'cryptogams', they are now considered to be as distinct from plants as they are from animals. They form a 'third kingdom' of life, a completely different form of existence. Yet we still treat them as if they were a peculiar kind of plant. Fungi are studied on plant courses and popularly regarded as part of 'botany'. Mycologists are always complaining about this. There are, we point out, at least five species of fungus for every wild flower in Britain.

What is a fungus?

Under the microscope, the living web of a fungus appears as a dense mesh of hollow tubes known as hyphae. These are the building blocks of fungal life, just as cells are the basic units of animals and plants. Hyphae are less than a hundredth of a millimetre in diameter. When they coalesce they form a mass of 'threads' called a mycelium, which has the appearance of fine cotton wool. The advantage of this kind of construction is that it enables the fungus to absorb what it needs from its surroundings, whether that be rotten wood, damp earth, dung or a pot of jam, without any need for internal channels or organs. It also enables the fungus to grow indefinitely, or at least as far as the food source allows. They can grow fast, too. Some species can put on a spurt of 6mm an hour, well in excess of any plant. A popular fallacy has it that mushrooms pop up overnight. Hence, 'mushrooming' has become a byword for something that spreads with disconcerting rapidity. In fact, each mushroom has taken weeks to grow. The reason they seem to appear so suddenly is that in the final stage the little buttons simply swell, by absorbing air and moisture, taking just hours to reach their familiar mushroom shape. This is why mushrooms are 90% water, and why most of them need moist air and damp soil or wood.

Another fallacy is that mushrooms are short-lived. It is, of course, the fruit body that is soon eaten or rots away. The organism that produces them, the mycelium buried in the soil, is capable of living a long time. There are 'fairy rings' – the marks in the grass left by the growing fungus – that are scores of metres in diameter and must be hundreds of years old. A single genetic individual can produce dozens of mushroom fruit bodies. In North America, evidence from DNA samples suggests that the mycelium of certain woodland mushrooms can cover several acres and must be hundreds, possibly thousands, of years old. Almost certainly fungi are among the oldest living organisms on the planet.

Fungi are an ancient form of life. They have had plenty of time to evolve and diversify. Their diversity is greater than the mind can easily grasp. In Britain, where they have been studied as intensively as anywhere in the world, we have about 12,000 described species, of which about 3,000 are larger fungi (macromycetes), easily visible to the naked eye. The rest are micro-fungi, requiring a microscope for identification. But that is not the end of it. New species are being discovered all the time, and the true figure must be well in excess of 12,000 species. Within Britain alone, some 460 new species were discovered between 1980 and 1989. At least 37 new species to Britain were recorded in 2010 alone (Kibby 2011). Throughout the world, an average of 1,500 species new to science are discovered *every year.* There may be 1.5 million species of fungus on the planet, perhaps more, and certainly not much less. But less than a tenth of that number has been described scientifically. In other words, perhaps 90% of the world's fungi are still unknown.

Even when we leave aside the micro-fungi, in Britain we are left with around 2,500 species that you might reasonably expect to find in the field. Getting to know that many species is quite a challenge. Don't worry! Hardly anyone does. There are much more manageable ways of getting to grips with fungi in the field. You can, for example, break them down into groups of related species. We can recognise a bolete from its pores, a brittlegill from its colour and chalky texture, or a milkcap from the juice that drips from the gills or cap when broken. Even a beginner soon gets to know at least some of the common fungi in the field from their general appearance – the yellow, black-spored tufts of Sulphur-tuft, the stiff apricot trumpets of the Chanterelle, or the rude and smelly beacon of the Stinkhorn. You learn them as you go, bit by bit. There are perhaps 250 fungi that one can recognise instantly, and maybe the same number again that can be named with a little help from a field guide. Once you know the basics, this world, you might say, is your oyster mushroom.

How mushrooms live

Fungi are often characterised as life's 'third way', inhabitants of the dark Third Kingdom. How does this alternative way of life work out in practice? Speaking very broadly, there are two kinds of fungi: those that live and feed by themselves, and those that do so by means of partnerships with plants (a third kind, fungal parasites, could be regarded as a partnership that has swung decisively in the fungus's direction). We digest our food internally. Fungi do so externally. With the help of a battery of biochemicals they break it down, and then absorb it. This is an economical way of life. You could think of fungi as guts without a skin – tiny, hollow tubes penetrating through the soil, rotting wood or living tissue, soaking up the juices as they go.

Let's take a closer look at the ways fungi live, starting with those that manage to get by on their own, the ones that recycle the annual deluge of fallen leaves and decaying wood.

Recyclers and rotters

Fungi are agents of decay. Theirs is a rotten world of decomposing waste matter: leaf litter, dead wood, dead bodies, dung and organic debris in the soil. The reason why all this debris does not choke the planet in short order is that it is recycled by fungi (with bacteria adding their ten percent's worth). From big bracket fungi to invisible moulds, they thriftily break down the waste and release the nutrients it contains. The amount of fungal activity needed to do this makes you gasp. An average wood produces about five tonnes of debris per hectare per year. The fungi get through this mountain of raw cellulose by sheer numbers. Fungi make up about 10% of the weight of living matter (biomass) in a wood. They are the weightiest component of all, bar the

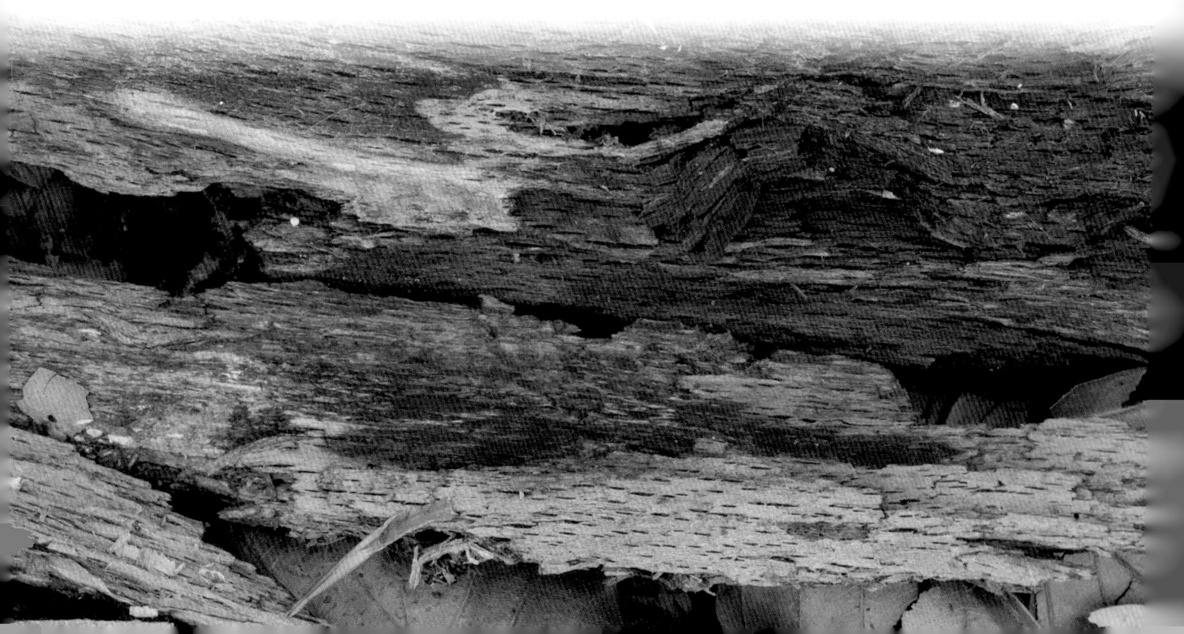

▼ **Wood stained green** by the Green Elf-cup fungus *Chlorociboria aeruginascens*.

◀ **Collared Parachute**
Marasmius rotula, a common rotter of dead twigs above or below ground.

▼ **A small army of Twig Parachutes**
Marasmiellus ramealis on old raspberry canes.

trees. You would require a convoy of dump trucks to remove the fungi of just a small copse. Yet all we see of them are their scattered fruit bodies in autumn.

Not that the lives of rotting fungi are all the same. Each wood has its quota of generalists and specialists. Many of the small brown mushrooms which you see poking their heads above the leaves have their mycelium in a damp layer close to the surface. Pick up a handful of leaves and you will often find they are stuck together with hyphae, and have bleached where the fungus has broken down the cell structure within. Among the commonest are species of *Collybia*, tough-shanked, tan-coloured mushrooms of the forest floor. An even larger number of species subsist on dead wood, from hard, dry, standing stumps to scraps of buried wood. Roughly a third of the larger fungi found in the forest subsist on wood. Managers who remove that component are subtracting a significant part of the wood's natural biodiversity – not only the fungi but all the myriad invertebrates and animals that depend on them.

Other fungi specialise in particular micro-habitats. Small species of *Marasmius* and *Micromphale* (both called 'parachutes') and, above all, *Mycena* ('bonnets' or 'fairy bells'), will sprout from individual leaves. Some are leaf-generalists, while others are restricted to a single species of plant, such as Beech or Common Reed. Our pair of British *Micromphale* species are Beech leaf-and-twig specialists. *Marasmius buxi* takes the risky course, in Britain at least, of growing only on the decaying leaves of Box, of which there is only a small supply, in the wild at least.

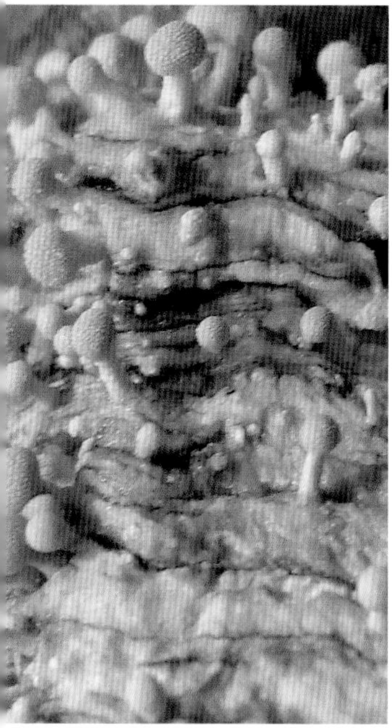

▲ **Ever wondered** what happens to discarded horns? Meet the Horn Stalkball *Onygena equina*.

Mycena belliae occurs on Reed stems and *M. pterigena* on Bracken fronds. *M. seynesii* occurs only on pine cones, as do all three species of *Strobilurus* and the Conifercone Cap *Baeospora myosura*. The little brown *Flammulaster carpophilus* is a beechmast specialist. The twiglet *Tubaria dispersa* subsists on half-buried haws beneath hawthorn bushes. Acorns have a small suite of specialists, including the yellow goblets of Nut Disco *Hymenoscypus fructigenus*, rather unfairly classed as a disease by foresters, since decaying acorns will never turn into oak trees.

Fungi can break down almost any natural material that contains carbon. Plant cellulose presents no problem to them (only a few animal stomachs can utilise it as efficiently). Certain bracket fungi also rot down lignin, one of the hardest structures in the natural world, the internal scaffolding that allows trees to soar to 30m or more without flopping over. There are even fungi that can break down oil, much to the annoyance of the petroleum industry. *Amorphotheca resinae*, also known as the creosote fungus, can 'eat' diesel and jet-fuel, growing so fat on its diet of explosive hydrocarbons that it blocks filters and pipes. Another, the Scaly Sawgill *Neolentinus lepideus*, enjoys the taste of creosote in railway sleepers and telegraph poles.

Some fungi scavenge animal remains. The soft tissues of animal corpses are stripped and broken down mainly by carrion-eating insects and bacteria. The great chance for fungi comes once the body has been stripped of soft tissue, leaving behind the bones, horns, claws, feathers and fur. They are gradually degraded and consumed by microscopic fungi. The best-known corpse fungus – because we can see it and enjoy its freakishness – is the stalkball, *Onygena*, which produces scores of little white matchsticks on rotting horns. There are two species, Horn Stalkball *O. equina*, which grows on the curly horns on a dead sheep's fleshless skull, and the Feather Stalkball *O. corvina*, which prefers damp, rotting feathers and is often found in old birds' nests. Both species are dining out on keratin, the fibrous protein that forms the toughest non-bony tissues of birds and animals.

Another feather-eating fungus, *Arthroderma curreyi*, has found a new habitat, courtesy of mankind – tennis balls. The balls need to go soft and green first, but at a certain point they turn white and mouldy as the fungus digs in. Apparently, *Arthroderma* will even attack plastic balls. Perhaps this is the answer to the mystery of why lost tennis balls are rarely found again.

Root traders

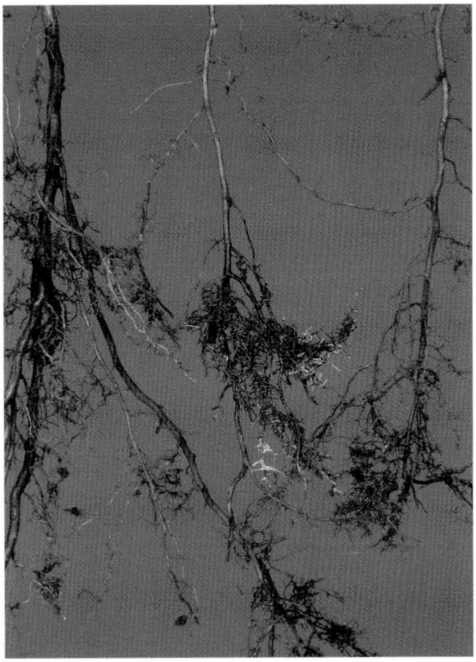

▲ **Roots of Silver Birch,** showing the white sheaths of the mycorrhizal fungus Brown Rollrim *Paxillus involutus*.

Decay fungi can be very abundant, but many woodland species, including most of the larger and more colourful ones, do not work in this way. Instead, they form a mutually beneficial association with the roots of living trees. These fungi are termed mycorrhizal, from two Greek words meaning 'fungus-root'. They include all the boletes and chanterelles, truffles and milkcaps, the poisonous Amanitas and spiny hedgehog fungi, and many more. About 40% of the world's woodland mushrooms are believed to grow with tree roots – although this is not always obvious since the fungi may fruit up to 100m from the trunk. The workface of these fungi is not the stately fruit body but the thick skin of compacted threads that wrap around the fine roots of its plant associate. Although this underground mesh of threads is invisible to us, it is very substantial; it is estimated that every kilogram of woodland soil contains at least 200km of fungal hyphae. On their own, the fine roots of a tree are good at sucking up water but hopelessly bad at finding enough nutrients to support such a large plant, especially in poor soil. The mycorrhizal fungi do it instead, absorbing nutrients through the web of their hyphae and supplying the root cells of the tree with a stream of soil ammonia, nitrate and phosphorus, as well as trace elements.

In nature, everything has its price. Mycorrhizal fungi 'charge' for their services in the form of glucose and fructose, simple sugars the green plant has 'prepared earlier' by photosynthesis. About a quarter of the products of photosynthesis are taken by the fungus, a heavy drain on the tree but one that is amply repaid by the supply of the nutrients necessary for rapid growth. Such partnerships begin at the seedling stage, and it has long been standard practice for foresters to gain a start on nature by inoculating the seedlings with mycorrhizal fungi before planting them in the nursery. Trees so treated grow twice as fast as those without. As they grow to maturity, a succession of different fungi can appear, all of them mycorrhizal species, forming stumpy sausage-like growths on the roots.

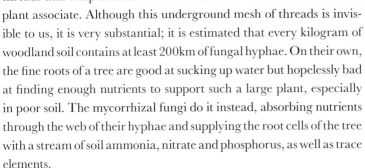

The mystery of exactly how the fungi extract minerals from the soil was dispelled a little by recent research at the University of Leeds. The team introduced flakes of biotite, a common rock-forming mineral, into a pot with a pine seedling inoculated with the mycelium of the Brown Rollrim *Paxillus involutus*, a very common mycorrhizal mushroom. After three months, they examined the biotite crystals under a microscope and found that the fungus had begun to bend and break down the mineral structure, using pressure as high as that found in a car tyre. As the crystal weakens, the fungus removes potassium and other nutrients and passes some of it on to the tree (Anon 2009). To put it as simply as possible, fungi can turn rock into soil. Trees, on their own, cannot.

Different trees have different fungi. Although there are generalists among the ectomycorrhizal fungi (that is, those whose mycelium is on the outside of the roots), many of them are confined to particular species of tree, or related groups of trees. Oaks, for example, share many species with Sweet Chestnut and Beech. Oaks have the largest number of associated species, followed by Beech. Pines, birches, Alder and willows are also heavily dependent on fungi. Many planted conifers, including larches and spruces, are too. Other trees, notably Ash, Rowan, Sycamore and maples, are also dependent on fungi but in their case the fungi are endomycorrhizal, that is they live within the plant tissues and do not produce mushroom-like fruit bodies. This is why non-native larch plantations are a better habitat for mushrooms and toadstools than native Ash woodland. Mycorrhizal mushrooms tend to like settled habitats, notably old woodland. Among the most barren habitats for larger fungi are recent woods of Ash and Sycamore colonising the sides of ravines and landslips.

Apart from trees, many other plants subsist with the help of fungi that sheath their roots, including moorland species such as heathers, wintergreens and bearberry, limestone plants such as rockroses, and alpine ones such as Dwarf Willow and Mountain Avens. Probably more plants than we know have such fungi on their roots. In the Burren, in western Ireland, one mushroom, *Cortinarius cinnamomeus*, was found associating with the roots of sedges.

▶ **A mass flowering of Yellow Bird's-nest** *Hypopitys monotropa*, a plant that grows with the help of a mushroom, *Tricholoma*.

Even more plant species have associate endomycorrhizal fungi. Since these are very small and do not produce visible fruit bodies (indeed, some of them appear not to produce fruit bodies at all), they are little known, especially as it is impossible to culture them in the laboratory. Few of us have even heard of their name, the Glomales. Yet they play a vital role, both in supplying their associated plant with nutrients and protecting it from disease. And they are also the reason why stable habitats, once lost, are hard to recreate. It is because the fungi are missing that bare ground fills up with weeds, rather than heather or rockroses. Weeds are often the plants, generally short-lived ones, which can do without fungi. For the same reason, one wonders how well recently planted trees will fare in the long term, especially in a changing climate (Merryweather 2001).

▲ **Ghost Orchid** *Epipogium aphyllum*, a plant that behaves like a fungus.

Among the most fascinating fungal partnerships are those associated with orchids. Most British orchids obtain at least part of their needs via the fungi inside their shallow, chunky roots, which enables some of them to reduce their leaves or (although it involves cheating on their partner) to ditch them altogether. The Bird's-nest Orchid *Neottia nidus-avis* taps the food supply of both fungus and tree, and is, effectively, a parasite. The equally leafless Ghost Orchid *Epipogium aphyllum* lives like a fungus, appearing briefly above ground only once in a blue moon, to flower and set seed. So far as we know, it has bothered to flower only once in Britain in the past 25 years.

How the equally leafless Yellow Bird's-nest *Hypopitys monotropa* survives was unknown until recently. In its case, the partner turns out to be a mushroom, one of several related species of *Tricholoma* ('knights'). These are normally mycorrhizal species of pine or willow. The Yellow

▲ **One fungus growing** on another: Parasitic Bolete *Pseudoboletus parasiticus*.

Bird's-nest seems to tap into this relationship and hijacks some of the tree's fungi, while giving little or nothing back. Other, non-British species of bird's-nest exploit different fungi, ranging from brittlegills to false truffles. One of the most remarkable 'fungalscapes' of recent years was a forest of Yellow Bird's-nests growing on a woodland bank in a dense ring, as if they themselves were the mushrooms.

Certain mushrooms also adopt this profitable cheating strategy. It had long been known that certain mycorrhizal species always, or nearly always, occur in the company of another mushroom: Fly Agaric *Amanita muscaria* and Peppery Bolete *Chalciporus piperatus*, for example, or the lovely Rosy Spike *Chroogomphus roseus* with Bovine Bolete *Suillus bovinus*. In each case, it turns out that the interloper is tapping into the shared bounty of both tree and mycorrhizal fungus. It is only one step from this to one fungus actually growing on another. Whether the Parasitic Bolete *Pseudoboletus parasiticus*, which grows attached to Common Earthballs *Scleroderma citrinum*, is strictly a parasite has been debated. It certainly looks like one. But there is some evidence that the association belies the bolete's name, and that the earthball does get something out of it. There appears to be a similar relationship between a bracket fungus, the Dyer's Mazegill *Phaeolus schweinitzii*, and the rare, or overlooked, Wood Bolete *Buchwaldoboletus lignicola*. In none of these cases can the pseudo-parasite survive without its host.

Intimate relations

There is more than one way of achieving a partnership. Mycorrhizal fungi are one way. But there are even subtler webs of life out there. Tiny fungi are embedded in the tissues of healthy leaves, just as there are fungi in the guts of cows and other ruminants, which help to break down the cellulose in their plant food. Some of these partnerships are not what they seem. Take the case of Choke *Epichloë typhina*, a yellow mildew that girdles grass stems in fields and meadows. On the face of it, Choke is a disease. It prevents the grass from flowering and seeding, and its toxins poison the hay, producing a condition in cattle and sheep called 'ryegrass staggers'. But closer investigation indicates a more complex picture. While Choke prevents some grass tillers from producing flowers, it stimulates others and actually increases the overall yield of hay. Its spores 'freeload' in the pollen, and so the fungus has a vested interest in the grass doing well. Moreover, it does a useful job. The toxins protect the grass from being chewed up by caterpillars and grasshoppers, or sucked by aphids. Instead, the insects, attracted by the sugary secretions of the fungus, chew up the fungus – a worthwhile exercise from its point of view, since some spores are likely to survive the passage through a fly's gut (Spooner & Roberts 2005).

▲ **Choke** *Epichloë typhina*, a 'disease' that may actually 'help' the grass.

Some micro-fungi share insects' homes. The galleries of the wood-boring ambrosia beetles are lined by a mildewed garden that is decorously browsed by the beetles whenever they feel peckish. A less benign association of beetle and fungus killed most of England's elm trees. Species of fungi known as vascular wilts use a particular kind of bark beetle as a vector to disseminate their spores. The tree dies when the fungus blocks the vascular systems of the tree, denying water to its branches.

Fleshy mushrooms and toadstools are an important food source. As anyone who has gathered wild mushrooms knows, the fruit bodies are consumed by maggots and woodlice (although some species attract more than others). The act of being eaten by a maggot or slug is, in a sense, an act of mutual benefit, since the fungus is effectively using the animal as a vector to disperse its spores. Mushrooms are eaten by a wide variety of animals, from springtails, mites, nematodes and fly maggots to voles, mice, squirrels and deer. Over 100 species of invertebrate, including worms, woodlice and beetle larvae, have been found in a single species, the hard black fungus known as Cramp Balls or King Alfred's Cakes *Daldinia concentrica* (although only five of them – a moth, a fly and three beetles – seem to be confined to it). Fungi also create plant galls that are shared by individual grubs or, in the case of large ones such as Witches' Broom (massed twiggy growths in birch trees), by a host of insects.

▲ **A fly parasite**, *Entomophthora muscae*, on a dead dung fly. Before slaying its victim, the fungus causes the fly to move to a position suitable for the dispersal of its spores.

Perhaps the nasty little fungi that take over the body of an insect for their own nefarious purposes first evolved as a more mutual relationship. The mildew-like growths of *Entomophthora* grow inside live flies, like animated cotton wool, and when fully developed direct the insect to crawl upwards or burrow downwards, as its biochemicals dictate, before finally sticking the dying fly to the spot. At this point, the fungus puts on a last spurt of growth and bursts through the punctured carcass to release its spores. The bloated bodies of gnats sometimes found in a garden pond or rainwater butt are mass victims of an attack by a fungus called *Entomophthora dipterigena*. Its relative, *E. muscae*, is the one that sticks houseflies to the windowpane, surrounded by a dusty cloud of spores.

The equally unpleasant fate of some insects, especially moth caterpillars, is to succumb to attack by 'plant-worms' or 'caterpillarclubs', members of the fungal genus *Cordyceps*. The mature fungus is shaped like a matchstick and its sole purpose is to release spores into the air. The business end lies below ground, where the fungus is embedded in the pupa, the dormant stage of a moth. Like a cunning torturer, the fungus allows just enough life to its caterpillar victim to enable it to turn into a pupa. By the time the matchstick appears, the pupa is dead, a husk enclosing a mass of mycelium. Other fungal species torment beetle grubs, flies, wasps or spiders. Two have turned 'vegetarian' and parasitise buried truffles.

Fungi such as truffles are practically begging to be eaten. They release powerful smells to attract large animals such as deer, pigs and dogs. At least some of the spores will work their passage unharmed, to be deposited elsewhere in a very convenient ball of dung. Certain fungi are able to take advantage of animals in other ways. The Rooting Poisonpie

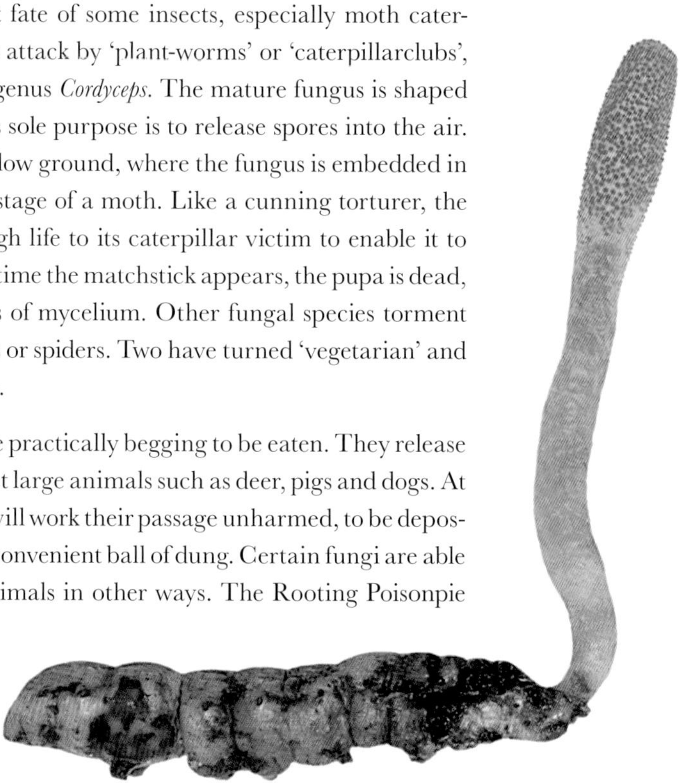

▶ **Scarlet Caterpillarclub** *Cordyceps militaris* emerging from the head of a moth pupa.

▶ **Rooting Poisonpie**
Hebeloma radicosum, a mushroom rooted in the underground latrine of a Mole.

Hebeloma radicosum has a long, thick taproot, like a dandelion, that can penetrate the nitrogen-rich underground nests of mice, the latrines of Moles or even wasps' nests. In Japan, there is another *Hebeloma*, *H. vinosophyllum*, which has, on occasion, been found growing over buried cows and sheep (hence its ghoulish nickname, the Corpse Toadstool), and presumably would not forego the chance of feasting on human remains either. It would be a useful clue at a crime scene, showing detectives not only where the corpse is buried but perhaps helping to establish when the foul deed took place. In Australia, the role of ghoul is played by *H. aminophilum*, which apparently specialises in growing on the corpses of kangaroos!

There may be more of these corpse-eating, urine-drinking toadstools than we realise. Small inkcaps, such as *Coprinopsis*, probably mark a nitrogen-rich patch of soil where a small mammal has urinated, or possibly where it lies buried. Another species found to share similar habits is *Calocybe constricta*, which turns up on lawns where dogs have urinated. This is a slender, medium-sized white mushroom, easily mistaken for a Field Mushroom (although its spores are white, not black). In the wild, it may be associated with the urine of that wild dog, the Fox.

Predators and parasites

A predatory mushroom sounds like a contradiction, like a playful snake or a cheerful donkey. Few would guess that oyster mushrooms, *Pleurotus* species, and their smaller relatives, *Hohenbuehelia*, are meat-eaters. Only under the microscope can one spot the toxic and sticky knobs at the end of their hyphae, which trap tiny eelworms as they slither through the rotting wood. Certain species of ascomycete fungus form hangman's nooses which fasten on a passing worm, like a lasso. The fungus then secretes an immobilising toxin and slowly liquidises its prey. Leaving nothing to chance, some of these fungi even secrete tempting scents to attract the worms. Think of the little struggling worms when you watch a strict vegan enjoy some oyster mushrooms.

Much better known are fungi which are out-and-out parasites, that is, they do harm to their host without any compensating gain. These are the plant diseases – a motley crew of rusts and smuts, cankers and scabs, curls and rots, blights and wilts. They are all too familiar to the gardener, forester and farmer, who unleash a deadly arsenal of chem-

▼ **The innocent-looking Oyster Mushroom** *Pleurotus ostreatus* feeds on small worms, as well as on rotting wood.

◀ Spores instead of pollen. A campion with the anther smut *Microbotryum violaceum.*

icals to try and control them. This is the science of plant pathology rather than field mycology. However, it is easy to get a false impression of the role of parasitic fungi in nature from our focus on crops and horticulture. Most wild plants, too, have associated fungi, many of which are confined to a single host plant. Some of them are hidden, others easy to spot, such as the purple anther smut *Microbotryum violaceum* found on campion flowers, or the rich orange blisters of Nettle Rust *Puccinia urticata*, or the thick white mould that often smothers the shoots of Shepherd's-purse.

▼ The very common Nettle Rust *Puccinia urticata.*

In nature, while the fungus may weaken or cause the death of individual plants, they rarely affect plant populations. Wild flowers, both common and rare, have been living side by side with their rusts and smuts for millions of years; indeed, they will have evolved together. Some of these fungi are themselves listed under the Biodiversity Action Plan, which implicitly recognises them as a legitimate part of the 'mini-ecosystem' of the host plant. (They offer an interesting dilemma to the nature conservationist: are these fungi an integral part of a plant's biology, or are they merely an unwanted 'disease'?) Real damage is confined either to artificial situations in which the natural balance is upset, or to recently imported plant diseases that lack natural controls.

Parasitic fungi represent a minority pursuit among field mycologists. However, interest in rusts and smuts seems to be growing, after a long period of neglect, and their study requires a good knowledge of the British flora. A few species are prominent enough to become honorary macro-fungi, such as the tarspot on Sycamore leaves, *Rhytisma acerinum*, or the orange horns of *Gymnosporangium* rust on Juniper branches. Forayers also look out for fungal galls – species of *Exobasidium* and *Taphrina*, which are sometimes conspicuous and even rather beautiful in their eerie way.

Certain fungi are parasites without seeming so. Jelly fungi include those familiar yellow or black blobby fungi attached to sticks and fallen branches. The best known is the Yellow Brain *Tremella mesenterica*, bright yellow clusters of floppy jelly found attached to branches of gorse, especially in winter. It seems to be living on the wood, like a bracket fungus, but is, in fact, a parasite of a much less conspicuous crust fungus, *Peniophora*, which shares its branch. There is a second Yellow Brain, *T. aurantia*, not recorded in Britain until the 1990s, which looks almost identical except that it has a different host, the very common Hairy Curtain Crust *Stereum hirsutum*. This quiet kind of parasitism is not uncommon among fungi. One finds it in species as different as Hazel Gloves *Hypocreopsis rhododendri*, a lichen-like fungus of Hazel twigs, and the bracket fungus *Skeletocutis carneogrisea* of conifer logs, which intermingle with the hyphae of certain bracket fungi (in the former case, the Glue Crust *Hymenochaete corrugata*, in the latter, the Purplepore Bracket fungus, *Trichaptum abietinum*). Another fungus with a hidden agenda is the Birch Mazegill *Lenzites betulinus*. This tan-coloured, fan-shaped bracket gains access to logs and stumps by attacking and destroying another fungus, the common and ubiquitous Turkeytail *Trametes versicolor*. Once the Turkeytail has been eliminated, the Birch Mazegill feeds on the rotting wood, as a typical bracket fungus. The technical term for this is 'secondary resource capture'.

Even more bizarre forms of parasite occur among mushrooms. Finding a piggyback fungus is always a foray highlight. These are little mushrooms that grow on top of bigger ones. The most frequent piggyback fungi are the two species of *Asterophora* that grow on the decaying hulks of brittlegills, usually Blackening Brittlegill *Russula nigricans*. Silky Piggyback *Asterophora parasitica* is small and dainty, whilst Powdery Piggy-

◀ **The little mushrooms of Silky Piggyback** *Asterophora parasitica* growing on the cap of Blackening Brittlegill *Russula nigicans*.

back *A. lycoperdoides* is usually covered with a brownish bloom of its own spores (the species name means 'like a puffball'), hence its alternative name, the Powdercap Toadstool. The unrelated Piggyback Rosegill *Volvariella surrecta* has similar habits, forming fungal gardens on the caps of Clouded Funnel *Clitocybe nebularis*. Evidently, this trick works better in some places than others, for the Piggyback Rosegill tends to turn up with any regularity in only a few places. Variants on this theme are the Splitpea Shanklet *Collybia cookei* and the Lentil Shanklet *C. tuberosa*, since these small, pale brown mushrooms emerge on long stems from rotting fungi half buried in the soil. In their case, fruiting is delayed. The mushrooms sprout from a resting stage, a hard-shelled tuber-like growth called a sclerotium, the 'splitpea' and 'lentil' of their English names.

Perhaps strangest of all is that shape-shifter of the mushroom world, *Squamanita*. When they were first described, *Squamanita* fungi were thought to be conventional mushrooms, with bright colours, funny smells and a swollen, scaly bulb at the base of the stem. They are rare and seldom seen, but once in a while enjoy an exceptional season and appear in comparative abundance. Such was October 2004, when reports came in first of Strathy Strangler *S. pearsonii* and then Powdercap Strangler *S. paradoxa*, both pungent, lilac-grey mushrooms covered in shaggy scales. Their true nature had been revealed only a few years earlier. Far from being orthodox fungi, they are a peculiar form of

▶ **Powdercap Strangler** *Squamanita paradoxa* – one mushroom turning into another.

parasite that takes over the body of their host mushroom and replaces parts of it with themselves (one is reminded of the horror film *The Fly*, where the body of the human researcher becomes intermingled with that of an insect). Hence, the fungus known as *S. paradoxa* consists of two fungi in one: the lower half is the host, the common Earthy Powdercap *Cystoderma amianthinum*, while the top half is the parasite. The join is obvious, for the bottom half is granular and bright yellow while the top is scaly and purplish brown. That is the meaning of their English name: they are the stranglers, consumers of the living corpses of their half-throttled victims!

Dual organisms

A more benign coupling of species is the double act between fungus and plant, known as a lichen. Lichens are fungi that are able, with the help of a layer of algae, to behave like green plants, and so manufacture their own food. This enables them to live on barren substrates such as bare rock and tree bark. This partnership is one of the most successful in the natural world. There are at least 1,700 species of lichen in Britain

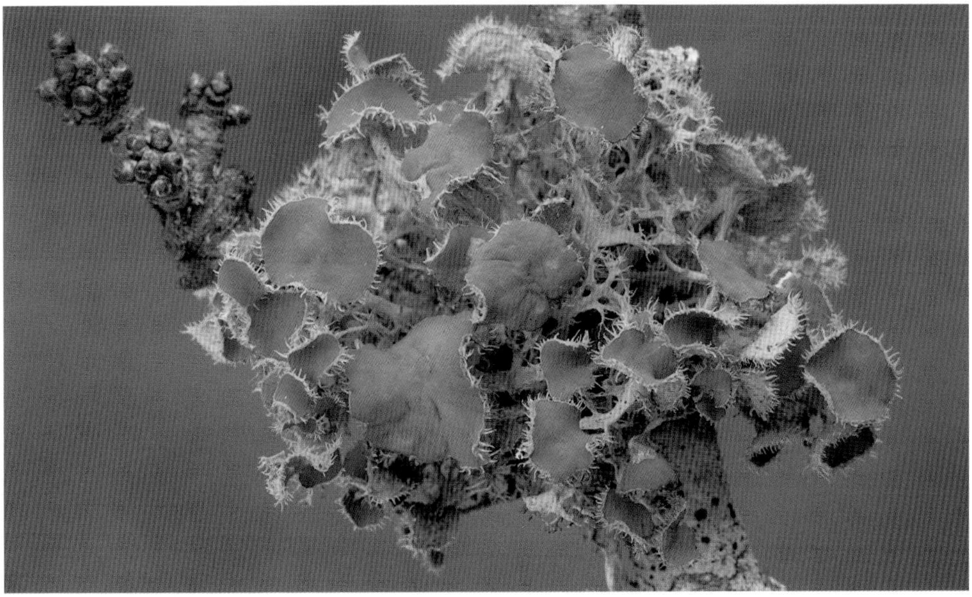

alone – almost as many species as there are native flowering plants. So long as the air is unpolluted and there is sufficient light, lichens seem to thrive almost anywhere, from city centres to open countryside, and from mountain tops right down to the high-tide mark. Lichens are sensitive to pollution, and so are of interest to environmentalists as indicators of clean air; certain species are confined to the super-clean, rain-washed air of the Atlantic coast, some of whose woods are lush wonderlands of lichens.

▲ **The striking disc-shaped fruit bodies** of the lichen *Teloschistes chrysophthalmus* reveal its fungal nature.

The fungal part of most lichens is a species of ascomycete. Their nature is most obvious when the lichen produces fruit bodies (apothecia), which often look like discs or tiny jam tarts, and resemble the fruit bodies of cup fungi. As fungi, they reproduce sexually by spores projected from little embedded flasks in the body (thallus) of the lichen. Many lichens have a second trick up their sleeve, for they also reproduce without sex by producing bits that break off and grow into genetically identical lichens. The colours of lichens – most often shades of green, grey and orange – are provided by their partners, the algae (or, for some species, cyanbacteria – see below). Algae, it seems, do most of the work. They manufacture the sugars that the fungus needs to survive, grow and reproduce. They pass it on when stimulated by the fungus to do so, in what seems like a master-and-servant relationship. What, if anything, does the alga get out of it? Protection, for a start. Living inside the thallus of a fungus enables the alga to survive in dry, windy, well-lit places where a free-living alga would soon frizzle up. And it seems the fungus also passes on trace elements from rock and bark that a healthy alga needs. The lichen's shape enables the alga to obtain the maximum benefit from sunlight, and so perform at its peak. Lichens on bark and rock are normally flattish or strap-shaped, but some (the 'fruticate' ones) form branches, enabling them (among other things) to catch the light by growing on the sunny side of the tree.

This relationship is obviously a very old one. Fungus and alga probably evolved together, so that you would be forgiven for thinking them to be a single entity. Indeed, lichens are treated taxonomically as though they were. Although the algae within them have their own individual scientific names, the lichen as a whole carries the name of the fungus (very few lichenised fungi can survive in a free-living state; when cultured separately, they become a shapeless, hopeless-looking mass). Although, strictly speaking, they are dualities, lichens are treated as species. And why not? Each one has its own characteristics and ecology. Each is a stable entity, and they are all identifiable.

A minority of lichens double up, not with algae, but with photosynthetic bacteria known as cyanophytes (as their old name of blue-green algae implies, these were once regarded as plants). Such lichens tend to have a dark thallus and, in some cases, a jelly-like texture. The most familiar are the dog lichens *Peltigera* species, found on bare

▶ **Heath Navel**
Lichenomphalina umbellifera – a lichen with its gill fungus partner.

ground on lawns, dunes and other places, and so-called because they have pointed pseudo-roots that resemble teeth. There are also a few lichens whose fungal partner is not a cup fungus but a mushroom. Most of these belong to the genus *Lichenomphalia*, of which the most familiar is the Heath Navel *L. umbellifera* (better known under its old name of *Omphalina ericetorum*). This exists in two contrasting forms: the lichenised part, which consists of blue-green flakes on bare peat or attached to *Sphagnum* moss, while the non-lichenised fruit bodies are small, pale yellow, trumpet-shaped mushrooms. As the English name indicates, seen from above navels do look a little like belly buttons.

Lichens are traditionally treated as separate entities from non-lichenised fungi. Specialists are called lichenologists, and their parent society is the British Lichen Society. Lichen hunters tend to look up, mushroom hunters down. They tend to hunt in small groups, while mycologists foray in larger parties. Indeed, the cultural differences between lichenologists and mycologists are arguably greater than the difference between lichens and fungi! Lichens will not appear in this book very often because of this cultural divide. If you are ever curious to know what makes lichenologists tick, I recommend *The Lichen Hunters* by the late Oliver Gilbert (2004). It was Oliver who invented the sport of 'adventure lichenology', in which the hardier kind of lichenologist heads for remote places carrying a tent, or takes an unusual habitat under his or her wing, such as disused runways or pylon bases. Compared with hard-core lichen hunters, we field mycologists have some catching up to do.

A world of slime

Lichens are fungi that are studied separately. Slime moulds, or myxomycetes, are not fungi but are traditionally treated as though they are. For a long time no one knew what to make of them. For part of their life, they behave like primitive animals, oozing and slithering in dark, damp places such as decaying logs, consuming bacteria, micro-fungi and other micro-organisms as they go. After a while, perhaps when the food runs out, they stop and undergo a strange metamorphosis. The oozing slime shrinks and solidifies and turns into what looks like a fungus. It is at this stage, often still a semi-solid blob, like melting wax, that we notice them. Fruiting slime moulds can be a variety of shapes, some like little sausages, others resembling fish roe, and others still more or less spherical, like miniature puffballs. Many are attractively coloured red, orange, yellow or with a range of iridescent colours under a lens, like fungal rainbows. Inside the fruit bodies, the spores form and ripen. Eventually the bodies dry out and break open, releasing the spores to begin the cycle again. They seldom remain in good condition for more than a few days.

We now know that slime moulds are neither animal nor plant. They are not even fungi, although they were long classed as offshoots, or distant cousins, of the fungal tribe. Slime moulds are, in fact, more closely related to certain soil amoebae, their probable ancestors. They occupy a group all of their own, the Mycetozoa. But they tend to live in the same damp, decaying habitats as fungi, and so are often found on fungus forays. At one time, slime moulds were quite popular with amateur naturalists, who would keep them in dried-out form in matchboxes. Today, their charms are known only to a shrinking band of enthusiasts (although they never fail to fascinate on forays and wildlife walks). They deserve to be better known. For the more determined, there is an excellent identification handbook available (Ing 1999) written by the foremost expert in the group, Bruce Ing. (At this time, Bruce Ing lived in Wales in a town called Mold; they found this most amusing in America.) It is the first for more than a century, although it lacks colour plates. Bruce tells me that a second edition, with colour images, is in preparation. Since 1999, 30 new species of slime mould have been discovered in Britain.

▶ **Slimy scrambled eggs** – the common slime mould *Mucilago crustacea*, found on grassses and other meadow plants.

Many slime moulds are small and inconspicuous. Although many species are quite common, they require careful searching in likely habitats. The ones we come across by accident are the largest species, such as *Brefeldia maxima*, which looks like whitewash, or *Fuligo septica*, which is bright yellow and resembles scrambled eggs or vomit, according to taste. You come across them in woodland, on bark, dead wood or leaf litter. Some species occur in grassland, moorland or wetlands, and many are characteristic of the rainy Atlantic coast of Britain. Less likely mini-habitats include coastal shingle, snow patches in summer and heaps of wet straw by the side of cornfields. Some species of slime moulds seem to be almost cosmopolitan, that is, they are found all over the world, as befits an ancient group of organisms. It may well be, however, that Britain is one of the best places in the world for slime moulds, along with mosses, liverworts and lichens, all lovers of cool, damp places in shaded ravines, the splashy sides of upland streams and gently rotting old trees.

▲ **Not a fungus.** The slime mould *Stemonitis fusca* forms bristle-pad-like clusters on dead wood.

▼ **The plasmodial stage of a slime mould,** *Ceratiomyxa fruticulosa*, is more like an amoeba than a fungus.

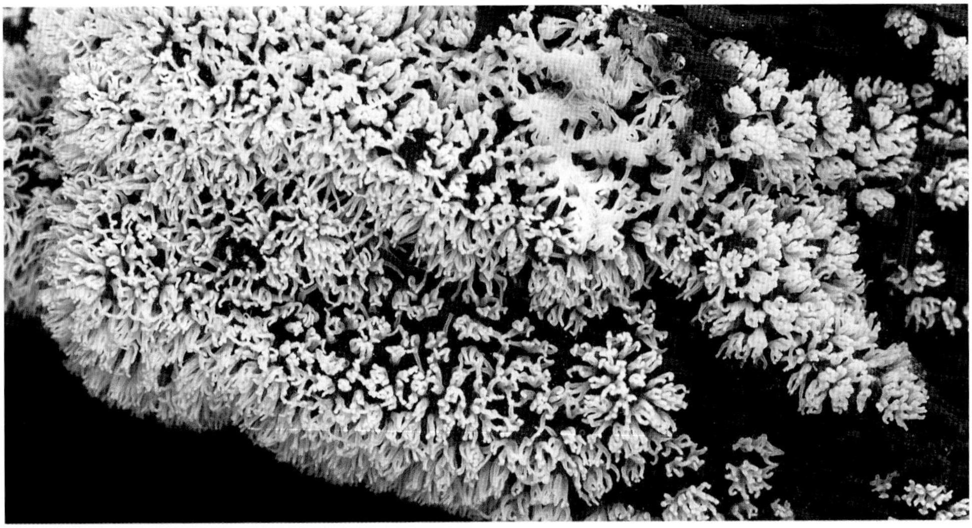

chapter three

What's in a name?

Having described how mushrooms and other fungi live, it is time to look more closely at the fungi themselves. All field guides to fungi set out the 'naming of parts' of a fungus – the bits one needs to know in order to identify them correctly. I do not want to go over the same ground, which is, in any case, rather dry and technical. Rather, I want to take a closer look at fungi through their names, both English and Latin. Names, I think, are more important than they are often given credit for. They are not just labels. Individually, each forms a kind of short description. And they allude to the cultural, as well as the scientific, nature of fungi. Collectively, fungal names blend poetry, science and everyday experience. Names, I believe, bring us close to nature.

Different words, similar things?

Let's start with 'fungi', the plural of fungus. This is one of those words that people pronounce in different ways, no one way being more correct than another. Some say fung-i, with a short 'i', others fung-aye, or funge-aye with a soft 'g' (as it happens, I belong to the fung-i school). To be consistent, perhaps we should say 'funge-aye', for the word is said to come from the Greek word *sphongos*, meaning 'a sponge'. Like sponges, fungi are soft and damp, and soak up water, swelling as they do so. Fungus is a word that casts a shadow. Although it applies equally to all life in this 'third kingdom', which is neither plant nor animal, one somehow associates it most with mildew and mould. This is ironic, since scientists now believe that certain 'mildews', such as the potato blight fungus and the downy mildews, are not fungi at all and may be more closely related to plants.

◄ **Candlesnuff Fungus**
Xylaria hypoxylon.

The study of fungi is mycology. The myco- bit is based on one of the earliest names for a fungus, the Greek word *mykes*, later Latinised as 'mucus'. The philosopher Hippocrates used it for a particular fungus utilised at the time as tinder, possibly the large bracket fungus now known as *Fomes fomentarius* or the Hoof Fungus. The term was picked up 2,000 years later by the Reverend Miles Joseph Berkeley (1803-1889), the founding father of fungus science in Britain. To the founder go the spoils, including the right to invent a name. Berkeley, who like every educated person of his day was well versed in the classics, liked the sound of it. Thanks to him, the name for the study of fungi is therefore mycology and not 'fungology' (although he did use that very word in a subsequent work!).

Many field guides to fungi have 'mushrooms and toadstools' in the title, as though the words mean different things (and you won't have to read very far for a third word to join them, 'agaric'). In fact, they all refer to the same thing: a mushroom-shaped fungus with gills on the underside of the cap. Culturally speaking, we associate 'mushroom' with edible kinds and 'toadstool' with non-edible, even poisonous ones. But in reality there are 'mushrooms' that are poisonous and 'toadstools' that are delicious. It is all rather confusing.

The words 'mushroom' and 'toadstool' come not from science but from folklore. Scientists prefer to work with words capable of precise

▼ **Hoof Fungus or Tinder Bracket** *Fomes fomentarius*, a massive bracket of old birch stumps, is found mainly in Scotland.

definitions, and so prefer 'agaric' for gilled fungi, 'bolete' for the plump ones with pores, and 'polypores' for those shaped like brackets. 'Mushroom', on the other hand, can mean different things to different people. Some would confine the word to those we can eat. Others will say, equally correctly, that any fungus with a cap and gills is a mushroom, edible or not. Surprisingly, given that some mushrooms are wholesome and delicious, the word has negative connotations. It was Stephen J Gould who pointed out that, while the arts 'flower', it is always crime and taxes that 'mushroom'. And, since 1945, we have lived in the shadow of that symbol of awesome destructive power: the vast, sinister, mushroom-shaped cloud of the atomic bomb. Mushroom is a very old word of uncertain origin. Some say it comes from the medieval French *mouscheron* (although that was once also the French name of the poisonous Fly Agaric!) Others suggest the original mushroom was in fact a 'moss' or *mousseron*, that is, a primitive plant that lacks a fixed shape and reproduces using spores. Another possibility is that mushroom comes from the same word as mousse. Just as a mousse of egg white and cream swells and solidifies with beating, so mushrooms seem to swell overnight from shapeless fluff to a solid, stately umbrella.

▲ **Rev. Miles Joseph Berkeley (1803-1889),** the founder of British mycology, describer of some 600 species of fungi.

In Britain, toadstools have long been the dark doppelganger to the wholesome mushroom (curiously enough, the toxin in the skin glands of toads has been detected in certain toadstools). Thanks to fairy stories and folk tales, the word 'toadstool' is redolent of witchcraft, venom and things that go bump in the night. The word may derive not from toads but from 'tode' (plural 'todes'), the German word for death. Toadstools, according to folklore, are poisonous, and eating them leads to illness and death. The name, as 'tadstole', first appears in a document dating from 1398, which also mentions 'frogstooles' (were they the edible ones?). In the Middle Ages, toads had an evil reputation, and it must have been easy to imagine them squatting on their noisome 'stools', malevolently eyeing the dark forest floor. Rather disappointingly, real toads do not seem much interested in toadstools. In the 1940s, a photographer managed to persuade a captive toad to crouch on top of a sturdy bolete for long enough to take a few snaps, which he sold to *The Times* newspaper (they are reproduced in *Mushrooms and Toadstools* by John Ramsbottom). Much as I like the word, you are not going to hear it very often in this book. My toadstools are all mushrooms.

The fact that we have two words for what is basically the same thing says more about us and our cautious eating habits than about biology. In countries where all kinds of fungi are gathered for food they make no such distinction. In France, they are all *champignons*, in Germany *pilze*, and in Italy simply *fungi*. It is because there is no real difference between a mushroom and a toadstool that 18th-century savants preferred the word agaric, another word borrowed from ancient writings. The Greek scholar Dioscorides used *agarikon* to mean 'of the countryside', or, as we might say, 'natural'. It was originally applied to a particular fungus that was collected as a cure-all for a range of illnesses, including dysentery, fever, colic and asthma. Dioscorides's miracle cure is probably Agaricon *Laricifomes officinalis*, a large bracket fungus not found in Britain but which grows on larch trees in southern Europe (the species name *officinalis* indicates a 'herb' stored at a pharmacy and used for medicinal purposes; literally 'from the office'). Today, the

▶ **The button stage** of Fly Agaric *Amanita muscaria.*

best-known fungus to retain the word agaric in its name is that Disney-esque wonder, the Fly Agaric. But it also survives in *Agaricus*, the genus in which the common Field Mushroom belongs, and also to the order Agaricales or gilled mushrooms.

That some fungi are poisonous was known to the ancient Greeks and Romans, and must have been common knowledge in prehistoric times when everyone hunter-gathered for the pot. By the Middle Ages, the English, at least, had grown to be cautious about eating wild mushrooms, not least because they were mysterious and seemed to defy natural laws. They were regarded as 'excrescences of the earth', which imbibed poison from the rotting damp in which they grew. Some said they formed from dung, or the slime left behind by snails. Gerard's *Herbal* advised against gastronomic experiments, for most wild fungi would undoubtedly 'suffocate and strangle the eater'. 'Beware of licking honey among the thorn', he warned, 'lest the sweetness of the one does not countervail the sharpness and pricking of the other.' Even edible mushrooms, cautioned Francis Bacon in his *Sylva Sylvarum* of 1627, are apt to produce wind and nightmares if consumed in excess. Such attitudes prevailed until comparatively modern times.

Names from the mists of time

The Romans recognised several fungi either because they were useful in medicine or because they were good eating (the Emperor Claudius was particularly fond of them, which made it easy for his wife to murder him with a poisonous one). The most valuable of all fungi, even more valuable than the truffle, was a mushroom called *boletus*. One of Martial's epigrams noted that while a messenger could be trusted to carry precious metals and expensive clothes, he was likely to gobble up a *boletus*. It was literally more valuable than gold. What the *boletus* was is uncertain. It was probably not what we know as *boletus* today, and the consensus is that the most sought-after mushroom of all time was the scarlet-capped Caesar's Mushroom *Amanita caesarea*, which unfortunately does not grow in Britain.

In one of the volumes of his *Historia Naturalis*, written around AD 77, Pliny wrote about a fungus called *suillus* or 'little pig'. In preserved form it could be used as a remedy for fluxes from the bowel, while, gently pressed against the offending part, it had the power to shrink piles or remove freckles, boils and other blemishes. This *suillus* was very probably a bolete in the modern sense, a plump fungus with a porcine

appearance. In Italy, they still call them little pigs, *porcini*, while *Suillus* survives as a generic name for the smaller boletes.

Pliny's name for truffles, *Tuber*, is also still the scientific name of the most valuable European truffles. Otherwise, our oldest names for fungi are English folk names. Certain fungi have long attracted attention because of some peculiarity, for which explanatory legends sprang up. The puffball, for example, was said to appear wherever a wolf had farted; the French name for a puffball is still *vesse-de-loup*. The story, silly as it is, lives on in their formal name, *Lycoperdon*, which could be translated as 'that which a wolf has spoiled'. They were also known as fusse-balls or puck-fists, the 'fusse' (pronounced 'fuzz') being the fine dust within. Gerard, the herbalist, believed that the dust could cause a form of temporary blindness known as 'poor-blinde', a notion that science has failed to endorse. More usefully, fusse-balls could be dried for kindling, or used to staunch the flow of blood from cuts. But they were 'in no way eaten', cautioned Gerard.

Gerard and his contemporaries also knew the Stinkhorn *Phallus impudicus*, or, as the English called it, according to Gerard, 'the Prick Mushroom'. Gerard's earthiness did not extend to his accompanying wood-

▲ **Common Puffballs**
Lycoperdon perlatum still with their spines. The 'puff' of spores is activated by raindrops falling onto the surface of the fungi.

► **Plums and Custard**
Tricholomopsis rutilans, an old name taken from its contrasting rich colours.

►► **Shaggy Inkcap**
Coprinus comatus, also known as Lawyer's Wig.

Fungi with long-established common names

Morel	*Morchella esculenta* and relatives
Orange Peel Fungus	*Aleuria aurantia*
Summer Truffle	*Tuber aestivum*
Coral Spot	*Nectria cinnabarina*
Candlesnuff Fungus	*Xylaria hypoxylon*
Dead Man's Fingers	*Xylaria polymorpha*
King Alfred's Cakes, Cramp Balls	*Daldinia concentrica*
Witches' Butter	*Exidia glandulosa*
Bog Beacon	*Mitrula paludosa*
Stinkhorn	*Phallus impudicus*
Devil's Fingers	*Clathrus archeri*
Common Bird's Nest	*Crucibulum laeve* and relatives
Puffballs	*Lycoperdon* species and relatives
Giant Puffball	*Calvatia gigantea*
Beefsteak Fungus	*Fistulina hepatica*
Chicken of the Woods	*Laetiporus sulphureus*
Dryad's Saddle	*Polyporus squamosus*
Turkeytail	*Trametes versicolor*
Dry Rot	*Serpula lacrymans*
Jew's Ear	*Auricularia auricula-judae*
Chanterelle	*Cantharellus cibarius*
Horn of Plenty	*Craterellus cornucopioides*
Cauliflower Fungus	*Sparassis crispa*
Fairy clubs	*Clavaria* species and relatives
Wood Hedgehog	*Hydnum repandum*
Grisette	*Amanita vaginata*
Tawny Grisette	*Amanita fulva*
Fly Agaric	*Amanita muscaria*
Panthercap	*Amanita pantherina*
Deathcap	*Amanita phalloides*
False Deathcap	*Amanita citrina*
Destroying Angel	*Amanita virosa*
The Blusher	*Amanita rubescens*
Parasol	*Macrolepiota procera*
Shaggy Parasol	*Chlorophyllum rhacodes*
Honey Fungus, Bootlace Fungus	*Armillaria mellea* and relatives
Field Mushroom	*Agaricus campestris*
Horse Mushroom	*Agaricus arvensis*
Wood Mushroom	*Agaricus silvicola*
Yellow Stainer	*Agaricus xanthodermus*
Lawyer's Wig, Shaggy Inkcap	*Coprinus comatus*
Common Inkcap	*Coprinopsis atramentaria*
Weeping Widow	*Lacrymaria lacrymabunda*
Sulphur Tuft	*Hypholoma fasciculare*
The Miller	*Clitopilus prunulus*
Fairy Ring Champignon	*Marasmius oreades*
St George's Mushroom	*Calocybe gambosa*
Field Blewit, Blue-leg	*Lepista saeva*
Wood Blewit	*Lepista nuda*
Plums and Custard	*Tricholomopsis rutilans*
The Deceiver	*Laccaria laccata*
Oyster Mushroom	*Pleurotus ostreatus*
Milkcaps	*Lactarius* species
Old Man of the Woods	*Strobilomyces strobilaceus*
Cep, Penny Bun	*Boletus edulis*
Slippery Jack	*Suillus luteus*

cut, which softened the Stinkhorn's undeniably phallic appearance by depicting it upside down! In the Netherlands, the same fungus was known as the Phallus, and this survives today as the scientific name of the genus.

Another interesting old name is Jew's Ear. The fungus of that name is rubbery and roughly ear-shaped, and grows most commonly on Elder trees. The pre-scientific world was ready with an explanation. It was a reminder of Judas Iscariot, who betrayed his master, Jesus, and then, full of guilt and remorse, hanged himself on an Elder tree. In Judas's time, the Elder was as mighty as the oak but God reduced it to a feeble, worthless bush on which Judas's shame lives on in these mysterious rubbery ears. The scientific name, *Auricularia auricula-judae*, echoes the old legend. The Jew's Ear was a useful fungus, for, when boiled to a jelly in milk or vinegar, it could sooth inflammations and sore throats.

▲ **The arresting presence** of the Stinkhorn *Phallus impudicus*.

▼ **King Alfred's Cakes** *Daldinia concentrica*, looking burnt even when fresh.

The one thing everyone knows about King Alfred is that he burnt the cakes. He, too, has his own fungus, *Daldinia concentrica*, called King Alfred's Cakes because it is roundish and black, and looks as though it has been burned to a crisp. Other blackish fungi have appropriately dark names. The black jelly-fungus *Exidia glandulosa* has been known as Witches' Butter for at least 200 years, and was supposedly one of the unpleasant substances used in witches' potions. Dead Man's Fingers is an old and appropriate name for the dark lobes of *Xylaria polymorpha*, protruding from the ground as though a buried corpse had been disturbed.

One of the oldest common names is Fly Agaric, or Fly Mushroom, a name common to several North European languages. According to the 13th-century scholar, Albertus Magnus, this poisonous and easily recognised mushroom was widely used as a primitive insecticide. Portions of cap left in a bowl of milk became a magnet for flies which, having imbibed the fatal liquid, grew dopey and so

▲ Jew's Ear
Auricularia auricula-judae, a name that connects with ancient Christian folklore.

easy to swat. An alternative explanation is that the 'fly' was in the head of the person who ate the mushroom. In times past, delirium and mild insanity were attributed to insects buzzing inside the brain (hence the expression 'he has a bee in his bonnet'). As was well known, eating the Fly Mushroom produced such symptoms.

Perhaps because the British were so cautious about eating wild mushrooms, relatively few of the best ones have long-established names. In some cases we were reduced to pinching them from the French, such as chanterelle, cep, grisette and champignon. One genuine folk name, the Horse Mushroom *Agaricus arvensis*, may incorporate a pun. It is larger and coarser than the Field Mushroom *A. campestris*, hence 'horse', but it also commonly grows in paddocks where horses are kept.

A few other species were once gathered and sold at market, and so acquired names. The Field Blewit or Blue-leg *Lepista saeva*, named after its distinctive blue stalk, was a favourite in the Midlands and the north, where they evidently appreciated its distinctive perfume and rubbery texture, sometimes compared to tripe. St George's Mushroom *Calocybe gambosa* is an edible spring mushroom that supposedly appears around St George's Day, 23rd April. Perhaps its association with the patriotic saint was a sign of culinary respectability.

Other edible or useful fungi were named after their similarity to familiar things. The delicious Oyster Mushroom *Pleurotus ostreatus* does, indeed, resemble an English oyster, which was once the food of the poor, not the rich. The Lawyer's Wig or Shaggy Inkcap *Coprinus comatus* is a comic rendition of a lawyer's curly wig when seen from the back (and is also an example of a fungus with two names, equally popular). The Horn of Plenty *Craterellus cornucopioides* recalls the classical cornucopia of goodies, but, being blackish, is also the trumpet of the Last Judgement, the *trompette de mort.* The Candlesnuff Fungus *Xylaria hypoxylon* is the fungal world's equivalent of a once familiar substance, the white 'snuff' on a burnt candle-wick.

Sickener's sisters and sorceresses

When books about fungi came to be written, their authors found an almost total lack of common names. Some were quite content with that, but others, generally those with literary pretensions, hastened to provide names of their own. Unfortunately, few of them caught on. More than 40 different names have been coined for the puffball and not one of them is used today. One of the earliest and most delightful invented names was provided by James Bolton of Halifax, in his landmark *An History of Funguses growing about Halifax*, published in 1788. This was 'the spatter-dashed mushroom' or *Collybia peronata*, which drew attention to the similarity of its hairy stem with the shaggy gaiters then worn by country folk. Its name today is the Wood Woollyfoot.

The most determined effort to provide names for at least the more distinctive fungi was made in the late 19th century by W Delisle Hay. His *Text-book of British Fungi* (1887) is forgotten now, but his efforts have a quaint Victorian charm, exemplified by 'The Faun's Delight' for the rare and beautiful *Hericium coralloides*, or 'Beelzebub's Cushion' for the sinister *Boletus satanas.* He even thought he could improve on the few generally accepted names, so that the Deathcap became, for him, 'the Arch Bane', while its relative the False Deathcap was 'The Sorceress'. His waxcaps are 'hoods', his hydnums 'urchins' and his mushrooms 'pratelles'. He found 'Stump-tuft' more descriptive than Honey Fungus, and produced a host of inventive names for fungi he believed to be poisonous, including the Crocodile, the Leaf-bane, the Snake-in-the-grass, the Slayer, the Malignant and the Sickener's Sister. His judgement on this score was not foolproof. According to him, *Clitocybe dealbata*, which he named the Cream-clot, makes 'first-rate eating'. Had he tried it, he would have changed his mind. Among the consequences of eating *Clitocybe dealbata* is excessive salivation, peeing, vomiting and – appropriately enough – weeping.

Most truly popular names of fungi belong to groups of related species. Hence, we have puffballs, earthstars, stinkhorns, morels, ink-caps, milkcaps, boletes, earthtongues and cup fungi. Remarkably few

▼ **Coral Tooth** *Hericium coralloides*, a rare and beautiful fungus of large Beech logs, was dubbed 'The Faun's Delight' by W Delisle Hay in 1887.

▲ **Gilded Brittlegill** *Russula aurea*, one of the more distinctive species of this large and colourful genus. This one has golden yellow gills, hence the English name.

English names occur in the most widely used field guide of the 1960s and 1970s by Lange & Hora (1965) – and even those are in inverted commas, as though they were not really respectable. But not everyone agreed.

Ex libris: inventing names

Forayers are sharply divided over the merits of common names for fungi. Some are their earnest advocates, arguing that the lack of them is one of the great obstacles to their popularity. Others regard them as unnecessary, arguing that Latin names have never stopped children getting into dinosaurs, or prevented a gardener from knowing his Chrysanthemums. I remember going head to head with the redoubtable Michael Jordan over this on the Radio 4 *Today* programme. Michael considered the British Mycological Society's newfangled common names to be, at best, a distraction and 'absolutely the wrong approach'. He found them condescending and gratuitous, and said, rightly, that many mycologists use them only with reluctance, if at all. Although, on that occasion, I pitched in for the new names, I have some sympathy with Michael's stand. I find myself divided even in my own mind. Scientific names have a logic that, with a little effort, makes them easier to remember than common names. Moreover, to my ears at least, they have a sweet music lacking in most English names. On my forays we tend to use the new names only when I can remember them, which is less often than not. Other naturalists, including lichenologists, seem to be having the same debate.

The journey to find common names for all common and easily recognised fungi began in the 1950s. E C Large, a plant pathologist who had written a celebrated textbook, *The Advance of the Fungi*, as well as three novels and much more besides, made an impassioned plea for common names. Most other European countries have them, he pointed out. They have no problem with vernacular names. 'It is wrong that almost every British bird should have a good English name, while so many of our commonest fungi are nameless in the English tongue.' With the help and advice of colleagues in the BMS, he produced a list of 200 names. Unfortunately, despite exposure in the Society's *Bulletin*, they did not catch on. Clearly, the majority of field mycologists agreed with Lange & Hora that they could manage without them.

Since then, attitudes have changed. In 1981, Roger Phillips used every English name he could lay his hands on for his best-selling *Mushrooms and other fungi of Great Britain & Europe*, better known as the 'Pan guide'. When Kew Gardens published its monographs on truffles, puffballs and chanterelles in the 1990s, it found English names for them all. The trouble was that some of these invented names were truly awful. There was little memorability in names such as 'reddish-brown corky spine fungus' or 'strong-scented stephensia', which did not exactly make the best case for common names. They were not what E C Large had in mind when he spoke of 'good, short, rude names that young lips can pronounce'.

In 2000, the British Mycological Society made up its mind and began a serious attempt to provide fungi with imaginative but appropriate names that people could remember. Among the interested parties were the Association of Fungus Groups, representing Britain's local fungus groups and societies, the four government nature-conservation agencies and Plantlife, which administered the process under the umbrella of the newly founded Fungus Conservation Forum. There was no intention of providing names for *all* British fungi – there were far too many – but around 1,000 species, it was felt, *deserved* a name. They included fungi that had come into prominence through their inclusion in various protected lists, or as 'indicator species' in habitat surveys. The new names, it was hoped, would help to raise their public profile, or, as I might have put it, to put the fun back into fungi.

Where there was an accepted English name already, such as Old Man of the Woods, Slippery Jack, or Plums and Custard, it was retained. Where a species had more than one name, as in the Shaggy Inkcap/ Lawyer's Wig, it was decided to retain both. The task of finding brand new names for 400-odd species was given to Liz Holden, an experienced and active field mycologist based in the Scottish Highlands. For her inventive vocabulary of fungal forms she drew inspiration from such universal things as 'colour, shape, host, edibility, toxicity, taste, smell, texture, folklore and humour'. Most of her neologisms were binomial, which often meant joining words, as in brittlegill or fibrecap. Many are based on a defining characteristic, such as 'webcap' for *Corti-*

narius, referring to the distinctive threads that shroud the young fruit body. The unusual spore colour of *Entoloma* is commemorated in 'pinkgill'. The chalky-textured genus *Russula* became 'brittlegills', objectively enough (although some of us would have preferred 'crumblecap', to match their relatives, the milkcaps, and incidentally make possible some memorable, if silly, combinations like 'apple crumblecap'). Words such as Amanita and bolete, which are enshrined in the Oxford English Dictionary, were regarded as sufficiently English already.

▲ **The edible Horn of Plenty** *Craterellus cornucopioides* recalls the classical fable of the goat's horn that suckled Jupiter.

Liz Holden's names have an authentically fungal flavour. Textures are evoked in oysterling, jellydisco, tarcrust and woodwax. Recognisable shapes are celebrated in funnels, shanks, parachutes and bonnets. Non-mushrooms include brains, spindles, corals, crusts and brackets. Occasionally, a little humour is allowed in. 'The Flirt' is her name for *Russula vesca*, a toadstool whose reddish cap-skin shrinks to reveal its white 'undergarment'. Her name for *Tricholoma* is 'knight', which sounds rather obscure unless one knows the French legend of a mushroom so delicious that it was served only to men of rank.

The new names were published by Plantlife in 2003, and subsequently by Summerfield Books. Michael McCarthy, in *The Independent*, had fun with them, noting the applicability of certain names for rock bands (Smoky Bracket), Pirates of the Caribbean (Redleg Toughshank and his sidekicks, Black Tooth and Mudwort Smut), exotic dancers (Foxy Fibrecap, Feather Stalkball) or denizens of some Tolkeinesque legend (Drumstick Truffleclub, Skullcap Dapperling). The latest field guides have taken them up with enthusiasm, notably those by Phillips (2006), Sterry & Hughes (2009) and Buczacki (2012). The new *Checklist of the British & Irish Basidiomycota* (Legon & Henrici 2005), on the other hand, ignores them, as does Jordan (2004) in the latest edition of his *Encyclopaedia of Fungi*.

And some nicknames

Nicknames are unofficial names which one seldom finds in textbooks but which are, nevertheless, widely used (for they have been given an airing on websites and blogs). One of these is the 'Train Wrecker', the nickname of *Neolentinus lepideus*, which won notoriety for growing on the traditional planks of pine once used as railway sleepers. As the fungus softened and rotted the timbers, so the sleepers lost their ability to hold the rails together, resulting in repeated derailments. Today, when wooden sleepers are no longer available to it, the distinctive scaly caps of *Neolentinus* have turned their attention to telegraph poles, as well as fence posts, picnic furniture, and the like. Its officially recommended name is the less prejudicial Scaly Sawgill.

Among other nicknames used mainly in America but which are entering the language over here through the internet, are the Stinking Pinwheel *Micromphale foetidum*, the Flabby Crepidotus or Jelly Crep *Crepidotus mollis* and Stinky Squid Fungus *Clathrus archeri*, although its accepted name of Devil's Fingers seems just as dramatic. One of the best names, Woman-on-a-motorbike, unfortunately belongs to a non-British species, a parasol mushroom, *Lepiota naucina*, which has long, shaggy 'hair' falling from a crash-helmet-like boss. Equally amusing are the disrespectful names for those dreary 'little brown mushrooms' (or LBMs), the *Tubaria*s. One has been dubbed the Truly Trivial Tubaria, another, the entrancingly dull *T. tenuis*, the Totally Tedious Tubaria. With English old-world courtesy, the official name is currently 'twiglets'.

A recent 'Name-a-Species' competition in *The Guardian* came up with 'Hot-lips' for the disc fungus *Octospora humosa* from its resemblance to the fleshy lips on a Rolling Stones album sleeve. The flamboyant *Xerocomus bubulinus* became 'Ascot Hat'.

The glory and wonder of formal names

As most naturalists, and certainly every mycologist, will know, basic scientific names (often called 'Latin names', although they are frequently in fact Greek) contain two words: first the genus, followed by the species. An 'author citation', the name or names of the mycologist who first described it, is sometimes added afterwards. To most field mycologists and forayers scientific names are as familiar as a well-worn slipper, and it is a pity that few of us give much thought as to what they mean. For, clearly, a lot of thought went into them. What follows is, I hope, a revelation of 'fungosity' through the communal experience of those who first coined them.

▶ **The Sickener** *Russula emetica*, so named from its hot taste, which can upset delicate stomachs.

In a minority of cases the scientific name means exactly the same thing as the English common name. *Geastrum*, for example, means earthstar. *Lactarius* means 'milky ones', which is much the same thing as 'milkcap'. Other genus names are slightly comic. The Giant Puffball, for example, is *Calvatia*, derived from a word meaning bald, and inspired by its great hairless head-sized domes appearing through the grass. *Lacrymaria*, which means 'Mary's tears', is the Weeping Widow, a funereal mushroom that sheds black droplets of moisture.

More often, the genus commemorates some distinguishing feature. Species of *Volvariella*, meaning 'little purse', have a membrane at the base of the stipe the shape of an old-fashioned belt purse. *Marasmius* comes from a word meaning 'drying out', and refers to the way the mushrooms turn pale as they dry. *Stereum*, the name for crust-like fungi that grow on logs, simply means hard or stiff. Other names are more imaginative. *Gomphidius* means 'little peg', an echo of the drumstick shape of the young mushroom, with its little button cap. *Collybia* means 'little coin', a name suggested by the penny-shaped brown caps when seen from above.

▲ **Glistening Inkcap**
Coprinus micaceus, with its telltale scales like flakes of mica.

Many mushroom names are based on a kind of formula. A suffix that crops up regularly is *-cybe*, meaning head or cap. Thus we have *Clitocybe* (sloping caps), *Calocybe* (pretty caps) and *Inocybe* (fibre caps). Another is *-loma*, meaning fringe or border, referring to the texture of the cap rim. Among the *-loma* names are *Tricholoma* (hair-fringe), *Entoloma* (inner-fringe) and the classically inspired *Hebeloma* (young-fringe), derived from Hebe, the mythical personification of youth.

Other names were suggested by colour. *Russula* means reddish, and although by no means all *Russulas* are red, a great many are; some of the commonest and best-known species are as bright as cherries. *Melanoleuca* means black-and-white, a name these stately mushrooms, incidentally, share with the Giant Panda. *Leucocoprinus* means white dung-fungi, or, more specifically, white inkcaps.

Other names still are rooted in classical literature. *Amanita*, a genus that contains many poisonous species, is derived ironically from the ancient name for the Field Mushroom! (By sheer coincidence, *Amanita* is also a Malay word meaning 'peaceful woman'.) The genus *Mycena*, dainty fungi known as fairy-bells or bonnets, is named after the ancient Greek city of Mycenae, which was, in turn, inspired by the Greek word for a fungus, *mykes*. According to legend, the city was founded by Perseus who, finding himself thirsty, drank from water pouring from a mushroom that had sprung up at his feet. The name must have seemed appropriate for these little fungi, which have a dandelion-like hollow stalk containing fluid.

When it comes to species names, various part-words tend to be used over and over again. For anyone seeking to understand them, it helps to know that names ending in *-ides*, *-opsis* or *-aceus* are all versions of

◀ **A mushroom of many colours**: the green, orange, yellow or bluish Parrot Waxcap *Hygrocybe psittacina*. The species name refers to the Latin for parrot.

the same thing, and mean 'look-alike'. For example, *micaceus*, the name of one of our commonest inkcaps, means 'like mica', and refers to the distinctive sparkling crystals on its brown cap. Names that end in *-ascens* or *-escens* mean 'turning into'. These generally belong to mushrooms that change colour as they get older (you can speed up the process by bruising them), so that *Hygrocybe nigrescens* turns from off-white to black, while *Cortinarius purpurascens*, like us, bruises a deep purple-red. Those species that are smaller than their neighbours in the field guide are often given diminutive endings such as *-ellus*, *-illus* or *-cellus*, meaning, in effect, 'little ones'. Those ending in *-olens*, meaning 'pertaining to smell', are noted for their strong scent, pleasant or otherwise. Names ending in *-phila*, meaning 'loving', are associated with a particular habitat. For example, *Psathyrella ammophila* 'loves' the sand; its full name might translate as 'the little fragile one that likes the dunes'.

▼ **Named after its colour**, the Orange Peel Fungus *Aleuria aurantia* appears on bare ground on tracks and roadsides.

There are probably more colour names among the mushrooms than in any other group of living things, a sign of how important colour is in identification. Mycologists soon acquire an eye for subtle shades. For example, the formal names of yellow fungi include no fewer than 40 different shades. Among them are *aurata* (golden), *citrina* (lemon), *crocea* (saffron), *lutea* (golden-yellow), *straminea* (straw), *ochroleuca* (ochre plus milky-white), *luteovirens* (yellow-green) and *vitellina* (egg-yolk). The milkcap *Lactarius chrysorrheus*, which oozes a rich yellow liquid when broken, means 'gold-flowing milk'. The name *icterina*, shared by several fungi, is derived from a Greek word meaning jaundice, that is, a bright, bilious yellow.

Similar inventiveness went into the naming of reddish toadstools, which vary from *aurantia* (rich orange), *coccinea* (bright red, as in the red dye, cochineal), *sanguinea* (blood-red), *testaceus* (brick-red), *cuprea* (coppery), *rubiginosa* (rusty), *hysginus* (flesh-coloured) or *vinosa* (the colour of red wine). *Cortinarius cinnabarinus* is named after an artist's pigment, cinnabar or mercuric oxide. The bolete *Xerocomus armeniacus* has nothing to do with Armenia; it shares the scientific name of the apricot, *Prunus armeniaca*, and is named after its apricot colours. The name *miniata* derives not from 'miniature' but from the Latin name of red lead, *minium* (even though the Vermilion Waxcap *Hygrocybe miniata* is, indeed, small and neat).

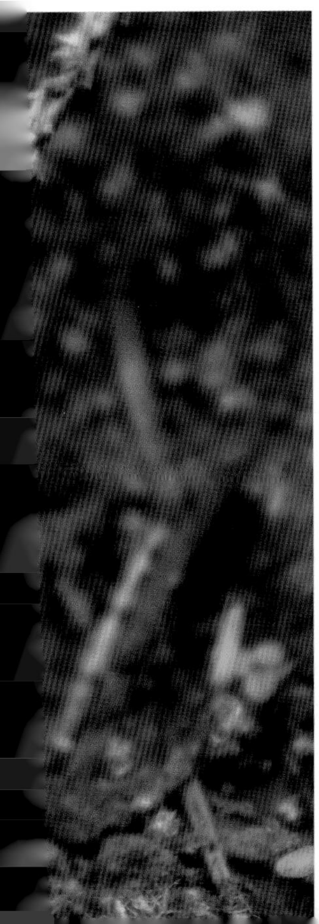

Perhaps the greatest imaginative effort of all went into the legions of brown mushrooms. Among them, the earnestly peering scholars managed to distinguish *cervinus* or *cervicolor* (the colour of deer), *badius* (bay-brown), *spadiceus* (date-brown), *hepaticus* (liver-brown), *hunnuleus* ('coloured like a young stag') and, best of all, *xerampilina* (the colour of 'withered vine leaves'). Botanists might be forgiven for assuming that *Hebeloma vaccinum* grows among *Vaccinum* or bilberries. In fact, it means 'the colour of a cow', that is (or was), brown.

A few formal names were clearly intended to amuse. Generations of naturalists have delighted in *Phallus impudicus* and its sauciness in putting forth such an obscene shape (one which Beatrix Potter found herself unable to draw). And to give a much more recent example, the species name of the colourful webcap *Cortinarius poppyzon* means a 'clicking of the tongue': an appropriate expression of delight in discovering so fine a fungus. Perhaps we shall come to call it the Wolfwhistle Webcap.

chapter four

Mushrooms on parade

Having considered a lot of fungal names and their meanings, it is time we put them in some sort of order. Fungi are classified by the way their spores are dispersed, so that one major group, the Ascomycota, squirts them out of little pockets called asci, while the other, the Basidiomycota, has them perched on top of an inflated, balloon-like part called a basidium. These two groups contain all the larger fungi found in Britain, a few hundred in the case of the 'Ascos', more than 2,000 with the 'Basidios'.

◀ **Golden Scalycap**
Pholiota aurivella on a fallen Beech trunk in the New Forest, Hampshire.

The variety of larger fungi is astonishing. Plants are restricted to a basic structure by their need for leaves, shoots and roots. The fruit bodies of fungi are much more plastic. Like plants, fungi can be broken down into natural groups which in most cases are easy to recognise in the field. There are many that share a basic mushroom shape, of course, but there are others of quite different appearance, shaped like balls, coral, clubs or brackets. Some have pores, spines or folds in place of gills. Some form shapeless crusts on fallen boughs and logs. Then there are the underground truffles, varying from small, cherry-like growths to larger ones that, frankly, resemble Badger droppings. There are fungi that look like burnt cakes, cups (or saucers), or lumps of jelly. Morels and their relatives are sometimes described as brains on sticks. My intention here is to set out this wonderful variety by introducing the main groups with a few words on each to give at least an idea of what they are like, and how many species there are. The common names are those recommended by the British Mycological Society, and the scientific ones from the *Checklist of the British & Irish Basidiomycota* (Legon & Henrici 2005).

Estimated number of species of British fungi

Basidiomycota (or Basidiomycetes)
c.3,500 species, consisting of:

Boletes	73
Mushrooms and toadstools (Agaricales)	c.2,200
Hedgehog fungi	32
Chanterelles	12
Gasteroid fungi (Gasteromycetes)	72
Club and coral fungi	c.100
Polypores	c.60
Corticoid fungi	c.375
Jelly fungi	c.200
False truffles	32
Rusts and smuts	c.360

Ascomycota (or Ascomycetes)
c.5,600 species, consisting of:

Cup fungi (Discomycetes)	c.1,600
Flask fungi (Pyrenomycetes)	c.2,300
Lichens	c.1,700

These approximate figures exclude the fungi known as anamorphs which, to cut a long story short, have different reproductive characteristics and so are named separately, even though they might (or might not) be the same species as sexually reproducing fungi.

Total number of British fungi, large and small: c.12,000

The main groups of larger fungi found in Britain

Basidiomycota

Fungi whose spores develop on a structure known as a basidium.

Mushroom-shaped fungi with pores

Boletes *Boletus, Leccinum, Xerocomus, Suillus* and smaller genera

About 73 species. Boletes are plump, fleshy fungi that have a spongy layer of pores instead of gills. The archetypal bolete is the Penny Bun or Cep *Boletus edulis*, perhaps the most sought after edible mushroom in the world. But the group also includes the lankier, rough-stemmed *Leccinums*, the smaller *Xerocomus* species and the often sticky-capped *Suillus*, as well as various smaller genera. The pore colours vary from cream and yellow to red or pink, darkening as the fungus matures, while their stipes often bear an interesting pattern of nets, dots or scales. Some change colour when cut or bruised. Most boletes grow as partners on the roots of trees or, in a few cases, on rockrose and other plants.

Mushrooms with gills

There are around 2,200 species of gilled mushrooms, or agarics, and new British species are discovered every year. Gills are the thin flaps underneath the cap of a mushroom that radiate from the centre, like spokes. They carry spore-bearing structures called basidia, which pop off the spores when ripe, sending the dust-like spores swirling into the dank air beneath the cap. I have divided the vast variety of gilled mushrooms into recognisable groups, some of which belong to a single genus, and others to groups of related genera.

Rollrims *Paxillus, Tapinella*

5 species. Rollrims are relatives of boletes but have gills on the underside of a flattish or funnel-shaped cap. These are easy to peel off. The cap of the commonest species has an inrolled rim, like a piecrust.

Spikes *Gomphidius, Chroogomphus*

4 species. Flat-topped mushrooms with slimy caps and decurrent gills (that is, they run down the stem below the cap). One of them has a little telltale spike, like that on an old-fashioned German helmet.

◀ **The Bovine Bolete** *Suillus bovinus*, like all boletes, is mushroom-shaped but has pores, rather than gills. This one is strongly associated with pine.

Milkcaps *Lactarius*

75 species. Milkcaps are easily recognised by the milky latex they exude when broken or damaged. They are medium-sized mushrooms with flattish caps that become funnel shaped at maturity. Some are

smooth, others fluffy with a pleasing fringe, and their colours vary from cream through shades of yellow, orange and brown to pink or reddish. Milkcaps have a crunchy texture and many have fiery hot or sour tastes.

Brittlegills *Russula*

This is a huge genus, with 145 species and counting (although only 20 or so are regularly encountered). You can recognise a brittlegill by its crumbly texture and gills that snap off easily. Many of the brightly coloured mushrooms in woods are brittlegills – polished reds, yellows, oranges, purples, pinks and greens, while the spores vary from white to yellowish. Like milkcaps, some have a hot taste, and in some cases also interesting smells (fruity, shellfish, marzipan, etc).

▲ **Yellowdrop Milkcap** *Lactarius chrysorrheus*. The bright yellow milk and association with oak are diagnostic.

Parasols *Macrolepiota*

9 species. Tall, stately mushrooms with scaly caps and a double ring around the stem which one can slide up and down. The umbrella-like cap usually has a central boss from which the scales radiate outwards.

Dapperlings *Lepiota, Cystolepiota, Leucoagaricus, Melanophyllum, Chamaemyces*

74 species. Small to medium-sized mushrooms with white spores, some with scaly caps and stem rings (many of these are poisonous), others with smooth caps. Some have intriguing rubbery or camphor smells, while the two species of *Melanophyllum* have blood-red or green gills respectively. *Chamaemyces* is covered with 'dewdrops' that stain it with spots.

▼ **Beechwood Sickener** *Russula nobilis*, a hot-tasting species strongly associated with Beech.

Powdercaps *Cystoderma*

8 species. Attractive little fungi covered with tiny golden or brick-red granules all over the cap and stem, with a smooth bit just below the gills. Very occasionally, they are parasitised by fungi called stranglers (*Squamanita*) which take them over, producing fungal monsters, part strangler, part powdercap.

Amanitas *Amanita*

39 species. Sturdy, medium-sized mushrooms with white, crowded gills that are free (that is, not attached to the stem). Many have a club-foot at the base (clavate) or a stem that emerges from a membranous bag (volva). Most include a

stem ring, those without having a flattish cap with striations at the edge. Some have the remains of a veil sticking to the cap, forming pale shreds or spots. This genus includes many well-known mushrooms, including the Blusher, the Panthercap, the Fly Agaric, the Destroying Angel and the Deathcap. The formal name was thought familiar enough to become an English name, too.

▲ **Scarlet Waxcap** *Hygrocybe coccinea* is bright red, like fallen cherries, with a greasy cap.

Rosegills *Volvariella*

11 species. Like Amanitas, these white mushrooms emerge from a bag or volva, but they have rose-pink gills and spores. For a small genus, they have an inventive range of life-styles: some grow on rotten wood, one does well on the straw of cornfields, while a third is a piggyback, growing on other mushrooms.

Waxcaps *Hygrocybe*

51 species. These are often brightly coloured mushrooms with a polished, sometimes sticky or slimy cap, and thick, waxy gills. Most are grassland species. They are identified using cap textures – dry, greasy, or slimy (viscid) – as well as their beautiful colours, with reds, yellows and greys predominating.

Woodwaxes *Hygrophorus*

22 species. Mostly pale, fleshy mushrooms with white spores and a waxy texture. Some have dry caps, others are slimy. Most of them grow in woodland, sometimes late in the season.

Honey fungi *Armillaria*

6 species. Tough, brownish tufted mushrooms, most of which grow on logs and stumps, with the help of black 'bootlaces' or rhizomorphs. Most have stem rings and all have small scales on their honey-coloured caps. The common Honey Fungus *Armillaria mellea* is a notorious parasite of trees in plantations and gardens.

Knights *Tricholoma*

45 species. Medium-sized, thickset mushrooms with domed caps, some with striations or scales, and often sinuate (wavy) gills. Their colour ranges from pure white and yellow to more nondescript browns and greys. Most grow in woodland and some have distinctive smells, such as meal, gas or soap.

Cavaliers *Melanoleuca*

19 species. More elegant than the knights, they often have tall stems and flattish, thin-fleshed caps. Most are in shades of brown that go pale in dry weather. Under the microscope many have strange cells shaped like harpoons or clubs.

Funnels *Clitocybe, Leucopaxillus* and smaller genera

48 species. These are funnel-shaped mushrooms, some tall and stately, others small and easily missed. Many have strong, distinctive smells of aniseed, hay, meal, cucumber, or, in one case, the inside of a henhouse. Some are fairly easy to recognise, others fiendishly difficult.

Blewits *Lepista*

11 species. Robust mushrooms with smooth, rounded caps, a firm flesh and gills that easily separate from the cap. Technically, they are similar to *Clitocybe* but have pinkish, not white, spores. The best-known species, the Field and Wood Blewits, have bluish-violet stalks.

Deceivers *Laccaria*

9 species. Tough little brown mushrooms (or, in one case, a little violet mushroom) with thick gills and a deceiving range of shapes and sizes. The stipe has striations that are often characteristically twisted.

▼ **Clouded Funnel**
Clitocybe nebularis is a large, funnel-shaped species the colour of a thunder-cloud. One of the commonest late-season mushrooms, it is often found growing in circles or 'troops'.

▲ **Burgundydrop Bonnet** *Mycena haematopus*, like most 'bonnets' (formerly 'fairy bells'), grows on decaying plant material.

Shanks and toughshanks *Collybia* and related genera
35 species. A ragbag group of woodland mushrooms with very tough stalks and the texture of cartilage. Some grow in clusters, others in large numbers on decaying leaves on the woodland floor.

Navels *Omphalina* and smaller genera
20 species. These tiny, funnel-shaped fungi grow among moss on lawns and peat bogs (and sometimes plant pots). A few form an association with algae as a kind of half-lichen. Many have delicate translucent colours, and one is a beautiful shade of blue-green.

Parachutes *Marasmius*, *Micromphale* and smaller genera
36 species. Mostly small, delicate-looking fungi with domed, furrowed caps reminiscent of an expanded parachute. Many grow attached to debris such as twigs and decaying leaves. A few have tough 'horsehair' stalks, while *Micromphale* species smell of rotting cabbage or radish.

Bonnets *Mycena*, *Hemimycena* and smaller genera
93 species. Small, delicate mushrooms with conical, bell-like caps and slender stalks, which are often hollow and sometimes latex-filled (one common species 'bleeds' red juice). Some grow in tufts on debris and stumps, or on the decaying leaves of particular plants. Colours range from pure white through shades of brown and grey, enlivened by the odd candy-pink, purple or even hairy one.

Piggybacks *Asterophora*
2 species. A pair of little white powdery mushrooms that grow on the backs of other mushrooms. Always a favourite find on fungus forays.

Pinkgills *Entoloma*
156 species. A large and challenging group of mostly smallish mushrooms with pink gills (the spores, which are also pink, are in strange geometric shapes). Many species are characteristic of old grassland or heath. Colours range from shades of brown and beige to more attractive dark blues and violets (which fade with age).

Shields *Pluteus*
28 species. Mostly smallish mushrooms characterised by round caps and gills that are pink and free (i.e. not attached to the stem). All of them grow on rotten wood, including woodchip and sawdust. Some have attractively patterned or brightly coloured caps. They may be indicators of ancient, or at least lightly managed, woodland.

▲ **Pelargonium Webcap** *Cortinarius flexipes*, a common webcap with a distinctive point ('umbo'), growing in moss under birch.

Webcaps *Cortinarius*

228 species. The largest mushroom genus, most of which grow in woodland. Webcaps have tobacco-brown spores and a veil or cobweb of fibres that covers the gills of the young mushroom and later adheres to the stem. Many webcaps are attractive, with bold shapes, bulbous stipes and subtle shades of red, violet, yellow and orange, along with a bewildering array of stripes, sheaths, rings and speckles. Unfortunately, most are difficult to name, even with the help of the microscope.

Rustgills *Gymnopilus*

12 species. Medium-sized orange-brown mushrooms that grow in tufts on decaying wood, so-named because the yellowish gills develop rusty brown spots as they mature.

Poisonpies *Hebeloma*

32 species. A tight-knit group of pale brown, brown-spored mushrooms, poisonous by repute, with a characteristically inrolled, pie-crust-like cap. Many smell of radish and have droplets on the gills. Not a group for the faint-hearted.

Aldercaps *Naucoria*

16 species. Dull little brown mushrooms with brown gills, which grow in alder swamps.

Fibrecaps *Inocybe*

108 species. Another large and challenging genus of smallish, brownish, brown-spored mushrooms. Yet they have their charms. Whilst most fibrecaps share the same basic build, many have intriguing scents and combinations of fibrils, bulbs, crystals and even 'hair'. They are poisonous, too.

Tufts and brownies *Hypholoma, Psilocybe*

35 species. Tufts are yellowish, dark-spored fungi that grow in large masses on decaying wood and stumps. They include our commonest mushroom, the Sulphur Tuft *Hypholoma fasciculare*. Brownies are smaller, with bell-shaped caps, and include the notorious Magic Mushroom or Liberty Cap *Psilocybe semilanceata*.

Conecaps *Conocybe*

64 species. A large group of small fungi with long, slender stems and cone-shaped caps that grow in grassland, woodland or dung. They all look the same.

Fieldcaps *Agrocybe, Bolbitius*
15 species. Another group of rather nondescript grassland fungi. One common species fruits on lawns in the spring, and another is common on woodchip. The Yellow Fieldcap *Bolbitius titubans* is a beautiful yellow, but so slimy it is almost impossible to pick. Technically speaking, the cap skin of fieldcaps is made up of rounded, not thread-like, cells.

Twiglets *Tubaria, Simocybe*
12 species. Little pale brown mushrooms without much character. They are not quite as boring as they look, for some species grow on fallen berries or twigs.

Scalycaps *Pholiota*
25 species. The scaliest of mushrooms, most of these yellow-brown species grow on logs, stumps or woody debris, often in large tufts. There is usually a sheath or stem ring, and some are sticky, as well as excessively scaly.

Roundheads *Stropharia*
16 species. Dark-gilled mushrooms with a stem ring and often a slimy cap. Among them are several attractive blue-green species. Most grow on rich soil or dung, often in pasture or nettle beds.

Mottlegills *Panaeolus, Panaeolina*
9 species. Dark mushrooms with a tall, slender stem, bell-shaped cap and black spores, usually growing on dung in grassland. The brownish gills are characteristically mottled, like leopard skin, and, under a lens, may have pale edges.

Brittlestems *Psathyrella*
72 species. A difficult genus of delicate-looking mushrooms with slender, brittle (because hollow) stems, black spores and small bell-shaped or flattish caps – a bit like inkcaps, without the ink. Some species grow in tufts and many are hygrophanous, that is, they change colour on drying, becoming paler.

Inkcaps *Coprinus, Coprinopsis* and related genera
104 species. At maturity these mushrooms deliquesce, that is, they gradually dissolve away into an inky fluid containing the black spores. Their caps have an interesting range of scales, sparkles and pleats. Most are fragile and short-

▼ **Magpie Inkcap**
Coprinopsis picacea, tall, elegant and distinctive, but with an unpleasant whiff of halitosis.

▲ **Field Mushroom** *Agaricus campestris*, a familiar sight in pastures, particularly those grazed by cattle and horses.

lived; just a few are robust, including the well-known Lawyer's Wig or Shaggy Inkcap *Coprinus comatus* and Magpie Inkcap *Coprinopsis picacea*. Many of them grow on dung, straw or rotting vegetation.

True mushrooms *Agaricus*

40 species. These are mushrooms in the strictest sense, fleshy relatives of the Field Mushroom *Agaricus campestris*, which start as 'buttons', with baby-pink gills that darken as the mushroom matures. All have a stem ring, and some have soft cap scales. The flesh of some species turns yellow or pink when bruised. They occur in a wide range of habitats but are best known from rich soil in grassland. Not all true mushrooms are edible: beware those that smell of ink. It is phenol you can smell, and comes with a guaranteed tummy ache.

Oysters *Pleurotus, Hohenbuehelia*

17 species. These mushrooms grow on wood and have either very short stems or none at all: they are all cap and gills, and often grow in clusters. The flaring shape of the best-known species recalls the shell of the now defunct British oyster (and supplies the scientific name for such fungi, 'pleurotoid'). Secretly, these fungal oysters catch and consume tiny worms in the rotting wood.

Oysterlings *Panellus, Arrhenia, Melanotus* and related genera

28 species. These are the smaller oysters, with tiny stems, growing on rotten wood and other substrates (which, in *Melanotus*, have included doormats and the anchor ropes of boats).

Cockleshells *Lentinellus, Lentinus*

7 species. More shell-shaped fungi, most of which are rare. They grow on dead wood on standing or fallen trees.

Spores born on spines

Hedgehogs *Hydnum*

3 species. *Hydnum* hedgehogs have soft, mushroom-like flesh as well as prickly spines instead of gills. The commonest species, Wood Hedgehog *Hydnum repandum*, is known in restaurants as *pieds de mouton*.

Tooths *Hericium, Hydnellum, Phellodon* and smaller genera

29 species. Our three species of *Hericium* are spectacular fungi that grow on dead wood and resemble coral or mops. The others are tough, woodland fungi that grow free on the ground with a bracket-like cap supported on a stipe. Most of them are rare, and as a group they are of conservation interest. In this book, I call them hedgehogs.

Spores born in fleshy folds

Chanterelles *Cantharellus, Craterellus* and smaller genera

12 species. Delicious woodland fungi that have wrinkles and folds instead of gills. They include the well-known Chanterelle *Cantharellus cibarius* and the black Horn of Plenty *Craterellus cornucopioides*.

▲ **Golden Spindles** *Clavulinopsis fusiformis*. The spindle-shaped clusters are usually seen in grassland, but in this case are in mature woodland.

Coral and club fungi

Corals *Ramaria, Ramariopsis, Clavulina*

26 species. Wonderful fungi shaped like underwater corals, with massed, tightly packed branches. They come in a lovely range of colours, too – golden yellow, salmon pink, even violet. Unfortunately, they are not always easy to identify. A monograph by Brian Spooner is in preparation, to be published by the Royal Botanic Gardens, Kew.

Clubs and spindles *Clavaria, Clavulinopsis, Pterula* and other genera

33 species. 'Fairy clubs' are attractive yellow, orange and white fungi that form clubs and spindles in short, wet grass.

Cauliflower fungi *Sparassis*

2 species. Our only common cauliflower fungus, Wood Cauliflower or Brain Fungus *Sparassis crispa*, is unmistakable: a crisp, yellowish, cabbage-like growth at the base of pine trees. It tastes nice, too.

Gasteroid fungi

72 species. These are fungi whose spores are liberated with the help of exterior agents such as raindrops, flies or wind. They are 'stomach fungi', so-named after the bag-like puffballs. They are not all related but they all have a bag-like shape, at least to begin with.

Earthballs *Scleroderma*

7 species. Earthballs are similar to puffballs but have a thick, leathery skin covered in warts or little spines. Broken open, they smell of burning rubber.

Stalkballs (or stiltballs) *Tulostoma, Battarrea*

5 species. A quintet of rare and weird puffballs that grow on a tall stalk. Two are protected species.

Puffballs *Lycoperdon, Calvatia, Bovista* and small genera

24 species. *Lycoperdon* are the true puffballs that release their spores in puffs from a little aperture. The Giant Puffball *Calvatia gigantea* grows to the size of a football or a small boulder. Both it and the smaller *Bovista* puffballs release their spores passively, as the fruit body dries and breaks open.

▼ **Arched Earthstar** *Geastrum fornicatum* in the process of pumping spores into the damp air.

Earthstars *Geastrum* and small genera

18 species. A delightful bunch of fungi that resemble starfish or little manikins. Their outer skin forms 'arms' that lift the central ball off the ground to do its business, releasing spores. Always a foray highlight.

Bird's-nest fungi *Cyathus, Mycocalia, Crucibulum, Nidularia*

10 species. Little fungi shaped like tarts or nests. The spores are contained within egg-like peridioles that go 'ping' when hit by a raindrop.

Stinkhorns *Phallus, Mutinus, Clathrus* and small genera

8 species. The smelliest of fungi, these are one form of 'fungal flower' with scents that attract flies that feed on their noxious gunk and then buzz off with spores stuck to their legs. They form wonderful shapes: cages, tentacles and, of course, the rude gesture of the Stinkhorn *Phallus impudicus.*

Crust fungi, brackets and other fungi

These are mostly fungi that grow on wood, usually dead wood, although earthfans, rosettes and some polypores grow on the forest floor. Many brackets form large fruit bodies that project from the trunk. 'Crusts' form irregular patches, usually on the undersides of logs and dead wood.

Earthfans *Thelephora*

27 species. Dark fungi that form tough fan-shapes that hug the forest floor. They often have a mouldy or earthy smell and have been known to appear in plant pots.

Rosettes *Cotylidia, Stereopsis*

5 species. A group of rare fungi that form rosette-like brackets on the ground.

Polypores or bracket fungi Many genera, including *Polyporus, Phellinus, Trametes, Skeletocutis, Inonotus* etc

Bracket fungi are an indeterminate group, but more than 60 species fall loosely into this category. These are tough, pored, sometimes woody fungi that grow on the trunks and branches of trees, forming a projection that varies in shape from a flat bracket to a rounded horse's hoof (known as a 'conk'). Most are wood-rotters on fallen wood or standing trunks.

Mazegills *Daedalea, Datronia, Gloeophyllum, Phaeolus*

6 species. This is a sub-group of bracket fungi named after their pores, which look like an aerial view of a maze. The archetypal mazegill, *Daedalea*, is named after Daedalus, the founder of the famous labyrinth of Crete that hid the monstrous Minotaur.

Crusts *Stereum, Hymenochaete, Peniophora* and other genera

An indeterminate group of at least 375 species characterised as resupinate, that is, spread out flat on a substrate, especially dead wood and fallen logs. The genera *Stereum* and *Hymenochaete* are specifically known as crusts. Nearly all need a microscope for identification.

▶ **An earthfan,** *Thelephora penicillata*, forms rosettes with tufted tips among moss on the woodland floor.

▲ **Yellow Brain** *Tremella mesenterica*, a jelly fungus.

Jelly fungi

Many of the c.200 British species of jelly fungi are small and need a microscope for identification. The following is restricted to the larger and more accessible kinds.

Brains *Tremella, Exidia*

43 species. Brains are shapeless jelly-like buttons, lobes and frills, found on wood and branches. The best known are the Yellow Brain *Tremella mesenterica*, a parasite on crust fungi, and the black *Exidia glandulosa*, known as Witches' Butter.

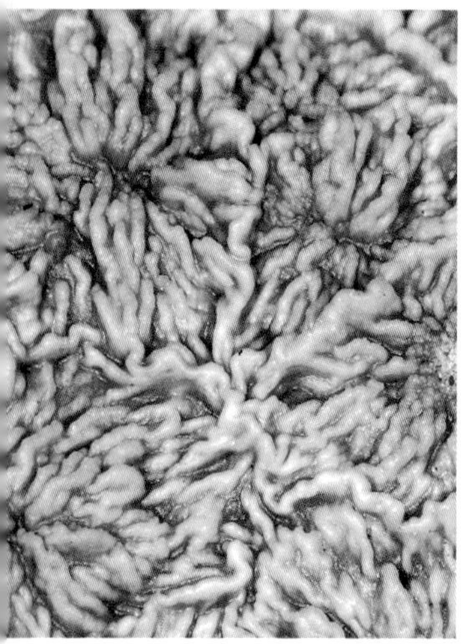

▲ **Wrinkled Crust** *Phlebia radiata.*

Jelly rots and cobwebs
Phlebia, Phlebiella and smaller genera

25 species. These are jelly fungi that resemble crusts or brackets. The best-known jelly rot is *Phlebia tremellosa*, a pinkish rubbery bracket covered in small bristles.

Stagshorns *Calocera*

5 species. These are the jelly world's fairy clubs – yellow or orange projections on dead wood, some like tiny antlers.

False truffles

False truffles *Rhizopogon, Hymenogaster* and other genera

32 species. Real truffles – including the expensive ones – are ascomycota. False truffles are basidiomycota and so unrelated, but they share the same round shape and underground lifestyle. You would not want to eat a false truffle. Many smell disgusting. But, since the job of a truffle is to be eaten and void its spores in the dung, something obviously likes them.

▼ **Coltsfoot Rust** *Puccinia poarum* produces rusty-red spots.

Rusts and smuts

Rusts Urediniomycetes

260 species. Rusts are parasitic fungi on a wide range of plants, and are more easily identified from the host than their individual characteristics. Hence, rusts are 'botanists' fungi'. They are named after the fruit bodies that burst from infected leaves, but while some are rust coloured, others are bright yellow or orange. Rusts have very complicated life cycles, often involving more than one host.

Smuts Ustilaginomycetes

c.100 species. Smuts, like rusts, also have a complicated life cycle. The most noticeable feature of these parasitic fungi is their dark, powdery spores, reminiscent of the smuts produced by smoke. Also known as bunts. Once best known as agricultural and horticultural pests, some rusts and smuts are now on the protected list.

Redleafs *Exobasidium*

13 species. Parasitic fungi, mainly of the heather family, that distort the leaves and shoots of the host. Some produce galls, others turn the leaves red.

▲ **Cowberry Redleaf** *Exobasidium vaccinii* colours the Cowberry leaves bright red to match the berries.

Ascomycota

These are fungi whose spores are contained in pockets and tubes known as asci. They work like water pistols, squirting the spores high into the air with, in a few cases, an audible pop. There are about 250 species of larger Ascomycota in all (plus several thousand smaller ones we won't bother with). Unlike Basidiomycota, a large proportion of the larger 'ascos' fruit in the spring. In addition, most British lichens are ascomycete fungi that have co-evolved with plants (or blue-green bacteria) in the form of algae.

Truffles *Tuber, Elaphomyces* and other genera

35 species. 'True' truffles, that is, the ones we enjoy to eat, are members of the genus *Tuber*: underground fungi with powerful scents. *Elaphomyces*, or hart's truffles, appeal more to deer and squirrels.

Candlesnuff and fingers *Xylaria*

6 species. The plump, dark bunches attached to wood are known as Dead Man's Fingers *Xylaria polymorpha*. The one with black-and-white antlers is known as the Candlesnuff Fungus *X. hypoxylon*, an old name that has survived the advance of electricity.

Jellydiscs and bulgars *Ascocoryne, Neobulgaria*

10 species. Fungi that resemble rubber buttons attached to dead wood. The best known is the ink-black Bulgar *Bulgaria inquinans*.

▼ **Candlesnuff Fungus** *Xylaria hypoxylon*. Its antler-like tufts are very common on stumps and fallen branches.

▲ **Lemon Disco** *Bisporella citrina*, whose bright yellow discs are very common on fallen branches in damp places.

Jellybabies
Cudonia, Leotia, Spathularia, Mitrula
8 species. More rubbery or jelly-like fungi, some of which are brightly coloured and resemble jellybaby sweets. The best known is the Bog Beacon *Mitrula paludosa*, which brightens dull ditches in spring with its vivid orange matchsticks.

Earthtongues *Geoglossum* and other genera
18 species. Characterful but easily overlooked fungi of grassland and moorland, either black or green, and variously shaped like tongues, pokers or lollipops. They are of interest to conservationists as indicators of old grassland and good spots generally.

Caterpillarclubs and truffleclubs *Cordyceps*
9 species. These bizarre clubs and matchsticks grow on the bodies of insects buried in the ground or on false truffles. The best known is Scarlet Caterpillarclub *Cordyceps militaris*, whose appearance has been compared with toy soldiers.

Discos *Bisporella, Hymenoscyphus* and many other genera
c.50 species (the term 'disco' is not sharply defined). Tiny, stalked cups like little goblets, attached to damp, rotting wood and various plants. The Lemon Disco *Bisporella citrina* is an unmissable bright yellow, the Common Grey Disco *Mollisia cinerea* a pretty shade of grey. The Snowy Disco *Lachnum virgineum*, of dead bramble stems, is creamy white.

▼ **Scarlet Elfcup** *Sarcoscypha austriaca*. The bright red cups are found on fallen mossy Hazel branches in early spring.

Spots and woodwarts *Nectria, Hypoxylon*
34 species. Pustules, warts, lumps and spots attached to wood and twigs, of which the best known is the red Coral Spot *Nectria cinnabarina*.

Cups, crowncups and elfcups
Peziza, Disciotis, Sarcoscypha and others
There are around 300 species in the cup-fungus family, the Pezizales, of which perhaps 50 are large enough to find easily. Named after their characteristic shape, they include the beautiful Scarlet Elfcup *Sarcoscypha austriaca*, the big, jagged-edged Violet Crowncup *Sarcosphaera coronaria* and the unmistakable Orange Peel Fungus *Aleuria aurantia*. Many species fruit in the spring.

Ears *Otidea*
5 species. Related to cup fungi but attractively elongated into Rabbits' ears. Nice colours, too, being mainly orange and ochre.

False morels and saddle fungi *Gyromitra, Helvella*
22 species. These poisonous (when raw) relatives of the morels have saddle- or brain-shaped heads, and in some cases look like half-melted candles.

True morels *Morchella, Mitrophora*
6 species. True morels look like bits of sponge on a hollow white stalk. The comely Common Morel *Morchella esculenta* is honey-coloured, the others dark. Morels are the most expensive wild fungi found in Britain.

Tongues, besoms *Taphrina*
20 species. These parasitic fungi produce distinctive galls on a range of trees. Some look like exotic fruit, such as the yellow mini-bananas on Aspen formed by Aspen Tongue *Taphrina johansonii*, the Pocket Plums *T. pruni* on plum trees, or the flame-coloured tongues produced by Alder Tongue *T. alni* on Alder cones. Another *Taphrina* produces Witches' Brooms or Birch Besom on birch trees.

▲ **Black Morel** *Morchella elata* is distinguished by the elongated head and mostly vertical 'ribs'.

Lichens

c.1,700 species. Lichens are 'dual organisms', that is, a combination of a fungus and a primitive plant, an alga (or in some cases a cyanobacterium). The fungal component is, in most cases, an ascomycete. The alga enables the lichen to manufacture its own food, like a plant, and therefore to grow on barren substrates such as rock and bark. Lichens are traditionally regarded as a separate study, lichenology, and in Britain they have been well studied and recorded.

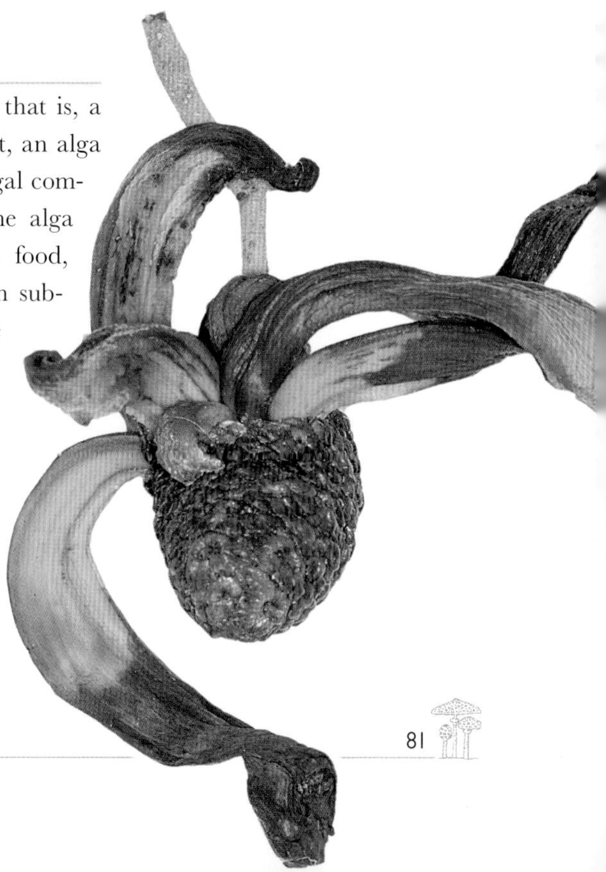

▶ **Alder Tongue** *Taphrina alni*, eerie, scarlet tongues emerging from alder cones.

chapter five

What mushroom is that?

'Fungi are hard to identify.' This is true. 'Fungi are easy to identify.' That is also true. Admittedly, a great many fungi, even some mushrooms and toadstools, require a microscope to spot the diagnostic features that separate one species from another. You cannot get very far with a hard genus such as *Inocybe* or *Galerina* without a toolkit of stains, reagents and slides. Moreover, they will drag you into the coils of taxonomic dispute, where experts debate and argue without, it seems, ever agreeing. But few of us will want to go that far. We can have a lot of fun with fungi without becoming at all expert. You can quickly name dozens of species you find on forays with no more than a pair of eyes and a hand lens. Ignore the 'little brown mushrooms' (LBMs) for now. There are plenty of big, colourful, shapely fungi that are as easy to name as wild flowers and ferns. And if you really hanker after the name of that LBM, you can always sneak it onto the pile of one of the folk with microscopes, who probably won't have much time left over for fieldwork.

There are certain things about mushrooms that you have to get used to. For a start, size doesn't count. Unlike animals, mushrooms and other fungi do not always grow to a predetermined size and shape. It all depends on how well grown (and doubtless how well fed) they are. Supermarket mushrooms are all the same size because they are grown industrially, in controlled conditions. But gather Field Mushrooms in the wild and you find them in all shapes and sizes, from little buttons to flat-tops the size of a saucer. Recently, I was admiring a rare mass fruiting of the Deceiving Bolete *Boletus queletii*, a handsome fungus with a date-brown cap and vermilion pores. The smallest were the size of

◀ **Drumstick stage of the magnificent Parasol** *Macrolepiota procera.*

a penny but the largest were more like a penny bun (that is, a large bun that probably cost a penny in 1840). As for shape, they were about as regular as the lumps of plasticene left over from a toddlers' playgroup. Colour is a more reliable criterion, but it, too, can be distressingly inconstant. Colours can wash off in the rain, or turn pale as the mushroom dries out. Some mushrooms even change colour, usually growing darker, if they are bruised, or as they grow older.

So to name mushrooms you have to concentrate on characters that are more or less constant. One of the best is the colour of the spores. Find a mature cap and smudge some of the gills on your finger (you can get better results by putting the cap under a glass on a sheet of paper or a piece of glass for a few hours; for species with white spores, use toned paper). Fungal spores come in a wide variety of colours, and you can identify the more subtle ones with a colour chart such as that published by the Royal Botanic Gardens, Edinburgh. Spores have a more or less fixed shape and size. A powerful microscope reveals their nature: a surprisingly wide variety, including ones that are smooth, spiny, warty, netted (reticulate) or, in the case of certain species of *Inocybe*, reminiscent of flying pigs!

▼ **Agaricus mushrooms** are mostly large and fleshy, with crowded gills and dark spores. This one, the Yellow Stainer *Agaricus xanthodermus*, is easily recognised by instantly turning chrome-yellow when the stipe base is cut. It smells unpleasantly of ink (phenol).

Another valuable clue is the way the gills are attached to the stem, or stipe, as we are supposed to call it. With 'free' gills, which characterise the genera *Amanita* or *Pluteus*, among others, there is a clear, ring-shaped space between the gills and the stipe, as one can ascertain by looking up at them (or using a dental mirror, if you do not wish to pick the specimen). Other gills are 'adnate', that is they are attached to the stipe, or 'decurrent', which means the gills run partway down the stem. You can also take out your x10 hand lens and check the gill edges. A pale, dark, mottled or toothed gill edge may help to identify a species. On *Paxillus*, the gills easily pull away from the cap. With inkcaps, they turn into ink.

You can also have a look at the average cap shape. Caps vary from bell-shaped to flatter 'berets', sometimes with a little bobble on the top. Others are more like funnels with hollow centres. The cap may be grooved along the margin (sulcate), or have bits of skin hanging down off it (appendiculate). The cap texture may be smooth, slimy, sticky or scaly. Some caps are downy or silky, or curiously wrinkled or cracked. Some species of *Lepiota* are positively fluffy. The caps of some species become frilly-edged (flexuose) as they get older. The stipe, too, has all sorts of diagnostic features. It may be ringed (or double ringed), pitted, powdery or marked with zones, like snake-skin. The base may have a bulbous swelling, or sit inside a membranous cup called a volva. Some species change colour when the base of the stipe is cut. The Deceiving Bolete I mentioned earlier turns a deep beetroot-red. The infamous Yellow Stainer *Agaricus xanthodermus* turns bright chrome-yellow, which is the best way of telling it from its edible look-alike, the Field Mushroom *A. campestris*.

Colour is an important character, but another, less expected one is smell, and another still is taste. We mushroom hunters do a lot of sniffing and tasting. Some mushrooms could be identified by a blind person by scent alone. Putting such elusive things as scent into words has exerted the imaginations of mycologists down the ages, some of whom, to judge from their wilder flights of fancy, might have been wine-tasters. One species has been confidently compared with a nurse's starched blouse, another with 'ladies of the street' i.e. cheap soap. Among the commonest fungal scents is 'new meal', in other words, fresh flour, and also pastry, marzipan and aniseed balls. More exclusive ones have furnished the mushroom's common name, as in Coconut Milkcap *Lactarius glyciosmus*, Curry Milkcap *L. camphoratus*, Cucumber Cap

▼ **Oldrose Bolete**
Boletus rhodopurpureus is a rare and colourful bolete that turns an instant deep blue when cut.

After Eight Mints (others say menthol) ***Lepista glaucocana***
Wine corks ***Russula adusta***
Bubble gum ***Russula fragilis***
Smelly feet ***Cortinarius camphoratus***
Eau de Cologne (or Parma violets) ***Lepista irina***
Composted elder flowers ***Pluteus petasatus***
Mint and blackberry jam ***Russula pseudointegra***
Harlots (i.e. cheap soap) ***Tricholoma saponaceum***
Hen coops ***Clitocybe phaeophthalma***
Laudanum ***Russula cavipes***
Old sherry casks ***Russula densifolia***
Poppy petals ***Mycena leptocephala***
Old mashed potato ***Cortinarius callisteus***
Russian leather (or cedarwood) ***Hygrocybe russocoriacea***
Snickers bars ***Tricholoma aurantium***
Stewed apples ***Russula fellea***
TCP ***Cortinarius obtusus***

▲ **Soapy Knight**
Tricholoma saponaceum smells of cheap soap, or, some say, 'ladies of the street'!
Listed above are some of my favourite smell analogies and comparisons.

Macrocystidia cucumis and Cabbage Parachute *Micromphale brassicolens.* Crab Brittlegill *Russula xerampelina* smells like rotting crab. *Cortinarius vulpinus* is said to smell like a sow on heat, *Russula amoena* of artichokes. Various species of *Pholiota* are said to smell of straw or sweetcorn. Some of my favourites are listed above.

Perhaps the smelliest genus of all is *Inocybe*, the fibrecaps, a tricky group of small or medium-sized mushrooms with snuff-brown spores. What they lack in physical presence, they make up for in pongs, which vary from over-ripe pears and bananas to 'musty barrel staves', dirty stables, cloves, truffles, pelargonium, honey, fish, acorns, urine and rotten meat. Quite a few smell, to put it as politely as possible, 'spermatic'. One common species, *Inocybe corydalina*, combines a nausea-inducing odour of over-ripe fruit with a well-known brand of toilet cleaner.

It's fun to make the best use of our taste buds, too (though not, perhaps, with *Inocybe*). Nibbling unknown mushrooms should be done with caution. Chew a little bit of cap for 30 seconds or so (some tastes take a little while to develop). Then spit it out. And do not taste anything known or suspected to be poisonous. The hot or bitter taste of raw milkcap *Lactarius* or brittlegill *Russula*, in combination with their smell, is a great help in distinguishing one from another. The hot ones are traditionally given to a newbie forayer. Once tasted, the slow-burning fuse of Rufous Milkcap *Lactarius rufus* will never be forgotten!

Touch is also a good way of confirming the evidence of your eyes. It helps to sort out which caps are sticky and which are merely shiny or silky. Identifying certain tricky little yellow waxcaps involves the 'kissing test', in which you touch the cap with your lips; the slightly sticky ones will adhere for a moment. This is possibly not something you should do on your own in a public place.

A final important clue to the identity of your fungus is its habitat. Many woodland fungi associate with particular trees, so that, after looking downwards at the specimen, you should look up at the canopy. Two brittlegills called the Sickener *Russula emetica* and the Beechwood Sickener *R. nobilis* (known a while back as *R. mairei*) are a similar bright scarlet with pure white stipes (and pure white spores), but one grows under Scots Pine and the other under Beech, and never the twain shall meet (the older guides included another beechwood *Russula*, *R. fageticola*, which was very close to *R. nobilis*, but recent authorities have concluded they are one and the same thing, which is always a relief). Similarly, the Saffron Milkcap *Lactarius deliciosus* has a False Saffron Milkcap look-alike, *L. deterrimus*, but the real thing grows under pine whilst the fake prefers spruce (there is, needless to say, a third and much rarer lookalike, *L. salmonicolor*, found under fir).

▼ **Goatcheese Webcap** *Cortinarius camphoratus* has a 'repulsive' smell of ripe goats' cheese. It is a native pinewood species.

Field guides

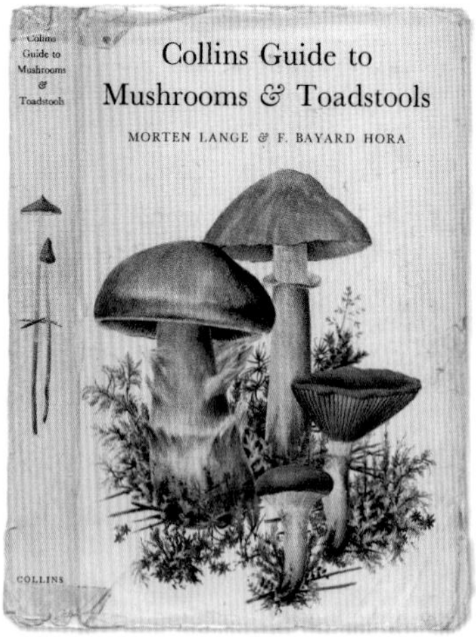

▲ **'Lange & Hora'** was the best field guide available in English during the 1960s and 1970s, although modern field guides illustrate twice as many species.

The job of a field guide is to enable you to identify the right species with the minimum of fuss. Every forayer needs a good field guide and, fortunately, today the best ones are very good indeed. Back in the 1960s and 1970s we had far less choice. The standard work then was the much-loved *Collins Guide*, Lange & Hora (1965). Field guides on fungi are normally referred to by the names of the authors, since they all share much the same title, that is, variants of 'Mushrooms and Toadstools of Britain'. Lange & Hora were quite a pair. Morten Lange was a Dane, a jovial Marxist with a passion for nuclear power. He alternated a respectable academic career at Copenhagen University with the leadership of the far-left Socialist People's Party in Denmark's parliament. F Bayard Hora, who adapted the work for a British audience, was a university lecturer at Reading University, and it was said that his book was particularly useful in the fields and woods of that part of Berkshire. Hora was a popular leader of fungus forays, and also a good fungal cook. He was reputed to be particularly fond of the very common Brown Rollrim *Paxillus involutus*, at that time thought to be harmless if cooked properly, but which is, in fact, deadly poisonous. It presumably did Hora no great harm, since he managed to live to the age of 75.

▲ **Morten Lange** (1919-2003), mycologist, radical politician and co-author of the first field guide on British mushrooms and toadstools.

Lange & Hora, which was illustrated with paintings by Morten Lange's father, Jakob, served us by default until 1981, when the 'Pan Guide' made its first appearance. The great strength of this book, *Mushrooms*, by Roger Phillips, was its photographs: crisp, beautifully reproduced plates with the mushrooms shown close to life size. Better still, each plate included specimens in different states of growth, and, where relevant, growing on their natural substrates. By coincidence, this book, like Lange & Hora, was ideal for forays near Reading. Many of the specimens were provided by Ted Green, from the countryside around Maidenhead and Windsor. The Pan Guide proved enormously popular, and has been reprinted many times, most recently by Macmillan in a slightly smaller format.

The next advance was a pair of field guides from the 1980s: one in 1987, by the French mycologist Marcel Bon, published by Hodder & Stoughton, and the other by our own Stefan Buczacki, published two years later in the short-lived Collins New Generation Guide series.

Both, it seems to me, are under-rated (it did not help their prospects that both went out of print early, although a reprint of Bon is promised). Bon broke new ground by illustrating over 1,200 species with excellent colour paintings by Denys Ovenden and John Wilkinson. It also usefully illustrated the spores of each species. Buczacki's guide was let down by its designer, for the illustrations are far too small. This was a pity, because the identification notes are excellent, with the key characters concentrated at the outset of each set of notes.

The most important guide of the 1990s was the *Collins Field Guide* by Courtecuisse & Duhem (1994). It includes no fewer than 1,750 species, and the illustrations by Bernard Duhem capture the tones and textures of fungi superbly (including the exact shade of the spore print, where it matters). The guide concentrates on agarics and boletes, and other large fungi are given rather short shrift. Hence it is not much use for identifying brackets, jelly fungi or even puffballs. It also tends to take a splitter's view of taxonomy at odds with the British view. The long-awaited *Collins Fungi Guide* by Stefan Buczacki was published in 2012. Billed as the most complete field guide to British mushrooms and toadstools ever, it illustrates and describes no fewer than 2,400 species. And, in addition to mushrooms, it includes a wide range of brackets, fairy clubs, puffballs and jelly fungi, including almost all the species likely to be found by the non-specialist. It even covers a large number of resupinate or crust fungi, although whether these are identifiable without microscopic drawings is a moot question. The illustrations have come under some criticism: although neatly executed, they are, to some degree, idealised and are less successful in capturing the elusive textures and sheens of fungi than are Bernard Duhem's. But the book is clearly laid out, up-to-date, as non-technical as it can be, and all the species are British.

For those who prefer photographs to artwork, the best book is the *Collins Complete Guide* by Sterry & Hughes (2009), who also took the pictures. They use all the recommended common names, and the notes are non-technical and easily understood. And, for once, it pays equal weight to larger fungi that are not mushroom-shaped, including a good range of brackets and cup fungi. It also has the merit of illustrating the species most likely to be found. The disadvantage of such books is that they tend not to show fungi at different states of growth, nor are all the diagnostic features always visible. Also well stocked with colour photographs is Michael Jordan's *Encyclopedia of Fungi*, first published in 1995

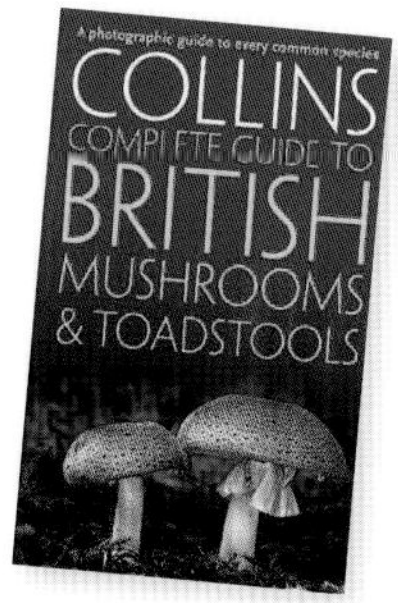

▲ ***The genus Hygrocybe* and *The genus Hebeloma*** – two of the detailed monographs available to today's mushroom-finders.

and revised in 2004. As the title implies, it is comprehensive, with sections on foraying, preparing as food and other topics. Most of the fungi were imaged *in situ* and the book is still a favourite with many, although too large to take into the field easily.

There are many more books that purport to be field guides. Most suffer the significant demerit of not including enough species. Others are aimed at wild-food enthusiasts and confine themselves to edible fungi (and their poisonous look-alikes). For the more experienced, there are specialist tomes dedicated to particular groups of fungi, such as the illustrated monographs produced at Kew – three so far, with a fourth, on coral fungi, in preparation – or the excellent *Fungi of Northern Europe* (also three, so far, on *Hygrocybe*, *Lactarius* and *Hebeloma*). From 2011 some excellent guides to popular genera are available under the authorship of one of Britain's most experienced field mycologists, Geoffrey Kibby. He has published an excellent guide to British Boletes, followed by *The Genus Agaricus*, *The Genus Russula* and *The Genus Amanita*, all of which are available from the NHBS website. They are colour-illustrated and of the highest standard, and anyone wishing to get to grips with these groups can hardly do without them.

Beyond that, there are multi-volume tomes on European fungi, of which the most attractive is the sumptuous *Fungi of Switzerland*, while the more recent *Funga Nordica* offers the current cutting-edge view of North European larger fungi. Hard-core forayers generally accumulate a fair-sized library of books, including a complete run of the wonderful *Field Mycology*, the journal for forayers everywhere, with all the very latest news on British and Irish fungi.

A more recent source of information is the Internet. There are websites on practically any aspect of fungi that might interest you. There is also a tremendous gallery of images out there; Google almost any fungus name and you will be presented with a parade of images. The Fly Agaric has 386,000 'hits', the Field Mushroom about 150,000. The British Mycological Society has its own site at www.britmycolsoc.org.uk. Some local or county fungus groups have their own sites, and so do individual mycologists, such as the well-maintained one by David Minter, called 'cybertruffle'. Websites are also good for spying on other people's mushrooms – there is a plethora of sites for the USA, and good ones for Australia, New Zealand, and (in English) Costa Rica and many other countries. It is in the nature of cyberspace that sites change from time to time, and that many prove to be ephemeral. Personally, I like books and libraries, if only because I prefer to ration computer time for fear that it might take over my life. I suspect websites represent the future and books the past, although I have yet to see Kindles and ipads on my fungus forays. But for entertaining browsing, websites undoubtedly offer a mycological feast of increasing sophistication and excellence.

▲ **The Cep or Penny Bun** *Boletus edulis*, one of the best-known edible mushrooms.

Chubby, homely shapes

Few of us can expect to become even tolerably familiar with all the larger fungi (let alone the legions of micro-fungi). There are just too many of them, and most of us have other things to do. But it is within the capacity of anyone interested in nature to learn to recognise at least some of the common ones we see on the lawn, in the park, and on woodland walks every year. So long as you choose an accessible group, it is also quite possible to acquire a specialist interest in quite a short time. And once you do, you have a good chance of finding species new to your neighbourhood, or even new to Britain.

One good group to start with is the boletes. It is easy to recognise a bolete as such, and many of them can be identified to species, with a bit of practice. They are rustic, satisfying fungi, with their homely, chubby shapes and subtle colours. There is a manageable number of them – about 70 species – and most have English names, if required. Boletes take you to attractive woods, parks and arboreta with mature trees, sunny rides and mossy banks. And, of course, they contain a fair number of species of culinary interest, including one of the best of them all, the Cep. One can get rather fond of boletes.

Another accessible group that is full of fungi with funny or outlandish shapes is the gasteroid or stomach fungi (formerly known as Gasteromycetes). They include the puffballs, the phallic stinkhorns, starry earthstars, bird's-nest fungi like tiny fruit tarts, and a rogue's gallery of greater freaks, such as cage fungi, stalkballs and the sinister Devil's

▲ **A 'troop' of Scarlet Waxcaps** *Hygrocybe coccinea*, in old, close-grazed grassland. Dry weather has caused their caps to upturn, exposing their thick, waxy gills, like the frilly petticoats of a can-can dancer.

Fingers *Clathrus archeri*, which looks a little like a half-buried squid. There is a first-rate illustrated monograph on the group, published by the Royal Botanic Gardens at Kew (Pegler *et al.* 1995). Again, there is a manageable number of them – around 70 species, and a number of rare ones that are of conservation interest. And they, too, have a few gastronomic stars, most notably the Giant Puffball *Calvatia gigantea*.

Slightly more challenging, but still approachable, are the waxcaps *Hygrocybe*. It is easy to recognise a waxcap as such, with their waxy complexion and bright, shiny colours, like well-sucked boiled sweets. They make a good group on which to test one's mycological teeth, with the help of an excellent illustrated monograph (Boertmann 1995) and a good showing in recent field guides. There are tricky waxcaps as well as unmistakable ones, but they have attracted a wide following, and are good ambassadors for fungi as a whole. It would be too much to suggest that if you can name a waxcap you can name anything, but they certainly offer a way in for other genera of wild mushrooms. I will return to them later because of their importance as indicators of old grassland rich in biodiversity.

Why fungi are difficult

Don't let this put you off. Many fungi are easy to name. For instance, one would need to be colour-blind to mistake the rich orange and gold tones of the porecrust *Pseudomerulius aureus* or the brilliant blue of the Cobalt Crust *Terana caerulea* for anything else. Many agarics and puffballs are as distinct as wild flowers. Even many rusts and smuts can be recognised, not so much from themselves as from the identity of their host plants. I have identified, cooked and eaten about 200 species of wild fungi, without once being poisoned.

And yet... flicking through the 300-odd plates of Courtecuisse & Duhem (1994), you come across page after page of mushrooms that all look horribly alike: 50 red *Russula* species, for example, and innumerable 'little brown mushrooms'. Do not even try to learn fungi from browsing a field guide. You will soon give up the struggle. The best place to learn about them is on a foray with a knowledgeable guide. The field guide then comes into its own as a means of confirming identification. A field guide is a tool, not an intellectual endurance test. We will never see more than a fraction of the fungi illustrated in Courtecuisse & Duhem, which is probably just as well.

▼ **The distinctive golden colour of the porecrust** *Pseudomerulius aureus*, on decaying pine wood.

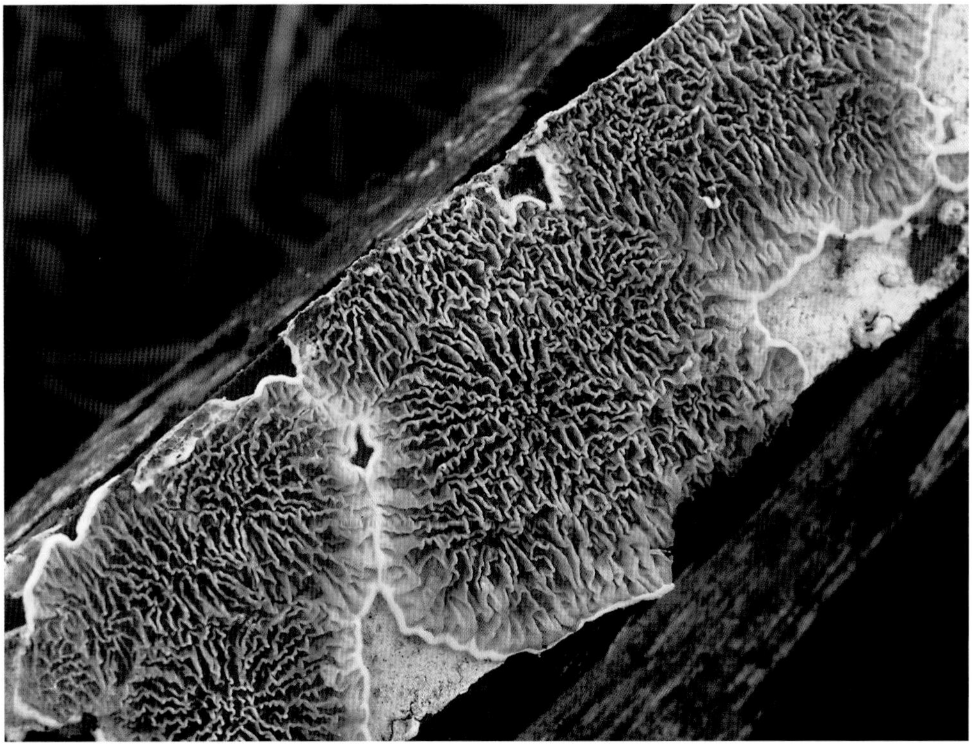

▲ **Pleated Inkcap** *Coprinopsis plicatilis*. The old inkcap genus, *Coprinus*, has been split up after DNA findings exposed its artificiality. So, more names to learn.

The reason why some fungi are difficult is at least as much to do with ourselves as with the fungus. It is all about the science of naming. Every time a new species is discovered, someone publishes a full scientific description (which, until recently, had to be in Latin). The name, description, and the specimen on which it is based (known as the holotype) should in theory enable the species to be identified without ambiguity for ever afterwards. In practice, life is not always like that. Many past descriptions were poor, while the specimen itself may be badly preserved, or even missing. Moreover, a great many dubious new names and descriptions have been made on the basis of insignificant differences, or on new interpretations as to what might constitute a species. This is why most species of British fungi have long strings of synonyms, that is, different names for the same thing.

Even today, with DNA and other advanced molecular techniques at our service, experts have difficulty agreeing. To take one example, Courtecuisse offers us seven species of black-staining waxcaps in his field guide. Boertmann, on the other hand, regards them as expressions of a single, variable species. Both are opinions. The lumping approach makes life easier for the rest of us, but who is right? Truth in taxonomy is a many-sided thing. There are rules, of course, but there is also wide scope for interpretation, especially when the differences between one species and another are based on a handful of variable characters. Some taxonomists like to cut their cloth very fine, others prefer broader interpretations. In one of his always-lively Notes & Records columns in *Field Mycology*, Alick Henrici (2009) summed it all up in lines by the poet William Cowper:

> 'Differing judgements serve but to declare,
> The truth lies somewhere, if we knew but where.'

The result is that different textbooks on fungi do not offer exactly the same set of species. The *Checklist of British and Irish Basidiomycota*, produced after long study and much argument in 2005, offered a consensus of what British mycologists consider to be genera and species. But it was contradicted in some places by the first volume of *Funga Nordica* (Knudsen & Vesterholt 2008), an equally authoritative review of European macro-fungi. Rather than being based on hard and fast lines, the naming of many mushrooms takes on the lineaments of a discussion.

Of course, these arcane arguments need not bother the average forayer. We can spot our Death Caps or Birch Polypores without entering into erudite arguments about taxonomy. Even DNA evidence is subject to interpretation (especially when, as they so often are, the results are counter-intuitive, and seem to deny the evidence of our own eyes). What molecular science *has* done is to dig the grave of the composite genus. Most of us grew up with large genera such as *Coprinus* (inkcaps) or *Collybia* (shanks), which were identifiable in the field as such (inkcaps, for instance, produce inky drops containing their spores). DNA has shown, beyond doubt, that such genera are artificial and include species that are not related at all. Inkcaps are no longer just *Coprinus* but also *Coprinella*, *Coprinopsis*, *Parasola* and more to come, no doubt. Fortunately, some big genera, such as *Russula* and *Lactarius*, seem to be genuinely monophyletic: an evolutionary form that has produced large numbers of closely related species, some of which may have evolved fairly recently.

Just as some old and familiar genera have been broken up, so some species have turned out to be 'species complexes', that is, not one species but several closely related ones. For example, at the turn of the Millennium, Dutch molecular mycologists showed that the familiar Poisonpie *Hebeloma crustliniforme* was not one species but a clutch of mini-species, not all of which could be separated easily by morphological characters alone (Vesterholt 2005). In other words, we now have species that cannot easily be recognised. We might reasonably complain that the genus *Hebeloma* is difficult enough already, without this sort of complication, but unfortunately human frailties are not recognised by science. All we forayers can do is to cut our cloth accordingly. For most of us, recognising a Poisonpie is good enough (certainly good enough to avoid eating it). It might be a species complex, but we can still treat it as an entity.

Deeper waters: scaly-stems and shield mushrooms

It might be a bit early in the book to explore even a little of the arcane world of the fungal taxonomist (and if you think so, feel free to skip this bit). But I want to give an example of why the naming of fungi can be almost hopelessly confused and entangled even when the fungi themselves may be quite recognisable. Take the boletes. They are easy to recognise as such from their pores and dumpy shapes, and time was when most of the species were recognisable, too. It is not so easy today, and especially not the lanky, scaly-stemmed boletes of the genus *Leccinum*. These are handsome, tall boletes, with relatively small caps, woolly scales on the stems and pale pores. They all grow in woodland, and are especially common in birch woods. When I started out, it was very easy to name a *Leccinum* (or scaly-stemmed *Boletus*, as they then were) because there were only two: the one with a grey cap was *Boletus scaber*, and the one with an orange cap *Boletus testaceoscaber*. Simple.

During the 1960s, several newly discovered but still reasonably distinct species joined the two originals, and an old generic name, *Leccinum*, was found to accommodate them. The new ones were the Slate Bolete *L. duriusculum*, a dull brown one that grows under poplars, the Ghost Bolete *L. holopus*, which is pale and appears through hummocks of spongy moss in boggy woods, and the Saffron or Yellow-cracking Bolete *L. crocipodium*, which is distinguished by a velvet cap which eventually breaks up into a crazy paving of yellow cracks (and eventually discolours to black).

So far, so good. Then, in 1970, Roy Watling caused a shock among boletophiles when, in his volume on boletes for the new *British Fungus Flora*, he listed several more, bringing the total to 13 species (Watling & Hills 2005). In the process, *Leccinum* boletes became potentially more difficult to name, since the identification of several now relied on changes in their flesh colour, which might take many minutes to appear. Even so, his keys still relied on macroscopic characters. With a sharp knife and patience, scaly-stemmed boletes were still fungi you could get to know in the field.

A quarter century on, and *Leccinum* was becoming much less manageable. A European monograph by Lannoy & Estades, published in 1995, listed no fewer than 36 species, or 'taxa' as they prefer to call them (since it gets around the problem of having to define what a species is).

▲ **This handsome mushroom has long been known as the Aspen Bolete** *Leccinum aurantiacum*. Some think it is not distinctive enough to be a species and should be swallowed up in another taxon, *Leccinum quercinum* the Orange Oak Bolete – or vice versa!

Not all were then known in Britain, but we soon started finding them, and the number of species on the British list rose to 30. The distinctions between them were finer than before, and rested particularly on the tones and shades of the cap and stem scales, although these are variable. Perfect fresh specimens were needed to make a diagnosis, and, to make sure, one needed to resort to scalpel, forceps and microscope slides to examine cells of the cap cuticle.

That was the position in 2000, when Geoffrey Kibby (2000) provided a user-friendly key in the very first volume of *Field Mycology*. I was probably not alone in feeling that, by this time, the cloth was being cut very fine indeed, and that insufficient account was being made of the natural variation between species. Where, indeed, do you draw the line? Five years later, another monograph appeared that took issue with Lannoy & Estades over this very question. The new one, by Bakker & Noordeloos (2005), took a close and sceptical look at variation within *Leccinum*, including new DNA data, and it came to a radically different conclusion. By this reckoning, there were not 30 British species but just 14. They found that the traditional characters of cap colour and colour changes in the cut flesh were more variable than had been allowed, and that some species also had a wider host range. So out went such taxa as *L. molle* and *L. oxydabile*; since there was insufficient evidence to support their separation, they were relegated to synonyms.

But this interpretation was far from a reversion to the status quo. Instead, the pack had been shuffled once again. For example, an unfamiliar species, Bakker & Noordeloos's *Leccinum cyaneobasileucum*, was found to be widespread and probably common in southern England, overlooked because it resembles a pale form of the well-known Brown Birch Bolete *L. scabrum*. A well-known species, the Aspen Bolete *L. aurantiacum*, was, by this analysis, reduced to a mere form of the Orange Oak Bolete *L. quercinum*. Meanwhile, other forms of Aspen Bolete with fluffy white scales have become *L. albostipitatum*.

British mycologists do not accept all of this. Instead, the authors of the *Checklist* decided to follow the 2005 revision of Watling & Hills' volume on boletes in the *British Fungus Flora*. We have, by this view, 17 species, including the retention of the Aspen Bolete as a good species, plus one or two others not recognised by Bakker & Noordeloos. The effect of all this reshuffling is that all field guides published before 2005 are out of date. At the time of writing, only Sterry & Hughes' photographic guide, published in 2009, was able to take account of the latest concept of the genus.

Even that is probably not the end of the story. 'Taxonomy isn't for those who need certainties,' concluded Alick Henrici. Nor can taxonomy live by DNA alone. *Leccinum* continues to supply 'excellent debating ground for thrashing out species concepts' (Henrici 2005).

To take just one more example, the 'shield' mushrooms of the woodland genus *Pluteus* are, like *Leccinum*, easily recognised in the field. It is a 'right little, tight little' genus, full of colourful, charming fungi. Every one of them has free gills, pink spores and a characteristic 'jizz' compounded of round, flattish caps, delicate build and a shared habitat of rotten wood. There is interest in the genus at present because of its association with dead wood and old trees. It is quite possible that *Pluteus* is to ancient woodland what waxcaps are to ancient grassland.

Pluteus, like *Leccinum*, has its own monograph, in this case one shared with the similarly pink-spored *Volvariella* in the *British Fungus Flora* (Orton 1986). Orton tended to take a narrow view of what constitutes a species. He described 43 species of *Pluteus*, some of which were separated by relatively minor variations in appearance or microscopic characters. The *Checklist* takes a radically different view, following a review of the genus by E Vellinga, published in the *Flora Agaricina Neerlandica* in 1990. By this view there are only 28 British species, five of which are so rarely recorded that their status is in doubt. This view of the genus is broadly shared by *Funga Nordica* (Knudsen & Vesterholt

▲ **Deer Shield** *Pluteus cervinus*, the commonest and one of the largest of the pink-gilled 'shields', growing on buried wood.

2008), the standard work on the fungi of Northern Europe, which lists 30 species, not all of which have been found in Britain.

The reason why experts come to such different conclusions is that this genus is full of problem areas where differences can arise (Kibby *et al.* 2010). Checklists and fungus floras cannot enter fully into the arguments, for their primary job is to list and describe recognised species. Instead, they make a decision that they can, if necessary, defend. For the time being, at least, we now have a relatively small number of shield mushrooms, some of which are well defined, and others, mostly the little grey ones, the subject of an ongoing learned discussion. The point is not entirely academic. *Pluteus* has the potential to be useful to woodland ecologists. Moreover, their role as late decomposers – fungi that move in on a tree at the point where it is turning into sawdust – may be of great importance in the ecology of natural woodlands. We underrate such species in Britain because it is a rare wood that is allowed to develop naturally. We rob the *Pluteus* mushrooms of their rightful habitat by clearing it all away.

So much for the labyrinths of fungal taxonomy. Taxonomists will go on arguing as long as there are taxonomists (which, in Britain at least, may not be much longer). Let them argue in their laboratories. What we must do is to get back into the field. Let us go for a foray.

chapter six

Natural habitats

Having met the main types of fungi and gained at least a glimpse of their world, let us now turn to the places where they live. Most species of larger fungi are found in natural habitats, that is to say, places that retain something of their original character and native vegetation, even though mankind may have farmed or managed them for centuries. Nearly all habitats in Britain are of this sort – not pristine wildernesses but farmed or otherwise managed places, where wildlife continues to survive, and, sometimes, thrive. Fungi do best on soils that have not been spread with artificial fertiliser, and which retain their natural wet bits and banks. Conifer plantations, which are poor in terms of flowering plants, can nevertheless be rich in fungi, so long as the ground is not disturbed by heavy vehicles.

Fungi need space to grow and fruit. They are happier on bare ground, leaf litter or among moss than competing with grasses and brambles. Micro-habitats are very important. One might notice very few fungi on the grassy forest floor, and then find two dozen species on an earth bank or a fallen log. In one of my local woods, most of the variety, including all the rarer species, is confined to the hinterland of a single old bank. Forayers soon get an eye for the most likely places: the roots of a spreading Beech, an old sand pit, now grassed over and grazed by Rabbits, or, in dry weather, the seepages around a pond or mossy streambank.

◀ **Beechwood Sickener** *Russula nobilis*, a hot-tasting and very common associate of Beech.

I have divided this section of the book on the places in which fungi grow into two. This chapter will look at the fungi of wild places, the best of which are often nature reserves or heritage land owned by bodies such as the National Trust. The following chapter will concentrate on fungi that grow closer to most of our homes, including the garden. Perhaps surprisingly, garden lawns can be exciting places to find fungi, including rare and exotic species. An increasing number of us are starting to cherish fungi on our own patch. They brighten up the autumn and suggest to us that our bit of the environment is not doing too badly. A lawn of fungi is fermenting with life.

Woodland

The habitat we associate with fungi more than any other is woodland. A much greater proportion of fungi are restricted to woods than is the case with flowering plants. The latter merely grow in the wood, taking advantage of the damp, shade and relative freedom from competition. But most woodland fungi grow directly on the trees, either as mycorrhizal species attached to the roots, or subsisting on decaying, and occasionally living, wood. Around a third of woodland fungi are associated with dead wood, and so any wood in which this resource is removed is instantly impoverished.

Perhaps surprisingly, the smallest group, in terms of species, is those that decompose rotting matter – the traditional role of fungi. Mushrooms can be very abundant on fallen leaves, and when you part the

► **Sycamore Tarspot** *Rhytisma acerinum* is abundant on Sycamore leaves in autumn.

▼ **Fungal landscapes:** the yellow-brown clusters of Honey Fungus *Armillaria mellea* on rotting stumps and branches often dominate the woodland floor in autumn.

surface layer you can find the white mycelium of the fungus binding the leaves together and turning them transparent. Yet, despite their numbers, they tend to be of the same few species – toughshanks, ink-caps and others – saprotrophs that recycle the harvest of debris and so maintain the fertility of the soil.

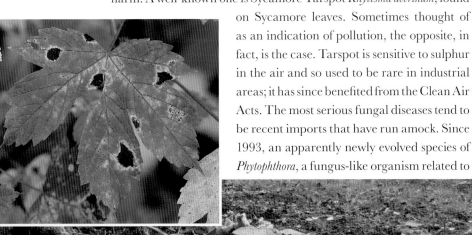

Another relatively small group is the fungi that attack living plant tissue. If the plants are of importance to us, we categorise these fungi as plant diseases. Among them is Oak Mildew *Microsphaera alphitiodes* that blights the tender foliage of oaks, including saplings, with a powdery white coating. Others include a variety of leaf-spots that discolour the leaves of many trees, shrubs and herbaceous plants but seldom do much harm. A well-known one is Sycamore Tarspot *Rhytisma acerinum*, found on Sycamore leaves. Sometimes thought of as an indication of pollution, the opposite, in fact, is the case. Tarspot is sensitive to sulphur in the air and so used to be rare in industrial areas; it has since benefited from the Clean Air Acts. The most serious fungal diseases tend to be recent imports that have run amock. Since 1993, an apparently newly evolved species of *Phytophthora*, a fungus-like organism related to

▲ **Giant Polypore**
Meriplus giganteus, a 'butt rot' (and therefore bad news for the forester), seen here growing on Beech roots just below the surface.

potato blight, has attacked the roots of Alder trees, killing perhaps 15% of all the trees in southern England. My local Crack Willows have been badly infected by an ultimately fatal black canker caused by a fungus, in combination with other diseases, such as scabs and wilts, which afflict a weakening tree. Beech often suffers from a bark disease caused by a fungus, *Nectria coccinea*, related to the common Coral Spot *N. cinnabarina*, which is spread by scale insects. Oak faces a number of potentially serious threats. One of these is another *Phytophthora*, *P. quercina*, the recently diagnosed cause of the condition known as 'oak die-back', in which the oak loses the outer parts of its crown and becomes 'stag-headed'. More recently, we have been invaded by yet another *Phytophthora*, *P. ramorum*, which causes the alarming-sounding disease known as Sudden Oak Death. It recently reached the Royal Botanic Garden Edinburgh, probably carried there on the soles of shoes from visitors who had unwittingly come into contact with its spores. Fortunately, Britain's oaks seem to be relatively resistant to the disease (it is named after American, not European, oaks), but it has devastated larch trees, especially in south-west England.

In conifer plantations the main threat comes from a bracket fungus, Root Rot *Heterobasidion annosum*. Root rots and butt rots, the name for brackets that appear at the base of the trunk, generally mark the end of the tree's life. The leathery fans of the Giant Polypore *Meripilus giganteus*, for instance, appear at the base of Beech trees that have either died or are about to give up the ghost. Brackets growing on the trunk, however, may actually prolong the life of a tree. Far from consuming and ultimately destroying the tree, they are rotting down the dead weight in the heart of the trunk, thus reducing the load on its decaying roots, and, some say, creating a more flexible, wind-proof cylinder in place of a solid trunk.

We have already mentioned the role of mycorrhizal and leaf-rotting fungi in woods. Alan Rayner (1993) compared this hidden fungal frenzy to the streets of a city. What we see above ground – standard lamps, fire hydrants, manhole covers and so on – are like the toadstools we see in autumn, the visible part of a network of underground pipelines, cables and sewers. So it is with fungi: the woodland soil, as well as the interior of every stump, log or sick tree, is alive with invisible networks that convert matter into energy and maintain the web of life. To us, fungi are objects that appear for a few weeks in autumn, impermanent and so, seemingly, insignificant. In reality, it is their dynamics that govern the eternal cycles of growth, death and decay. Theirs is a universe of threads, a form of woodland plumbing and arterial motion that we can scarcely comprehend, and of which we are barely aware.

The forest is also a battlefield. Fungi send out forage-lines that extend the organism outwards into new territory. You can sometimes see where rival lines meet up on a section of tree stump, where each fungal territory is marked out in black lines, like the boundaries of countries on a map. It is even more visible with lichens – which are fungi with an algal component – crowding the surface of a tree trunk, where the 'countries' can be different colours. Such territories must define the limits of growth for most fungi, but some seem just to grow and grow. The advance of one of the commonest genera of woodland mushrooms, the honey fungi *Armillaria*, is relatively easy to follow since its component threads are combined into bootlace-like rhizomorphs (literally, 'root-shapes') that help the fungus to move rapidly from resource to resource. In one case, its bootlaces were traced over 15ha of woodland and were estimated to weigh 100 tonnes – as much as the largest whales.

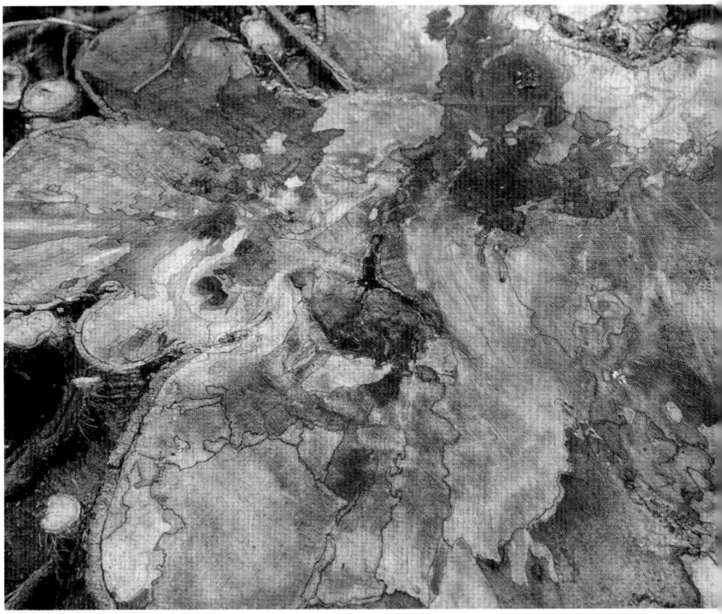

▲ **'Spalted' patterns** formed by the 'territories' of fungi on a decaying stump.

Which woods are the best for fungi? As for plants, it is often a case of the bigger – and more natural – the better. Woods with something like their natural quota of logs, stumps and over-mature trees will always support far more diversity than managed woods. Moreover, the naturally varied geology and uneven ground of ancient and natural woodland provides more small-scale habitats, including bogs, marshes and glades, which are colonised by different species of fungi.

As we are becoming increasingly aware, fungi, and especially mycorrhizal fungi, are sensitive indicators of pollution. Although Britain has no quantitative evidence from environmental monitoring, as the Netherlands does, there is broad agreement among forayers that things are not what they were. One reason may be the pollution of woodland soil from airborne nitrogen, added to a steady percolation of phosphorus from human settlement. The result has been a considerable increase in a few aggressive plants such as bramble, coarse grasses and, possibly, Dog's Mercury. This will have increased root competition with fungi. It is equally likely that some fungi have shared the fate of pollution-sensitive lichens. Woods in the west, where clean air blows in from the Atlantic, may well have a healthier fungus flora than those in the Midlands and south-east, although direct field evidence is lacking.

As we have seen, some trees have more fungi than others. Willows, Alder, birches and Scots Pine all have their distinctive fungi. Oaks are the centre of a particularly intricate fungal community, including large numbers of mycorrhizals or suspected mycorrhizals, such as boletes, milkcaps and brittlegills. They are also the host of two of our most distinctive brackets, the Beefsteak Fungus *Fistulina hepatica*, with its juicy flesh and realistic drops of 'blood', and Chicken of the Woods *Laetiporus sulphureus*, bright yellow and, when young, with the texture of chicken breast (not to be confused with another oak associate, Hen of the Woods *Grifola frondosa*, so named because its tiers of small brackets give the appearance of an excited hen). Overmature oaks on acid soil are particularly rich in fungi, including many rare species. It is the single richest habitat for boletes, with 57 associated species. More than 100 species of fungi have been recorded from rotting oak wood.

Beech is also rich in fungi, which can appear in spectacular numbers in a good season. It, too, has a large number of species that are more or less confined to old trees, and some of these have been used recently as indicators of fungal diversity. The thick leaf litter in beechwoods provides a banquet for fungi in autumn, and is a particularly

▲ **Chicken of the Woods** *Laetiporus sulphureus*, an immediately recognisable bright yellow bracket of oaks, yews and other hardwood trees.

good hunting ground for species of brittlegill, webcap and bonnet. Old or dying Beech trunks often sprout the horse's-hoof shapes of one of our largest brackets, *Ganoderma applanatum*, often known as the Artist's Bracket because you can score little pictures on its fine white pore surface (a similar species, Southern Bracket *G. australe*, is commoner and is equally art-friendly). Even the husks of beechnuts have their own fungi, such as the little horns of Beechmast Candlesnuff *Xylaria carpophila*. Unfortunately, many fine beechwoods in southern England took a pasting from the 1987 gale and, still more, from subsequent clean-up operations using heavy tracked vehicles. Some of the best sites for Beech fungi are now in parks rather than managed woods.

Birch woodland is another good habitat for fungi. Birch has no heartwood and so rots down quickly. More often than not, the fallen logs sprout fleshy half-moons of the Birch Polypore *Piptoporus betulinus*, whose pith was used both to 'strop' razors and to accept the fine pins of insect specimens. In Scotland and northern England it is joined by the Hoof Fungus *Fomes fomentarius*, a tough bracket once used as tinder, which has recently spread into southern England. But perhaps the best-known birch species of all is the Fly Agaric *Amanita muscaria*, whose colourful red caps, with their signature white spots, compliment the yellowing foliage and bracken as the days grow shorter.

Perhaps the most exciting woods of all, at least for the southern forayer, are the native pinewoods of Deeside, Speyside and Rannoch, in Scotland. They are the main home of at least 400 species of larger fungi, including many rarely found elsewhere, and have a fungal mycota similar to boreal forests in Scandinavia. Among their highlights are tooth fungi, a fine range of brackets and a good range of Red Data List species, including one of our largest agarics, Giant Knight *Tricholoma colossus*. Beneath the pines there is often a layer of Juniper, which has its own range of fungi, including two unusually large and prominent rusts, *Gymnosporangium* species, that do their best to look like jelly fungi.

Alder swamp has a small but highly distinctive suite of fungi. For one small genus, *Naucoria*, it is their main British habitat. The genera *Paxillus*, *Amanita* and *Russula* all have a species restricted to Alder, and there are also four special milkcaps. The specialist bolete, Alder Bolete *Gyrodon lividus*, has a luscious wavy cap and golden pores that turn blue at a touch. Most conspicuous of all is Alder Bracket *Inonotus radiatus*, which forms neat, yellow-fringed tiers of small brackets that 'weep' droplets of moisture when growing. There are also star species of *Taphrina*, gall-forming fungi that fruit on Alder cones. The galls of *T. alni* form weird flame-coloured tongues; once considered rare, it is now fairly common. Still rare is *T. amentorum*, whose galls are a rich crimson.

▲ **Birch Polypore** *Piptoporus betulinus* is one of the most widespread brackets, found in most birch woodlands.

Grassland

On the Continent, mushroom gatherers head for the woods. In Britain, we traditionally have gone instead to a patch of grass, perhaps a paddock with ponies, or the edge of an airfield or even a park, in the expectation of finding some Field Mushrooms. We associate grass with breakfast mushrooms, and also fairy rings, those enigmatic dark circles in the sward that suddenly sprout pale toadstools as summer nears its close. Those lucky enough to have a cottage lawn that has not been resown or treated with fertiliser may be familiar with the yellow, white and red waxcaps that colour the grass in October. They might also notice strange coral-like fungi, small yellow clubs and spindles in the wet grass, or dark slips of fungus that well merit their name of earthtongues.

Until the Second World War, England was a country of grass, with meadows and permanent pastures in every village. In my part of England, Wiltshire, the villages even had water-meadows, kept moist and green by a network of channels controlled by the local 'drowner'. The downs and uplands had extensive hillsides of springy grass grazed by sheep. Every spring the grass became scented by flowers, and in the autumn, barely noticed, they were coloured by fungi. But, as conservationists never tire of telling us, we have lost 95% of our permanent pasture to crop fields and arable leys in which the grass has been sown and wild flowers rigorously excluded. Semi-wild kinds of grassland have long passed out of modern agriculture and into the heritage business.

Grassland where there is still a good variety of fungi has therefore become circumscribed. Fungi are not like flowers, and lush natural meadows generally have a rather poor fungus flora: *Agaricus* mushrooms are the stars, but appear in varying numbers from year to year. More regular are members of that impossible 'little brown mushroom' genus, *Conocybe*. Pony paddocks sometimes produce football-sized Giant Puffballs *Calvatia gigantea*, often in a pocket of rich soil that also sprouts nettles. Such fields used to produce a good crop of dung fungi: inkcaps, roundheads and the dark bells of *Panaeolus* or mottlegills. But dung fungi have been hit hard by the drugs used to de-worm cattle, which have the side effect of producing chemically polluted dung. These chemicals have the same effect on fungi as nitrogen fertilisers. They kill them off.

▲ **Grassland fungi:** a colourful miscellany of waxcaps, pinkgills and spindles.

Most grassland fungi thrive best on nutrient-poor soil, where the grass is open and mossy and kept short by Rabbits or sheep, or by mowing. They do well on old, unfertilised lawns and churchyards. In the uplands, Britain still has plenty of fungally rich pasture, grazed by sheep and Rabbits and diversified by flushes, hummocks and banks. Here, one finds the greatest variety of those classic grassland fungi, the waxcaps, along with club fungi, earthtongues and the small, often bluish little pinkgills. Because of the great interest in waxcaps as biological indicators, I reserve them for discussion in a later chapter.

Most of the fungi mentioned so far seem to be saprotrophs that feed on decaying matter in the soil, including animal dung. There is another group of grassland fungi, less well known, that are mycorrhizal, in other words they infect the roots of plants. On limestone grassland, the most important host for these fungi is the Common Rockrose *Helianthemum nummularium*, a long-lived plant with woody trailing stems. Just as Dwarf Willow *Salix herbacea* on the tops of mountains represents a kind of dwarf alpine forest, so banks of rockrose on chalk hills could be said to be the temperate counterpart of *Cistus* scrub, the scented maquis of Mediterranean hillsides. Rockrose has a distinctive suite of mycorrhizal fungi, some common, some rare. One of the most conspicuous is a bolete, *Boletus luridus* (its common name, Lurid Bolete, is a straight translation), which has red pores and a crimson stem net. It seems odd to find such a large and fleshy fungus on an open hillside. It seems even odder when, as on St Catherine's Hill, near Winchester, it is joined by the Devil's Bolete *B. satanas*. Rockrose serves as an alternative host for some woodland fungi, such as a dwarf form of the Sulphur Knight *Tricholoma sulphureum* (which some regard as a separate species, *T. hemisulphureum*), with its powerful smell of gas, or the poisonous Panthercap *Amanita pantherina*. Other rockrose specialists include various species of webcaps *Cortinarius*, a poisonpie, *Hebeloma sordescens*, and several milkcaps *Lactarius* species. One webcap, the buff-yellow, mauve-gilled *Cortinarius calochrous*, is a very close relative of *C. cisticola*, an associate of *Cistus* bushes in southern Europe.

Another recent discovery is a suite of mycorrhizal fungi associated with Mountain Avens *Dryas octopetala*, which occurs at sea level in northern Scotland and western Ireland. In the Burren of western Ireland, that wonderful expanse of bare limestone masking a rich flora in its gaps and cracks, at least 35 species live among the mats of Mountain Avens. These include fungi more normally found in woods, including, unexpectedly, some that are normally associated with pinewoods. One of these is the Golden Chanterelle *Cantharellus aurora*, which has a brilliant yellow stipe and a contrasting nut-brown interior. Another is *Cortinarius odorifer*, whose lovely copper-brown caps smell strongly of aniseed, along with four other delectable *Cortinarius* species in the subgenus *Phlegmacium*, all robust, colourful fungi with slippery caps. All but one of them seems to be confined in Ireland to the Burren. In all probability, such fungi enable the Mountain Avens to thrive in the bare, thirsty rock-scape of the Burren, whilst the fungi receive their reward in finding a niche far outside their usual forests (Harrington 2001). Perhaps the association has lasted since the last Ice Age, when Mountain Avens and other cold-weather plants first put down roots and stayed. Many more fungi, particularly in the genera *Russula*, *Lactarius*, *Inocybe*, *Cortinarius* and *Hebeloma*, are associated with Mountain Avens in Europe, although their status in Britain has not yet been investigated.

Dung

When I lived in the Scottish Highlands I would quite often come across little gardens of fungi growing on decaying cattle droppings. As an image of recycling in action, it was hard to beat. Since returning to the south of England, however, I find them only occasionally, and then mainly in rough grazings, such as commons. The reason is that cattle are routinely dosed with ivermectin, a chemical that keeps the animals free of parasites, at the expense of reducing their dung to sterility. The end point, so to speak, of industrial farming has been to produce dung that is, effectively, poisonous. As a result, a large number of species, including fungi, have lost their habitat.

Of course, species that live on dung tend to lack the charisma of more colourful species. But some dung fungi, viewed closely and with as much sympathy as possible, are quite attractive. Snowy Inkcap *Coprinopsis nivea*, for example, is an elegant snow-white dome, with a floccose veil, like slightly lumpy ice-cream (*Coprinopsis* and *Coprinus* both come from the Greek word for dung). Under a lens, some of the 150-odd ascomycete fungi found on dung resemble half-sucked boiled sweets or fruit tarts. *Ascobolus stercorarius*, for example, forms yellow-green spangles, which darken to purple as the spores ripen, from lemon to blackcurrant, perhaps. Many dung fungi are more than usually poorly recorded. *Psathyrella hirta* is a fairly charismatic little mushroom bearing a white fleece on a brown cap, but there are few records, not because it is uncommon (people who know it often seem to find it) but because, by chance, it is not figured in any of the popular field guides.

Dung, especially herbivore dung, is rich in undigested and partly digested cellulose, as well as nitrogen and organic substances. What is more, it is water retentive, and in plentiful supply. Not all dung is alike, of course. In Britain, the most abundant source is from farm animals, notably horses, cattle and sheep. Among wild animals, deer dung is the most productive, and certain fungi specialise on Rabbit pellets. Two species are confined to the pellets of Mountain Hare. Species of micro-fungi have been found on the dung of mice, bats and birds (a yeast found on pigeon droppings is a potentially fatal pathogen of humans, if breathed in). Recently, three rare fungi were discovered feeding on the droppings of toads. Carnivore dung has a different chemistry, one less friendly to fungi, being richer in sugars and generally broken down instead by bacteria. Specialists studying dung fungi soon get used to their revolting substrate. To them, it becomes just another product of nature, like an old log or a dead corpse, and anyone who washes their hands too often is roundly mocked.

Dung fungi have spores that survive their journey through the guts of an animal, having been ingested with the grass or fodder. They fruit on the dung in succession, starting with micro-fungi such as pin-moulds *Mucor*, and the Dung Cannon *Pilobolus crystallinus*, another popular performing fungus of university courses, in which a glossy black spore-ball is blasted from the top of what looks like a tiny glass balloon. Equally remarkable is *Phycomyces*, a giant version of the pin-mould, whose sticky 'pinheads' attach to whatever blade of grass, animal leg or human trouser brushes against it.

Still more ballistic is *Sphaerobolus stellatus*, known as the Cannonball Fungus or Shooting Star, which ejects its round, sticky spore mass high into the air with an audible pop. This small, stellate, orange fungus, as delicate as blown glass, seems to be better known in America than in Britain. It has spread to flowerbeds where wood mulch is used (a sign that, to this fungus, there is no difference between rotten wood and

high-fibre dung – both contain cellulose). Its tiny cannons pepper the paintwork of parked cars and the white boards of New World houses from several metres' range. Once the spores have dried, they are impossible to remove without also removing the paint.

The moulds are followed a week or so later by fruit bodies of ascomycetes, most of which are disc-like in shape, and, for the really keen, can be induced to fruit by keeping the dung in a warm, damp container. This is also a good way of discovering new species – although identifying them is no easy task, since in many cases their taxonomy has not been fully worked out.

The fruit bodies of agarics begin to appear after nine days or so. For some reason, most agarics that live on dung have dark spores. They include species of inkcaps, mottlegills *Panaeolus* and brittlestems *Psathyrella*, all of which have blackish spores, plus some species of conecaps *Conocybe* and brownies *Psilocybe*, which respectively have brown or reddish-brown spores. Some grow on the dung itself, but others are more characteristic of manured ground, that is, the rich soil where the dung has broken down. Many dung fungi, especially the cup fungi, are tiny, and so rarely seen in field conditions. Instead they, too, can be grown on indoors, inside sealed bags and containers. These fungi are not as passive as they look. Some inkcaps conduct chemical warfare against other fungi, defending their tiny patch of weathering dung from all comers.

One dung fungus has gained far more fame than the others because of its rarity and strange appearance. This is the Nail Fungus *Poronia punctata*. It is about the size of a fingernail, white and dotted with black, and shaped like a golf tee, with a long black stalk that penetrates deeply into the dung. It is found only on the dung of ponies that feed on rough vegetation. In Victorian times it was regarded as common, but more recently it has become associated mainly with the New Forest, and is in steep decline all over Europe. It probably survives in the New Forest because there, uniquely, the ponies live as wild animals within a near-natural environment. Recently, it has turned up in other places in southern

▲ **Nail Fungus** *Poronia punctata* specialises in the dung of ponies grazing on heathland.

England, mainly heathland nature reserves where ponies have been introduced. For example, in 2005 it was spotted on Snelsmore Common, Berkshire, by Keith Tomey who, two years earlier, had introduced Exmoor ponies to control the invading gorse. There was a lot of it, too: 30 to 40 colonies across 100m of heath. I have seen it in quantity on Hartland Moor, one of the Purbeck heaths in Dorset, where Exmoor ponies are also used.

There is a second, much less well-known species of nail fungus, *Poronia erici*, which is confined in Britain to Scolt Head Island, on the north Norfolk coast, where it grows on Rabbit droppings. Curiously, it is quite common on the far side of the world, in Australia, where it also occurs on the droppings of kangaroos and wallabys. There are contending theories about where it originated. It could be a fungus that evolved with the kangaroo in the Australian bush, acquired a taste for Rabbit pellets, and then somehow found its way to Britain and the Rabbits of Norfolk. Alternatively, it might be a species with a worldwide but highly disjunct distribution that embraces both Europe and Australasia, but nowhere in between (although that would put it into a biogeographical category of one!)

▼ **Mosaic Puffball**
Handkea utriformis is a large puffball of commons and heaths which liberates its spores after breaking up, rather than through a pore, as in some smaller puffballs.

Dunes and heaths

Sand dunes are a surprising habitat for fungi. Apart from the dunes' lack of fertility and prevailing salt-laden winds, the delicate tissues of fungi seem ill-equipped to survive among sharp sand grains and shell fragments. On the other hand, there is usually plenty of dead vegetation (and Rabbit droppings) around, and the deeper layers of sand can be considerably damper than the surface. Micro-fungi in the roots of Marram and other grasses play an important role, enabling the grasses to capture the limited amount of nutrients, such as phosphorus, that is vital for their development. The larger fungi also help to bind the grains and fix the sand. Yet their activity is barely visible. Sand-dune fungi are less seasonally dependent than their counterparts inland, and finding their fruit bodies may require repeated visits over the course of a year.

The distinctive fungi of our dunes were first studied by Tom Wallace in the 1950s, and later by Maurice Rotheroe in the 1980s and 1990s. Maurice helped to put fungi on the conservation map by producing a steady stream of reports for the Joint Nature Conservation Committee (JNCC) on sand dunes around the coast of England and Wales. Their pages are full of fascinating fungi that are little known to most forayers. There is, for example, a mushroom called *Agaricus devoniensis*, whose stalk is buried deep in the sand, where it effectively functions as a root. There is a brace of tiny earthstars, which sometimes form rings in the short, sandy turf. There is also a little bird's-nest fungus, *Cyathus stercoreus*, which lives on Rabbit droppings, and a miniature oyster mushroom, *Hohenbuehelia culmicola*, attached to decaying culms of Marram Grass. There is a special dune puffball and a dune earthtongue. There is even a sand-dune stinkhorn, *Phallus hadriani*, protruding from a pinkish 'egg', which is said to smell of violets, or, according to others, of liquorice.

The fungi found on fixed dunes have much in common with meadows; there is a suite of waxcaps, for example, including one or two dune specialists such as the colourful Dune Waxcap *Hygrocybe conicoides*. More surprisingly, perhaps, there is a long list of fungi – some 78 species have been counted in the Netherlands – which depend on the mats of Creeping Willow *Salix repens* found in damp dune slacks. Most of these are probably mycorrhizal, infecting the roots of this miniature seaside 'forest'. Unfortunately for the forayer, most of these species are 'brown jobs' in the genera *Cortinarius*, *Hebeloma* and *Inocybe* that exercise the wisest wits of field mycology.

Lowland heaths have a lot in common with dunes. They form on poor, sandy soils inland, and are usually dominated by heather or grassland, often with small bogs in the depressions and valleys. Since the soil is deficient in nutrients, even the heather requires the help of fungi in its roots to thrive. Most of these fungi are microscopic, but they also include the Moor Club *Clavaria argillacea*, whose pale yellow clubs appear among mosses and lichens in autumn. Interestingly, something like a fungal war may be taking place below ground, with one set of fungi suppressing the spread of trees on this open heathland and another set encouraging it.

Among the commonest heathland fungi are the delicate 'fairy bonnets' and 'bells' of *Mycena* and *Galerina*, the latter being fiendishly difficult to identify. Indeed, many of the hardy mushrooms one finds on heaths are little brown jobs best left to those with microscopes. Places recovering from fires are good spots to look for discomycetes, or cup fungi, which sit close to the bare ground in parabolic shapes evolved for firing their spores upwards into the air.

▲ **A Dyeball** *Pisolithus arhizus* that has been split open to reveal the pea-like peridioles.

One of the most interesting fungi of dry, sandy soils is the Dyeball *Pisolithus arhizus*, also known as the Mule-dung Fungus because the massive spherical fruit bodies look as though an incontinent mule has passed that way. In America, it is known even less flatteringly as the Dog-turd Fungus, and has also been called the Bohemian Truffle because none but the most poor and desperate would be tempted to eat it. Recent DNA research has shown the Dyeball to be an associate of pine (and, more rarely, oak) that is found both in Europe and America, and it has been introduced into plantations elsewhere around the world. The large fruit body – it grows to the size of a tennis ball – is filled with pea-sized spore packages called peridioles, embedded in a blackish ooze, like rice crispies in a ball of tar. As the body ripens, its tough outer rind peels away to release chocolate-brown spores, some of which stick to the fungus. Beneath the ball, its 'roots' (rhizomorphs) form a sticky yellow mass that helps to bind the sand grains together.

This singular fungus, so-named because it makes a purplish dye, has been employed in the service of mankind to stabilise loose ground on industrial tips and wasteland. As a mycorrhizal species, it is also used to inoculate sapling trees and help them to grow on poor, dry soil. But in Britain, at least, it may be the Dyeball that needs the help. In one of its strongholds, on the sandy forest rides between Sandhurst and Ascot, in Berkshire, conservationists have preserved its habitat by cutting back invading scrub. And when the tracks on which it grows came to be resurfaced, Dyeball-friendly materials – local sand and gravel – were used instead of imported stone chippings. A modest enough task, perhaps, but it deserves a footnote as perhaps the first time anyone did anything to protect a rare fungus in Britain.

Mountains

Mountains have one of the most distinctive floras of any habitat. Well-adapted wild flowers form beautiful natural rockeries on the higher peaks. Moss and lichen enthusiasts would probably include mountains near the top of their list of places to visit. Mountain fungi are much less well known and, on the face of it, rocks and wind-blasted peaks seem unlikely habitats for species that thrive on damp, tree roots and deep soil. Yet, as we are discovering year on year, there are many alpine fungi, and some of them form partnerships with alpine willows and other plants. Without the fungi, many green plants would find survival on exposed mountain-tops difficult, if not impossible.

This is a habitat that Roy Watling explored in the 1970s and 1980s, and it now attracts a small band of hardy mycologists. Mountain agarics tend, like alpine flowers, to be colourful and petite. Many of those whose ecology has been investigated are mycorrhizal, that is, they are associated with plants, and above all with Dwarf Willow *Salix herbacea*. When they are in fruit, the mushrooms tower over the creeping mats of the willow, forming a strange alpine forest in which the natural order is reversed: the mushrooms become the 'trees' and the willow the understorey. This is a sight that must be familiar to mycologists in polar regions, but which perhaps few of us have witnessed in Britain.

Dwarf Willow is found in places where the snow lies late, and so, despite the exposure, tends to grow in places that are permanently damp and to some extent protected from winter frost and wind. One of its best-known associates is the Mountain Grisette *Amanita nivalis*, first found high up in the Cairngorms as long ago as 1823. It is one of our smallest Amanitas, a small, pale grey mushroom that noses from its protective cup like an acorn, before flattening out into a parasol. Its habitat is shared by two more recently discovered species, both named after their willow associate, the Mountain Waxcap, *Hygrocybe salicis-herbaceae*, and a milkcap, *Lactarius salicis-herbaceae.* A second alpine milkcap, *L. salicis-reticulae*, has been found growing among Net-leaved Willow *Salix reticulata*, a scarce but locally frequent mountain willow found mainly on the Breadalbane Hills of Perthshire. Other agarics that grow in this inch-high alpine willow forest include species of *Inocybe*, *Russula*, *Lactarius* and *Cortinarius*, counterparts of those that grow in lowland forests. As we have seen, Mountain Avens is another plant that depends on fungi. Among its associates is a dwarf form of the widespread Tawny Funnel *Lepista flaccida*. Dwarf Birch *Betula nana* is yet another fungally-dependent alpine dwarf shrub; in this case, small varieties of the same fungi help birch trees to thrive on poor soils elsewhere, among them, Fly Agarics and boletes.

This is an area where fit fungus forayers are almost bound to make discoveries. For example, Liz Holden succeeded in refinding the Arched Woodwax *Hygrophorus camarophyllus*, one of our 'lost' fungi, not seen since 1902, among mats of Bearberry on the lower slopes of the Cairngorms. On the Buttermere Fells, in the Lake District, John Taylor discovered a small brownish milkcap that still lacks a name. It may turn out to be the European *Lactarius nanus*, although further investigation is needed.

Another characteristic form of mountain fungus is *Lichenomphalia*, in which the fungus lives a kind of double life, part lichen and part gilled mushroom. *L. alpina* has a small, yellowish, trumpet-shaped fruit body which appears through a mass of greenish scales which, by custom, are given a separate name, *Botrydina*, although all the parts are interconnected with hyphae and form part of the same organism. Like some alpine flowers, this species is confined to mountains in central Scotland but descends to the coast in the far west. Evidently, its distribution is controlled by the need for constant humidity, rather than altitude.

In conservation circles, perhaps the most talked-about mountain fungus is the White Stalkball or White Stalk Puffball *Tulostoma niveum*, one of the first fungi to be investigated as part of the Biodiversity Action Plan. Interest was first sparked by its discovery, in the heart of a National Nature Reserve at Inchnadamph, Sutherland, in 1989. The tiny white balls appear mainly in winter, so the oversight is understandable. Its distinctive mini-habitat is mossy limestone boulders, and the association with moss may not be fortuitous. Many fungi, including the grassland waxcaps, often grow among the sponge-like comfort of mosses, as some protection against drought. Some, probably more than we know, form a more intimate partnership in which the fungus penetrates the cells of the moss. Since 1989, the stalkball has been found in two more sites, and doubtless more await discovery. As an inhabitant of exposed rocks in windy, drought-prone places, it would probably not survive long without its mossy comfort blanket.

▲ **White Stalkball**
Tulostoma niveum, a rare winter-fruiting alpine fungus of mossy boulders.

In polar regions, and in high European mountains, there are microfungi that appear and fruit at the edge of snow banks, or even in hollows formed under the snow as it melts. Such fungi are little known in Britain; one supposedly alpine species, a cup fungus found on the Isle of Skye, subsequently turned up in the very unalpine ambience of Cambridgeshire. However, Bruce Ing found a group of those 'honorary fungi', the slime moulds, under melting snow high up in the Cairngorms. The commonest species, *Diderma niveum*, forms a cluster of white balls on living or dead vegetation, and is a cold-climate cosmopolitan, occurring in both the Arctic and the Antarctic. More attractive, at least under a lens, are the bronze stalked balls of *Lamproderma cribrarioides* that pepper and blacken the shoot-tips of Crowberry and Alpine Clubmoss. It seems to favour the late snow beneath the chairlifts on Cairngorm, and so perhaps benefits from the compaction of the snow by skiers. Some 20 species of slime moulds are found under melting snow-packs in Scotland, but none of them occur in Snowdonia, presumably because the snow does not usually lie for long enough.

To see such things, most of us would have to make a long journey. It is time now to descend the high mountains, and poke around instead in the garden.

chapter seven

In our midst: our fungal neighbours

Gardens

Wherever there is something to consume and rot down, there will be fungi. Every garden, large or small, will contain scores, possibly hundreds, of species of fungi. Many of them are microscopic and so unlikely to attract notice. Others will be the contributory cause of disease in plants, such as rusts or mildews, and therefore undesirable (although not always: I knew at least one university professor who cultivated a sort of 'death garden' of fungal diseases as a source of practical course material). But many more exist harmlessly or beneficially, recycling nutrients and maintaining soil fertility. They rot down stumps and fragments of wood, and produce fruit bodies in a whole range of garden mini-habitats, from mulched flowerbeds and bonfire sites to compost heaps and plant containers. Edible mushrooms abound, from Shaggy Inkcaps on the lawn to, if you are lucky, summer truffles in the shade of a Beech tree. It would be hard to find anywhere with more variety within a small space than a traditional garden, with its lawn, borders and shrubberies – especially if the gardener has not been tempted by quick-fix fungicides and lawn fertilisers.

The most conspicuous garden fungi are on the lawn. Certain species, such as the Haymaker or Brown Mottlegill *Panaeolina foenisecii*, Spring Fieldcap *Agrocybe praecox*, Pleated Inkcap *Parasola plicatilis* and the Fairy Ring Champignon *Marasmius oreades*, may be more common there than in any other habitat. Older lawns produce a much greater variety of fungi that overlaps with semi-natural grassland, and are best considered there. More recently sown ones support a smaller range, but

◀ **Fruiting cups** of Green Elfcup *Chlorociboria aeruginascens*.

where there is enough woody debris in the soil they make up in numbers what they lack in diversity. The large lawn of the house where I used to live sat on a raft of debris, including building timbers, and, in the right season, used to sprout spectacular fungal gardens of Shaggy Inkcap *Coprinus comatus*, Weeping Widow *Lacrymaria lacrymabunda* and Bulbous Honey Fungus *Armillaria gallica*. Inkcaps are a distinct group of mushrooms whose black spores are shed in drops of liquid; as the mushroom matures, its tissues begin to deliquesce and seem to melt in front of one's eyes. The distantly related Weeping Widow is tougher, but 'weeps' black drops from its gills that splash the ground like inkblots.

The best-known lawn mushroom is the Fairy Ring Champignon, the tough, buff-coloured agaric that creates circles and half circles of bare ground as if the lawn is suffering from a vegetable form of ringworm. Rings often form when the turf has been taken from natural grassland, although they can also, in time, turn up on sown lawns and football pitches. Whether or not they are a problem depends on what the lawn is for. Some gardeners regard even a few daisies as a blemish. Others welcome a little natural variety within an otherwise dull and inert expanse of turf.

Older lawns, such as those of country cottages and hotels, can support a wide range of fungi that are characteristic of natural grassland. Some of our most exciting sites for those colourful mushrooms known as waxcaps are on lawns (I will say more about them in the next chapter), and lawns also produce little yellow and white spindles of fairy clubs and those dark slivers of fungus known as earthtongues. Rare or little-known fungi can crop up on unimproved lawns. Shelley Evans had the good fortune to find *Dermoloma magicum* on hers, a recently described species that has not yet made it into popular field guides and so probably goes unnoticed, despite being a remarkable mushroom that starts off pale brown, then bruises red, and finally turns black. A year or two later, she went one better and found a new European species just yards from the back door: a jelly fungus called *Efibulobasidium rolleyi*, otherwise known only from Tahiti and Iowa in the United States. Admittedly, its small brownish blobs are not the kind of thing that anyone except a mycologist would spot (although it looks more interesting under a microscope). But it shows that one need not wander far to discover little-known fungi. They are there, right under our noses.

Flowerbeds have their own distinctive fungi. What may appear will depend on what material has been used to fertilise and mulch the ground. Rotting dung has numerous associated fungi, of which the most famous is the Horse Mushroom *Agaricus arvensis*, which was formerly cultivated in beds filled with dung from fields and stables. Dungy ground often produces cup fungi in the spring, especially the deep-brown Bay Cup *Peziza badia*. The rose garden is the place to look for another spring-fruiting species, Shield Pinkgill *Entoloma clypeatum*, with its characteristic dimpled cap. Where the beds have been enriched with straw or wood fibre, you often find bird's-nest fungi, which look like fruit tarts for dolls (the 'gooseberries' or 'eggs' are spore-bearing structures called peridioles).

Well-composted flowerbeds sometimes produce the tall Stubble Rosegill *Volvariella gloiocephala*, which is one of the few fungi to have benefited from nitrogenous fertiliser and so has become a common species in arable fields where the land has been rested before ploughing. It is sometimes mistaken for a Field Mushroom (although it has a membranous cup or volva at the base of the stalk). This misidentification presents no real danger since it is theoretically edible, although, as you might expect from a fungus that lives on chemical fertiliser, it does not taste of much. Digging can occasionally turn up buried truffle-like fungi (although the best edible one, Summer Truffle *Tuber aestivum*,

▼ **Stubble Rosegill** *Volvariella gloiocephala* exploits man-made niches on composted ground and arable fields.

grows on tree roots, usually Beech). The first, and so far only, British specimen of the Steppe Truffle *Gastrosporium simplex* was discovered by Margaret Holden while she was weeding out some goldenrod from her garden. Another mycologist-gardener, Shelly Stroud, came across the euphemistically named Strong-scented Stephensia *Stephensia bombycina* in her garden in Breconshire, a truffle that draws attention to itself by an overpowering stink of blocked drains or over-ripe Camembert. The apparent association of truffles with gardens may be because that is where most of us do most of our digging.

Beds where woodchip mulch has been used are one of the most exciting new habitats for fungi. Many of the fungi, which can appear in great numbers for a year or two, are exotic species, the same ones having turned up in gardens and amenity plantings across the world during the past decade or two. I return to these in more detail below.

▲ **Turkeytail** *Trametes versicolor*, one of the commonest bracket fungi on decaying branches, stumps and logs.

Logs and stumps provide a very important habitat for fungi, and wherever large chunks of wood are left to rot you can expect to find seasonal crops of bracket fungi, woodwarts *Hypoxylon*, barkspots, oyster mushrooms and other species. Which species are present will depend on the tree. In general, native trees have more species than ornamental ones. One of the commonest is Turkeytail *Trametes versicolor*, so-named from its fan-shaped fruit bodies, with alternating dark grey, yellow and white bands. Oyster Mushroom *Pleurotus ostreatus* is another frequent and, usually welcome, fungus on garden log piles. At least one garden in my village produces a fine harvest of Summer Truffles, hidden among fallen leaves beneath a line of planted Hornbeams – although, since they look like half-buried Badger poo, only the initiated are likely to spot them for what they are. A common species that attracts attention by its strange shape is the Candlesnuff Fungus *Xylaria hypoxylon*, like tiny, ashen-tipped antlers or, as an older generation thought, burnt candle wick.

Another garden micro-habitat is the compost heap. Fungi are active agents in the process of decomposing dead vegetation into nutrient-rich soil. Because of the heat generated within the heap, these fungi are 'thermophiles' that can withstand heat beyond the tolerances of soil fungi. These species are mainly microfungi, but a few agarics regularly turn up and fruit at the surface of the heap, such as the little inkcap *Coprinopsis cinerea,* various species of brittlestem *Psathyrella* and the little Redspored Dapperling *Melanophyllum haematospermum*, which looks like just another 'little brown mushroom' until you turn it over and discover its blood-red gills. The same sorts of fungi also thrive on the warm, comforting environment of heaps of manure.

▲ **Orange Mosscap** *Rickenella fibula*, a tiny, funnel-shaped species usually found in carpets of moss.

Bonfire sites are one of the less likely garden habitats. The technical name for fungi that grow on burned ground is phoenicoid (phoenix-like), in honour of the fabled bird that was consumed in the fire, only to be reborn from its ashes. In the wild, they are presumably species that appear after forest fires (or, in other parts of the world, near volcanoes), and at other times survive in the soil as dormant spores. First to appear after the embers have died down are tiny discomycetes, especially the pinkish-orange crusts of *Pyromena* species, or *Anthracobia*, which produces orange discs like scattered seeds. Later on, larger fungi may appear, including cup fungi, morels and even toadstools such as certain inkcaps and the orange-brown Bonfire Scalycap *Pholiota highlandensis*, which is rarely found anywhere else (the scientific name is misleading: the fungus was named in America, but in Britain is just as much at home in the lowlands).

Fungi will even grow on garden wall tops and other dry places, such as the edges of a gravel drive. Among them are tiny, delicate, trumpet-shaped species of navel *Omphalina*, oysterling *Arrhenia* or mosscap *Rickenella*, which seem to survive by forming partnerships with mosses and liverworts. The very lucky may find the Winter Stalkball *Tulostoma brumale*, a drumstick-shaped stalked puffball that occasionally turns up among crumbling mortar on mild, damp days in winter and early spring; its other habitat is sand dunes.

Most of the larger fungi of gardens are harmless and, indeed, quietly beneficial. The one to watch for, though, is the Honey Fungus *Armillaria mellea*, aka the gardener's curse. This is a honey-brown toadstool with dark brown cap scales and a stem ring, and usually grows in tufts. It often occurs harmlessly on stumps and buried wood, as it did in my garden, living on dead matter as a saprotroph. But some strains of it turn aggressive and parasitic, penetrating the roots of living trees and producing a 'butt rot' that will eventually topple and kill the tree. It has also attacked root crops such as potato. Once Honey Fungus takes hold, the only remedy is to dig up and destroy the infected roots (or, says one advisor, move house). The fungus's dark secret lies in the black bootlace-like threads, rhizomorphs, with which it moves from stump to stump, like the runners of a strawberry plant.

▲ **Bad news for gardeners.** The massed fruit bodies of Honey Fungus *Armillaria mellea.*

The Honey Fungus has another trick up its sleeve: it glows in the dark! The glow is faint, and you need dark-adjusted eyes to see it, but break off a piece of damp, rotten wood in which the fungus is growing and you may observe a faint, eerie glow that, to some eyes, is greenish. It is nothing compared to the glow of some tropical fungi, but it is still thrilling. What benefit the light brings to the fungus is unknown. It may be an incidental by-product of fungal chemistry, without a useful function.

▼ **The bootlace-like rhizomorphs of Honey Fungus** *Armillaria mellea,* exposed where the bark has fallen away.

Encouraging fungi in the garden is easy. The advice is essentially the opposite of that given for formal gardens. That given to encourage insects and wild flowers by 'green gardening' also works pretty well for fungi. Here are some tips:

- Practise organic gardening by avoiding fungicides, broad-spectrum weedkillers and lawn fertiliser.
- Use natural mulches such as wood fibre or rotted compost.
- Learn to love those mossy patches on the lawn. When mowing, remove the clippings. This reduces a build-up of nutrients and so helps fungi such as waxcaps and coral fungi, which thrive best in open, mossy conditions.
- Stick to the same site for garden bonfires and compost heaps: it helps the fungi to build up their numbers.
- Cherish mature trees, especially native ones such as oaks, Beech, birches and willows. Cherish large logs and stumps even more.
- So long as you can identify them, collect and consume the edible ones to your heart's content.
- And if there are plenty of fungi already, keep up the good work!

Indoor fungi

Fungi in the garden is one thing, but few of us want mushrooms in the house, unless they are edible ones safely packed away in bottles and jars. The list of least welcome fungi is headed by Dry Rot *Serpula lacrymans*. The English name is a misnomer, for Dry Rot needs damp and humidity to thrive. Its formal name is fun: *Serpula* means 'little snake', whose wriggles match the sinuous patterns of the fungus's brownish, pancake-like fruit bodies. *Lacrymans* means to weep. Whoever named it was referring to the droplets that form on the ripe fungus, as if 'weeping in regret at the havoc it has made,' according to one characteristically sentimental Victorian mycologist. Once Dry Rot has taken hold, the householder faces a large bill, and the tears will not be confined to *Serpula lacrymans*.

Strangely, Dry Rot has never been found in a natural habitat in Britain. It is confined to structural timber and presumably spread to Britain from abroad once our ancestors started to build timber houses and boats. It was common enough in the past to be regarded as a plague, and I can still remember its disgusting fungussy stench in abandoned wartime Nissen huts on an airbase where we once lived. In modern homes, efficient ventilation has made it virtually a thing of the past, along with fleas and bedbugs, but in places where flooding is a growing problem, like a cold lava it creeps in and smothers everything – bricks, floorboards, water pipes, leather shoes, books, furniture, everything – turning what was once comfortable habitation into a scene from Edgar Allan Poe's *Fall of the House of Usher.*

A less harmful species is the Cellar Cup *Peziza cerea*, whose buff-coloured cups sometimes appear in damp corners and cracks in cellars. It is an adaptable species that currently thrives on rotting sandbags thrown up during a flood and subsequently left to rot. It is also associated with toilets, especially men's toilets, appearing on walls left damp and peeling from a leaking cistern, and was probably much commoner in this habitat when the loo was halfway down the garden path. Cellar Cup is not harmful in itself, but it is a warning that nastier problems, such as Dry Rot, might be on the way.

Much more attractive indoor fungi are certain exotic and colourful species that grow in plant containers and hanging baskets. If there are liverworts in your plant pot, then the little Redhead *Loreleia postii*, which grows on them, may not be far behind. Much more obvious is the bright yellow Plantpot Dapperling *Leucocoprinus birnbaumii*, also called the Yellow Houseplant or Pot Plant Mushroom. It is a tropical species that first turned up in heated greenhouses but is now colonising hanging baskets and plant pots. It has also begun its leap into the great outdoors where it has been found, for example, on a handy heap of woodchips made from recycled Christmas trees, in Highgate Woods, Middlesex. Other tropical mushrooms have appeared in hothouses, including *Collybia multijuga*, a pale mushroom with a brown centre that grows in 'troops' at Kew, and *Agaricus endoxanthus*, a dark-capped relative of the poisonous Yellow Stainer Mushroom. These interlopers do not seem to harm the plants they grow with, which is just as well, since they are impossible to eradicate, short of replacing the soil.

Fairy rings

As every lawn-owner knows, mushrooms sometimes grow in circles. Although the mushrooms appear only now and then, their presence is visible all year round as a dark ring in the grass. Closer inspection shows that, at least with the most common ring-maker, the Fairy Ring Champignon *Marasmius oreades* ('champignon' being a French word for edible mushroom), the ring is double, with an outer zone of darker, slightly lusher grass, and an inner one where the grass grows poorly, with earth showing through. Such rings range from a few feet to several metres across, and still larger ones have been detected on aerial photographs, looking like faint archaeological impressions. These have long been called fairy rings, as well as fairy dances, fairy courts, fairy walks and, in bygone Sussex, hag tracks. In the days when people believed in fairies, the rings were supposed to mark the places of moonlit revels where the little folk transacted their business, cast spells and danced the night away (perhaps with some of them sitting out a dance on the handy little toadstools). Sheep dared not bite the 'sour' grass of the ring lest they be poisoned or fall under enchantment. Today, some of us still believe in fairies of a different kind. In 1999, an image of a fairy ring appeared in Charles Fort's *Fortean Times*, a journal dedicated to strange phenomena, whose correspondent suggested 'earth energies' or aliens as the cause.

Folk tales about fairy rings are common to the whole of Europe, though perhaps they reach the pinnacle of imaginative fancy in Germany, where they are known as 'hexen', or witchcraft rings. The probable basis for the tales is the circle of apparently trampled ground, for, it was reasoned, what else could have made it but troops of tiny feet? By the late 17th century, Robert Plot thought that he had found a more rational explanation: the rings surely marked the patch of scorched earth where lightning had struck (and mushrooms do often appear after a thunderstorm). Others suspected the alleged rutting habits of moles. One explanation did link the rings with mushrooms, but only indirectly: the latter, it was reasoned, grew on the circles of slime and putrefying earth left by wandering slugs. Unlike Plot, Gilbert White, the naturalist of Selborne, drew his conclusions from observation and evidence. He stripped fine turf from the downs for his 'garden-walks', and noted that it abounded with fairy rings 'which shift situation continually, discovering themselves now in circles, now in segments, & sometimes in irregular-patches, & spots'. On these strips and circles of dark turf he

◀ **Plantpot Dapperling**
Leucocoprinus birnbaumii, a bright yellow, cosmopolitan intruder in plant pots and hanging baskets.

sometimes found puffballs and deduced, rightly, that their spawn had been brought in with the turf.

In the year before White's death in 1793, the botanist William Withering discovered the true cause of the mysterious rings. He found traces of a fungus in the bare ground of the ring, but none in the lusher grass beyond. He identified the species responsible as *Agaricus oreades* (now *Marasmius oreades*), and the mushroom has been known ever since as the Fairy Ring Champignon. Years followed before anyone understood the mechanism responsible. It is simply a matter of growth and biochemistry. On an even substrate, fungi tend to grow outwards in a circle, like mould on a jar of jam. The ring marks the line of active growth, where troops and circles of little mushrooms appear when conditions are right. The fairy ring fungus competes with the grass by producing

toxins, resulting in that narrow strip of 'trampled' earth. The band of taller grass beyond is benefiting from the nitrogen released into the soil by the growing fungus – fungal fertiliser.

The older the fungus, the larger the ring. Really big fairy rings are restricted to old grassland, and are made not by the Fairy Ring Champignon, which can manage only 10m or so, but mostly by the St George's Mushroom *Calocybe gambosa*. One enormous ring, made by the Trooping Funnel *Clitocybe geotropa* and only detected by aerial photography, measured 800m across, which, at an assumed growth rate of between 20cm and 70cm per year, would indicate an age of at least 1,100 years, and possibly as much as 4,000 years! Large fairy rings are a good indicator of ancient grassland. They mark the slow march of an immortal mushroom, like the outermost ring of an enormous tree. Today, it is the piecemeal nature of old grassland, more than fungal biology, which sets a limit to their size.

▼ **A relative of the blewits,** *Lepista panaeola* (formerly *L. luscina*) – this species has somehow avoided an English name – forming a large fairy ring in grassland, Quantock Hills, Somerset.

At one time, the Fairy Ring Champignon was thought to be the only fungus that creates visible rings, but, in fact, many grassland species do so, and certain woodland ones, too, (although the latter are generally 'tethered rings', tied to tree roots). Perhaps the most spectacular of all fungal rings is a circle of stately scarlet Fly Agarics *Amanita muscaria* formed around a tree. Among the grassland species that sometimes form rings are Field Mushroom *Agaricus campestris*, Field Blewit *Lepista saeva* and Meadow Puffball *Lycoperdon pratense*. Unlike the Fairy Ring Champignon, they stimulate but do not suppress the grass, so that their rings form zones of lush, dark grass without the inner ring of bare ground. Yet other grassland species, such as waxcaps, have no visible effects on the grass, and their rings are composed of the fruit bodies alone.

Some gardeners dislike fairy rings because they spoil the purity of an even, bowling-green turf. Others find the circles and patterns attractive, and regard the mushrooms as free autumn bounty, suitable for mushroomy winter casseroles (although one needs to be aware of the Fairy Ring Champignon's poisonous look-alike, Ivory Funnel *Clitocybe rivulosa*, which also forms rings on garden lawns). Getting rid of fairy rings is difficult. With no chemical remedies available, the gardener has little choice but to dig out the soil around the ring and replace it with sterilised loam before resowing the turf. As Gilbert White discovered, soil from almost any turf taken from wild grassland on downs, dunes or commons will contain fairy ring fungi – nature's revenge!

The global fungal weeds

Ever since they invented machines that could reduce a small tree to a pile of chips in minutes, woodchips have been used widely as mulch, which suppresses weeds whilst enriching the soil beneath in a similar way to compost or stable bedding. When not in use, the chips are commonly left in the open in piles, where they start to rot. This is a form of gardening that has particular appeal to cash-strapped public authorities, since it allows them to maintain flowerbeds without pesticides and without a gardener. Its appeal knows no boundaries, and woodchip mulch is now used the world over, from Cape Town to Helsinki.

Although weeds have difficulty gaining a roothold in the loose layers of flakes, fungi have no such problem. In the past, some fungi were associated with rotting heaps of sawdust, among them the rare Golden or Sulphur Bolete *Buchwaldoboletus sphaerocephalus*, which forms mighty

◀ **Redlead Roundhead**
Leratiomyces ceres (formerly known as *Stropharia aurantiaca*), a copper-coloured coloniser of woodchip mulches. Its scientific name has changed twice in the past ten years.

tufts of golden mushrooms, each the size of a currant bun. In recent times, equally strange and exotic fungi have begun to turn up on beds of woodchips. One of these is the mysterious copper-coloured mushroom dubbed the Redlead Roundhead, one of the few fungi one can identify with confidence from a speeding train. My first sight of it was in the car park of the Eden Project, in Cornwall, where Green Alders had recently been planted to screen out unsightly cars from the botanical wonders beyond. It was a dull, grey morning in mid-November but the copper mushrooms crowding the beds looked like pirates' treasure – thousands of doubloons, strewn across the beds. It was as if the God of botany had complimented the Eden Project with a rain of bright copper pennies.

▲ **Fluted Bird's Nest** *Cyathus striatus* grows in clusters, like tiny scallop shells, on well-rotted wood and woodchip mulch.

Until the first years of the 21st century, this mushroom was scarcely known in Britain. Almost overnight, it turned into a common species. The odd thing was that this new fungal 'weed' was hardly known in the wild, and no one knew from whence it came. It is found on woodchip beds around the world, apparently equally as at home in North America, South Africa, Australia and New Zealand as in Western Europe. There is even doubt about its name. When I was admiring it at the Eden Project, it was called *Stropharia aurantiaca* and had started to appear in the latest field guides by that name. However, that name was based on a misidentification and so is invalid (the name actually belongs to a colour form of the native *Leratiomyces squamosus* var. *thraustus*). Since then, its name has changed twice. DNA analysis proved that it was the same species as a fungus called *Psilocybe ceres*, and which has itself been shifted to *Leratiomyces ceres*. Maybe we should stick to the English name! The view today is that the Redlead Roundhead is a native of Australia, which, as it were, jumped onto the global bandwagon of suburban woodchip beds. Another woodchip fungus is spreading even more rapidly. This is *Agrocybe rivulosa*, a pale, nondescript mushroom with a characteristically wrinkled cap, first found on a pile of Sycamore woodchips at Leek, Derbyshire, in 2004. Six years later, it has become one of the commonest flowerbed agarics in the country but still, at the time of writing, lacks an English name.

Fungi can exploit changing conditions as quickly as this because they produce so many spores. Unlike most plant seeds, spores are smaller than grains of dust, and so they form a kind of aerial plankton that can be blown miles, or perhaps hundreds of miles, from their point of origin. Fungi will rapidly germinate and colonise flakes of wood as soon as it is moist and starting to soften. Since there is nothing to check their growth under these artificial circumstances, fruit bodies can appear in spectacular numbers within a year or two of mulching.

Conifer chips and bark chips, widely used in Britain, seem to support fewer fungi than hardwood chips.

Woodchip beds in full 'bloom' are reminiscent of mushroom farms. Native species, too, take advantage of this man-made 'fast food'. Some observations suggest a succession of species, from early colonisers such as species of *Coprinopsis* and *Psathyrella* to a brief fungal explosion in the second or third year, followed by a tailing off as the chips lose their nutritive value. In 2000, Jonathan Revett found a kind of devil's garden of exotic fungi on the woodchip dunes of a children's play area. What looked, from a distance, like discarded rubber tyres turned out to be close-massed rings of the normally rare bird's-nest fungus, Fluted Bird's Nest *Cyathus striatus*. With them were the sinister spires of dog stinkhorns, normally a woodland species, and gargoyle-like outgrowths of Elfin Saddle *Helvella lacunosa*, 'like a black mass of satanic melted candles', bounded by a miniature hedge of Upright Coral *Ramaria stricta*. Municipal borders and flowerbeds have become a good place to find morels, both the ordinary Morel *Morchella esculenta* and Black Morel *M. elata*. On this habitat, these normally spring-fruiting species are appearing with increasing frequency in the autumn, too (but, since so many of these places are by roadsides and car parks, gathering them as food might not be wise). In view of its recent predilection for towns, the Black Morel is now known in America as the Urban or Landscape Morel. At least 150 species of larger fungi, natives and aliens alike, have been found thriving on woodchips.

▼ Like something from a horror film: Devil's Fingers *Clathrus archeri* is spreading in gardens where woodchip mulch is used.

Even more exotic fungi sometimes turn up. Devil's Fingers *Clathrus archeri*, for example, looks like a prop from a cheap sci-fi film, a rosette of flesh-coloured tentacles smothered in an evil-smelling, spore-laden gunk. A native of Australia, it is still quite rare in Britain, but has become a backyard species in parts of the United States, where its lurking presence causes anxious sniffing at parties and barbecues. Another spectacular fungal weed is a large, tufted mushroom with red-brown scales, recorded for the first time in 2003. It, too, has suffered a succession of name changes. Its current name is *Agaricus subrufescens*, but it is better known as *A. rufotegulis* (meaning 'red roof-tiles', after the colour and layering of its cap scales) or *A. blazei*. It occurs in North and South America as well as Eurasia, under different aliases. Since *A. subrufescens* is the oldest, this name takes priority, despite being also the least memorable. The mushroom has attracted attention because, in addition to a pleasant smell and taste, it is of medicinal interest and has a potential application in cancer treatment. It was first described from North America, where it was apparently cultivated locally before the Cultivated Mushroom *A. bisporus* swept all before it.

Another woodchip hitchhiker has attracted attention for other reasons. The Blueleg Brownie *Psilocybe cyanescens* is a powerfully hallucinogenic 'magic mushroom', apparently more potent than our native one, Liberty Cap *P. semilanceata*. Small and caramel-brown with a wavy cap margin, its stipe gradually turns a psychedelic blue, hence 'blue leg'. Until recently, it was known only from the flowerbeds of Kew Gardens, where it has maintained a precarious existence for a century. But since the authorities started to use woodchips on forest tracks it has escaped into the wild and is now colonising the woods around London; it has also turned up in Ireland. They are known in the illegal drug trade as 'cyans'. It seems to be a native of California, where it is regularly grown from spores and used as an illegal recreational drug.

Another reputedly hallucinogenic fungal weed is *Gymnopilus dilepis*, and this one also looks the part. Starting as a tan-coloured button, it soon turns attractive shades of purple, from mauve to deep plum. With its contrasting yellow gills, it looks like a small version of our common *Tricholomopsis rutilans*, long known as Plums and Custard. When, as is usual on woodchip heaps, the caps grow packed together, this is another fungus that is hard to ignore. Previously known only as a plant-pot alien in greenhouses, it was first found outdoors in the 1990s and is now locally frequent in south-east and eastern England on rotting chips and compost heaps. It is a native of south-east Asia and Australia, and, once again, seems to thrive on the internally generated heat and jungle damp of woodchip piles.

Our global fungal weeds (in Alick Henrici's memorable phrase) seem to be a harmless and attractive addition to our wildlife. Where their presence is thought educational and interesting, the mulch could possibly be managed, for example by raking the old mulch to one side instead of removing it, to allow fungal colonisation of the fresh stuff underneath. Not that they seem to need much help from us. They are one of the current winners in life's lottery, vivid emblems of our increasingly suburban, ever more homogenised, climatically warmed planet.

God's fungi: churchyards and cemeteries

In the lowlands, country churchyards and urban cemeteries are among the best places to find a variety of fungi, particularly grassland ones, all conveniently localised within 'God's acre'. Churchyards and some cemeteries are essentially parks with graves, offering a variety of trees set in short and often mossy grassland. In my own corner of England, a favourite foray venue is a small churchyard at the edge of Savernake Forest. It invariably provides a good assortment of waxcaps, including the famous Ballerina or Pink Waxcap *Hygrocybe calyptriformis*, and coral fungi, including the rare Violet Coral *Clavaria zollingeri*, with its uniquely rich purple colour. There are also various species of little blue or grey *Entolomas*, and tufts of Clustered Domecap *Lyophyllum decastes* which, I notice, often seems to grow on graves, possibly on the decaying coffin wood beneath. Such places are islands of strange diversity. In their isolation, they form refuges, in effect fungal nature reserves, often preserved by kindly custodians who appreciate them.

In the Chilterns, many similar old churchyards have been surveyed by Richard Fortey, the celebrated author and palaeontologist

▼ **Violet Coral** *Clavaria zollingeri*, a scarce and beautiful coral fungus of old grassland, including lawns and churchyards.

▲ **The mysterious** *Amanita inopinata* started appearing under Yew and Lawson Cypress in churchyards and gardens from the 1980s.

(Fortey 2000). They contain patches of species-rich (i.e. nutrient-poor) grassland, kept short by mowing, with patches of moss on and amongst the old headstones. Waxcaps are particularly plentiful, with a dozen or more species in the best sites, including such rarities as Slimy Waxcap *Hygrocybe irrigata* and the colourful Orange Waxcap *H. aurantiosplendens*. Although most of these are on chalky soil, Fortey found that no two churchyards are alike. One, at Rotherfield Greys, produces regular crops of the scarce Yellow Foot Waxcap *H. flavipes*, with its distinctive splash of bright yellow at the base of the stalk, while another at Highmoor Cross specialises in the Crimson Waxcap *H. punicea*, a stout, handsome mushroom which is usually found in good company.

Churchyards are good places to look for fairy clubs and coral fungi, too. The turf at Rotherfield Greys church can be richly speckled orange with Meadow Coral *Clavulinopsis corniculata*. Some of Fortey's Chiltern churchyards share one of the specialities of my Savernake Forest church, the densely branched, reputedly poisonous Ivory Coral *Ramariopsis kunzei*. Still rarer is the tufted, smoky-pink Beige Coral *Clavulinopsis umbrinella*, confined in Oxfordshire to the churchyard at Highmoor.

Cemeteries can be among the best places to find fungi in cities, and they are popular venues for fungus forays. One good site, North London's Kensal Green Cemetery, sandwiched between the Grand Union Canal and the busy Harrow Road, yields a notable list of rarities, including the pinkish-brown, cucumber-scented Poplar Knight *Tricholoma populinum* and the sturdy Slate Bolete *Leccinum duriusculum*, both under poplars, as well as the attractive Snakeskin Grisette *Amanita ceciliae*, so named from the fragments of veil on the cap that resemble a cast snakeskin. Here, waxcaps are confined to the lawns by the old catacombs, but one grave regularly produces constellations of the little Beaked Earthstar *Geastrum pectinatum*. I cannot think of a better fungal compliment! Paul Sterry told me a graveyard fungus story about another earthstar called *G. striatum* (its unimaginative common name is Striated Earthstar). At Eastleigh Cemetery, Hampshire, a noted place for this species and other rare earthstars, it fruits prolifically on several graves, but most commonly of all upon the sepulchre of one Alfred Coffin!

Yet another north London cemetery, Abney Park, is now a nature reserve. Here, the headstones have been swallowed up in woodland. It has a long and exciting list of fungi, and is especially notable for bracket fungi and slime moulds. Other examples include North Watford Cemetery, in Hertfordshire, that county's best waxcap site. Surrey's Brookwood Cemetery is, at 150ha, the largest in Britain, and boasts 23 species of waxcaps growing in the short grass between the graves. Alan Legg and others have recorded 400 species of fungi from Darlington West Cemetery, in County Durham.

Perhaps the most remarkable churchyard fungus of all is *Amanita inopinata*. This is an Amanita that looks more like a parasol mushroom, or that dark and uniquely shaggy bolete known as Old Man of the Woods *Strobilomyces strobilaceus*. Instead of the coloured cap and white 'spots' of the Fly Agaric and its relatives, *A. inopinata* has a skin of thick, greyish, cottony felt which disrupts as the cap expands into shaggy lumps and warts. To add to its oddity it has salmon-pink gills, unlike the other members of the genus whose gills are snow-white. The name *inopinata*, appropriately enough, means 'unexpected' or 'surprise', for the mushroom was unknown to science when it was discovered in Kent by Irene Palmer, in 1981, and subsequently described by Kew's Derek Reid. It soon turned up elsewhere in south-east England, especially in churchyards where it usually grows on bare soil under Yew or Leylandii. Since it was inconceivable that such a mushroom could have been missed, it was suspected to be a recent introduction. Sure enough, it has been found to be quite widespread on the far side of the world, and seems to be particularly at home in New Zealand (although, since it is associated with European Cupressuses, it may not be indigenous there either). Why it should choose churchyards over any other habitat remains unknown.

▲ **The thick grey cap** of *Amanita inopinata*.

That concludes our tour of wild and not-so-wild habitats. But the question remains: do mushrooms and other fungi tell us something about the environment in which they grow? Is there something special about rich and diverse sites, or do mushrooms occur more or less at random? From what we know of flowering plants, we would expect them to be very fussy about the ground they choose. And we would be right.

chapter eight

Earthtongues, waxcaps and hedgehogs:

what fungi tell us about the natural environment

Conservationists have long known that some species of flowering plants and ferns are confined mainly to old, undisturbed woods (though more so in some parts than others). For example, in eastern England, Primroses and Wood Anemones grow mainly in woods that are known to be ancient, that is, at least 400 years old (this is about as far back as historical evidence will permit us to go). The same seems to hold true of mosses and lichens, some of which depend on conditions of constant humidity that would be destroyed by clear felling. The rule holds good for insects and other small invertebrates too. There are moth and beetle species that are rarely found away from old woodlands that are rich in plants and dead wood.

It begins to look like a general rule. The oldest habitats are also the best, especially when they are also large and relatively undisturbed. It is only here that we can appreciate the wonderful biodiversity that has built up over a long age. Today, habitat re-creation is all the rage, but it will take centuries to match the diversity of old woods, pastures and heaths. For that reason, it is vital to hang on to them. They are, literally, irreplaceable.

Fungi are no exception to the rule, although, as usual, we know less about them. One group that has attracted enormous interest in recent years is the grassland fungi. These are often attractive, and tend to fruit fairly regularly, unlike some of the shyer woodland species. Surveys by field mycologists and others have provided a mountain of evidence that grassland fungi are good indicators of old grassland. Moreover, they have given us a very different idea of the value of grassland on poor soils. Many of these are relatively poor in flowering plant diversity and so were discounted when it came to conservation assessments. Yet they are not poor in fungi.

◀ Tooth fungi and oak leaves.

Mushrooms of old grassland

Wild flowers and fungi do not always share the same turf. Fungi need space to thrive. They like open, mossy turf, kept short by grazing or, in the case of lawns, mowing. They do not like long grass, which is too shady for them to fruit. Fungal diversity peaks in old grassland that has not been agriculturally 'improved'. These include chalk downs, limestone grassland, grassy heaths and commons, and dune slacks, as well as permanent pasture.

▼ **An earthtongue**, probably a species of *Geoglossum*, appearing like miniature standing stones in short, sheep-grazed turf.

The fungi that cause the greatest excitement are the brilliantly coloured waxcaps *Hygrocybe*, but there are also earthtongues, erect slivers of dark fungi shaped like arrow-heads or adders' tongues, coral fungi as brittle and beautiful as underwater reefs and a host of smaller species, some of which are deep blue with salmon-coloured gills. Some species are considered to be rare and threatened by the march of human progress. They feature on conservation Red Lists across northern Europe.

While mossy grassland was known to support interesting fungi, there was little attempt in Britain to compare one site with another until the 1990s. The hero of the hour was the late Maurice Rotheroe, a former journalist turned freelance mycologist, who set himself the task of surveying the fungi of dunes and upland pastures, and assessing their relative importance. His reports to English Nature and the Countryside Council for Wales helped to make conservationists more aware of the fascination and importance of large fungi, and they also drew attention to their sensitivity to habitat change.

To evaluate grassland sites, Rotheroe borrowed and adapted for British use a technique devised by field mycologists in Scandinavia. This involved waxcap species, which, with a bit of skulduggery, could be used to relate the number of species seen on a single visit to a predicted total of species present. He refined the technique to include other grassland fungi that are just as habitat sensitive as waxcaps. These he divided into four groups, whose initial letters spell 'CHEG'. 'C' is for the coral or club fungi, known in the trade as 'clavarioid fungi'. 'H' is for *Hygrocybe*, the waxcaps. 'E' is for *Entoloma*, the mostly small fungi with salmon-pink gills, including the little blue ones just mentioned. The quartet is completed with 'G', which stands for earthtongues (*Geoglossum* and other genera), those bizarre black and green fungal tongues. For the purposes of completion, a few extra genera of grassland fungi are buried within the CHEG formula, so that, for instance, the small genera *Dermoloma* and *Porpoloma* lie within 'H' as honorary waxcaps. 'CHEG' has become the standard 'formula' for fungal grassland surveys. The beauty of the method is that the trained eye can evaluate the fungi of a patch of grassland more or less at a glance. All the surveyor has to do is to add up the scores to arrive at the CHEG number, making it an easily understood quantitative assessment.

The drawback is that it assumes a certain level of expertise. After all, it is not likely you will do justice to a great site if you can recognise only half a dozen kinds of waxcap. (*BBC Wildlife* got around the difficulty by launching a simplified key that identifies blocks of species by their colour. This does at least provide a rough indication of a site's diversity). In practice, the waxcap score is usually higher than the rest of the 'CHEG' fungi because naturalists know them best. Fewer of us are at home with earthtongues and pinkgills, which generally need a microscope to determine. Even so, Rotheroe's surveys revealed several sites in South Wales with a score sufficiently high to warrant the phrase 'nationally important', and to suggest that South Wales was one of the richest places for grassland fungi in Europe. Since then, the CHEG method has revealed many more rich grassland sites, and, perhaps surprisingly, some of these are on lawns. A hotel lawn in rural Leicestershire has one of the highest CHEG scores in the country. Another small place seemingly blessed by nature is the lawn and bank of Charles Darwin's house at Downe in Kent, which, at the last count, had a CHEG score of 40, including 20 waxcaps, nine *Entolomas* and eight fairy clubs. Of course, lawns can be old grassland, too. In many areas, old cottage and manor-house lawns and churchyards are among the main refuges of 'waxcap grassland' in our intensively farmed lowland countryside.

The method has been useful for bolstering the case for protecting a site. It was tested in law in the case of Llanishen Reservoir, near Cardiff, a disused Victorian lake used for sailing and other water sports. The reservoir is a noted site for its pond life and Grass Snakes, but what persuaded the Countryside Council for Wales to designate the place as a Site of Special Scientific Interest was the diversity of waxcaps and other grassland fungi growing around its banks. It is one of the best of its kind in Wales, with at least 29 waxcap species recorded. The designation was promptly challenged by the owners, who wanted to develop the site, but it was upheld by the High Court in 2007. This is as clear a legal justification as we have for designating sites for their fungal interest. Unfortunately, the owners, Western Power Distribution, have persisted with their redevelopment proposals, the latest one being to drain the reservoir and fill it with rubbish (BBC 2011).

▲ **Scarlet Waxcap** *Hygrocybe coccinea.*

▼ **Date Waxcap** *Hygrocybe spadicea,* a rare waxcap of calcareous grassland.

A happier conservation case, also in Wales, was at Llanerchaeron Mansion, an 18th-century house owned by the National Trust. Its modest lawn proved to be a veritable garden of fungi, including the exotic Violet Coral *Clavaria zollingeri*, the rare Olive Earthtongue *Microglossum olivaceum*, and a rainbow of waxcaps. The house was about to undergo extensive restoration owing to the attentions of a less desirable fungus, Dry Rot, which might have resulted in the use of the lawn as a builders' dump. Fortunately, the National Trust was persuaded to take steps to protect the lawn during the work, and Rotheroe even arranged a mycological teach-in for workers on the site.

Fungal flowers

Let us take a closer look at these 'fungal flowers', the waxcaps. What are they exactly? To begin with, they are very brightly coloured. Their colours are accentuated by their waterproof 'skin', which reflects the sunlight like fine satin. There are waxcaps for nearly every colour of the rainbow – buttercup yellow, fiery red, parrot green, mellow orange. Even the

▲ **Blackening Waxcaps,** *Hygrocybe conica = nigrescens*, in various stages of maturity.

► **Cedarwood Waxcap** *Hygrocybe russocoriacea*, distinguished by its strong smell.

▼ **Splendid Waxcap** *Hygrocybe splendidissima*, a beautiful waxcap of western and northern grasslands.

▲ **Spangle Waxcap** *Hygrocybe insipida*, one of the smaller species of unimproved grassland.

▲ **Snowy Waxcap** *Hygrocybe virginea*, the commonest waxcap, often found on lawns.

grey ones have a subtleness of tone and sheen that sets them apart. The name 'waxcap' refers to their texture – cool, thick and waxen, almost as if they were made in a factory. Some are slippery to touch ('lubricous') or even slimy ('viscid'), and if you try to pick these they slip through your fingers. The name *Hygrocybe* means 'water-cap', and, more than most fungi, they are cool and damp to touch, as if containing a bubble of moisture within a plastic envelope.

It was in the Netherlands that the mycologist Eef Arnolds (1989) first spotted something else: that waxcaps are commonest in exactly the kind of unsown, unfertilised pasture that was fast disappearing during the agricultural boom of the 1970s. Some species are more tolerant of agricultural improvement than others, but as a group waxcaps are reliable indicators of mycologically rich grassland.

There was a snag. Until recently, waxcaps made a surprisingly poor showing in field guides, and so it was difficult for a non-specialist to get to grips with them. This was not helped by a rift among European taxonomists over the precise characters which constituted a species. Where *do* you draw the line between one species and another? Was the waxcap that blackens when you touch it one species, or two, or, as one arch-splitter argued, seven? Did a slight difference in surface stickiness, or a barely discernible difference in tone, constitute sufficient reasons to split a species? Or should one allow for a reasonable range of variation? It depends where you draw the line, and on who wrote the field guide.

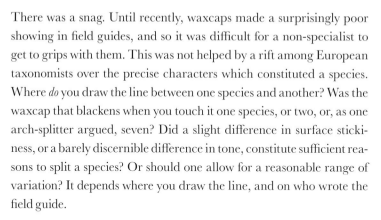

Fortunately, a fungal hero rode up in the nick of time to save us from a futile and endless academic debate. David Boertmann of Denmark is the author of a magnificent and affordable monograph, *The genus* Hygrocybe, which came out in 1995, just as everyone was getting keen on grassland fungi, and waxcaps in particular (it is now available in a new, revised edition). Not only is every species well illustrated in colour and accompanied by non-technical descriptions, but Boertmann took

a commonsense 'lumper's' line on taxonomy. That awkward group of indistinguishable blackening waxcaps was judged to be no more than forms of a single variable species, *Hygrocybe conica*. This certainly made life easier for the forayer. He also ignored a slight difference in stickiness and gill colour between the two common yellow waxcaps: they are both, he decided, versions of the same thing, *H. chlorophana*, the Golden Waxcap. Boertmann's masterpiece is now widely used throughout Europe as the accepted authority for naming waxcaps.

A good monograph makes waxcaps accessible, but it does not make them easy. In theory, every species can be named in the field using Boertmann's field characters, which are thoughtfully summarised in italics at the start of each species description. In practice, one constantly comes across specimens that do not key out easily, and often seem to contain characters of one species mixed with those of another. In such cases microscopic examination is necessary (as it may be for specimens in less than perfect condition). For example, a churchyard near my home in Wiltshire produces some very pretty golden-orange waxcaps that agree in most respects with Boertmann's description of *Hygrocybe chlorophana*, though that species is normally bright yellow. One day, I must get my microscope out.

Fortunately, some waxcaps are unmistakable, and most others can be narrowed or nailed down from a combination of shades, shapes, textures and scents. The nondescript-looking Cedarwood Waxcap *Hygrocybe russocoriacea* gives itself away with its powerful whiff of polish, or, as its species name proclaims, 'Russian leather'. Put a Honey Waxcap *H. reidii* on the radiator overnight and it will fill the room with sweetness. Oily Waxcap *H. quieta* has a soapy tang that older books compared with that of bed-bugs (although, as a two-tone waxcap, yellow above and orange below, even those with no sense of smell will have no trouble). Boertmann also urges us to use what he calls the kissing test. Touch a waxcap to your lips, and you can tell right away whether the texture is rubbery, sticky, rough or smooth. But specimens must

▲ **The Ballerina or Pink Waxcap** *Hygrocybe calyptriformis*, an unmistakable waxcap that is fairly common in Britain, although rare throughout the European mainland.

be picked with care, preferably with a special fungus knife, since pressure may release water from the underlying tissue and create a false slipperiness.

Even in the best places, waxcaps tend to form local hotspots within a larger, more barren area. Places worth searching carefully include roadsides or tracks, or short turf close to old mines and quarries. One of the best sites in south-west Scotland is associated with serpentinite, a rock rich in magnesium. Britain still has a vast acreage of 'waxcap grassland'. When Boertmann held a course on waxcaps at Abergavenny, in South Wales, in October 1997, he found enough species within a few hours to provide the course with sufficient material for the entire weekend. In lowland Europe, by contrast, waxcaps are in short supply. In the Netherlands, Eef Arnolds estimated that only about 200ha of waxcap grassland remained in the whole country – and that was 30 years ago (1988).

First in the Netherlands, and later in Denmark and Sweden, the link between waxcaps and old grassland was thoroughly investigated. The countries of Northern Europe share broadly the same species, and so the international survey results are comparable. Once similar surveys also got underway in Britain, we realised that we are an important country for such fungi. In fact, we have more top-quality sites – that is, those with 17-32 species of waxcap – than the Netherlands, Denmark and northern Germany put together. Sites 'of regional importance', with 9-16 species, are almost commonplace in the British uplands, while you might easily find 4-8 species 'of local importance' on your local common or village green – or even, if you are lucky, on your lawn.

There are some interesting differences between the waxcaps of Britain and our Continental neighbours. One of the prettiest and best-known species is the Pink Waxcap *Hygrocybe calyptriformis* (sometimes known as the Ballerina because as the cap expands it splits and curls up at the edges, like a tutu). It is locally common in Britain, and found on lawns and in churchyards, as well as in the open countryside. Yet it is vanishingly rare in continental Europe. In Denmark, it is confined to a single site, and in the Netherlands it is almost as rare. Neither of the two European waxcap specialists, David Boertmann and Eef Arnolds, had set eyes on it before coming to Britain. This is why the Pink Waxcap was on the original British Red Data List – because it was on everyone else's Red Data List. Possibly it is an oceanic species, like the Bluebell, fond of clean Atlantic rain and so restricted to the westward fringe of Europe (although this is certainly not so in North America, where it seems to prefer conifer woods!).

Experiments by Gareth Griffith and others at the University of Wales, Aberystwyth (Griffith *et al.* 2002, 2004), have proved that waxcaps are acutely sensitive to chemical fertiliser. A few, notably Snowy Waxcap *Hygrocybe virginea*, Meadow Waxcap *H. pratensis* and Blackening Waxcap, will linger in improved grasslands, and even colonise sown lawns after some years (Blackening Waxcap appeared on my lawn about 15 years after it was reseeded). But the majority of species are more environmentally sensitive. Given the right management, some of them, at least, could be coaxed back. Arnolds (1989) suggested that grassland could be made more waxcap-friendly by withholding fertiliser and increasing the stocking levels – and then waiting.

The average application of fertiliser in Britain is 120kg per acre per year, more than enough to wipe out all but the most tolerant waxcaps. In the even more intensively farmed Netherlands the equivalent figure is, or was, a rather frightening 263kg. Liming, too, is harmful, for it increases the biomass of bacteria at the expense of fungi. Improvement also reduces or stamps out the pockets and carpets of moss on which waxcaps seem to depend. In the Netherlands, the super-slimy species Parrot Waxcap *Hygrocybe psittacina* and Glutinous Waxcap *H. glutinipes* have a particular affinity with generous pockets of moss. Perhaps the moss acts as a sponge and maintains the necessary humidity. Or perhaps waxcaps have a more direct association with moss along the lines of that of mycorrhizal fungi and trees.

Not that all waxcaps share a common ecology. A few occur mainly on lime rich soils. Rather more prefer somewhat acid soil that is species-poor in terms of flowering plants. Several are found only on high ground, and a few even venture into woodland (where their distant relatives in the genus *Hygrophorus* hold sway) – as they do quite commonly in other parts of the world. Nor do they all appear at the same time. October is probably the best month overall, but in mild years you can find impressive troops of waxcaps in December. A few, such as the little red *Hygrocybe helobia*, tend to fruit earlier in the year and so may be under-recorded. Others, such as the Cedarwood Waxcap, are late-season species. This means, of course, that you have to make more than one trip to a site to discover its full potential.

While waxcaps as a whole may be in decline, some are much commoner than others. One of the rarest is the Date Waxcap *Hygrocybe spadicea*, named from its brown cap, the colour of dates, which contrasts well with its primrose-yellow stalk and gills. It seems to prefer dry and moderately lime-rich soils. Fortunately, its appearance on the Biodiversity Action Plan made forayers more *spadicea*-conscious, and resulted in a modest cache of new records, some in unexpected places. In 2006, the Date Waxcap suddenly fruited well, with new records all over the place, suggesting that it might not be rare so much as shy-fruiting.

Waxcaps have proved difficult to study, for they have so far resisted attempts to culture them on laboratory media. We have no idea yet of how to grow them from spores (those of the common Snowy Waxcap managed to produce a germ tube, but growth stopped soon after that). Clearly, their growth requires a certain special something, not yet defined but which must surely offer a clue to their localised distribution. Their mycelia are practically undetectable to the human eye. Eef Arnolds considered waxcaps to be saprotrophs, that is, feeders on humic matter in the soil, although he also suspected some sort of symbiotic relationship with mosses.

Recently, something of their physiology has been elucidated using spectrometry and the techniques of molecular biology. The results indicate that waxcaps derive their carbon from recently fixed carbon dioxide, and not from dead plant material. This means either that they are mycorrhizal – partners of plants – or that they find it by some unknown, novel means. In this context, it may be noteworthy that sites which are good for waxcaps are often poor in pinkgills *Entoloma*, and vice versa.

Signpost to the woods

Conservationists have long been fascinated by habitat indicator species, that is, plants or animals that seem to be confined, more or less, to near-natural, undisturbed places. Their presence can be taken as a sign of quality, and the more indicator species, the higher the diversity.

We have long grown used to the idea that about half of our woodland flora is of the stay-at-home sort, and that they are rarely found away from old woodland, at least in the drier parts of the country. The idea has practical applications. For example, indicator species were used by the then Nature Conservancy Council as evidence of sites of high quality when producing 'inventories' of ancient woodland during the 1980s.

We also know that this same rule applies to grassland fungi, albeit for slightly different reasons. Since they produce quantities of light spores that can float in the air, fungi presumably have no trouble dispersing them. Waxcaps and other species are probably restricted by their sensitivity to chemicals in the soil. How about woodlands? Woods support a greater variety of fungi than any other habitat. Are some species restricted more to old woods, in the same way as plants such as Wood Anemone and Herb-Paris?

Undoubtedly this is the case, but good evidence is hard to come by. The most probable reason why fungi should be restricted to older woods is that they depend on large living trees, logs and stumps. These are routinely removed in commercially managed woodland, and so we might expect such species to be confined to woods in which there are plenty of old trees and not too much tidying up. There *are* fungi that seem to be confined to old wood, living or dead. That is why the Government has protected two of them, Oak Polypore *Piptoporus quercinus* and Bearded Tooth *Hericium erinaceus*, which respectively fruit on over-mature oaks and Beech.

We also know that natural woods of the sort we no longer have in Britain can be almost incredibly rich in fungi. In North America, scientists became suddenly interested in the biodiversity of old forests when, after a series of legal challenges in the early 1990s, logging was banned in parts of the Pacific North-west to preserve the habitat of the Northern Spotted Owl. The teams set up to study these old-growth forests discovered a great many other species that are at least as vulnerable to disturbance as the owl, and they include no fewer than 234 species of fungi. One, the Noble Polypore *Bridgeoporus nobilissimus*, became a minor wildlife celebrity. This is a colossal bracket – the type specimen weighed 136kg! – although its appearance has been unkindly compared with a doormat. We seem to respect species that qualify for the *Guinness Book of Records*, and the consequence was that each Noble Polypore site was protected with an exclusion zone of 240ha. No ground-disturbing activities can take place until a risk assessment has been carried out. In other words, the ecological needs of the irreplaceable polypore must come before profit.

Closer to home, Scandinavian mycologists have produced similar lists of old-forest fungi. In Sweden, they resulted in a book, *Signalarter*, or 'Signal Species', which attempts to identify 'biotopes' of high conservation value, together with their characteristic species. In Denmark, the loss of native biodiversity from that country's natural Beech forests led two mycologists, Jacob Heilmann-Clausen and Morten Christensen, to seek easily identifiable fungi that are confined to large logs and stumps (or 'coarse woody debris', as the surveyors preferred to term them). Further field testing led to a refined list of fungi that could be used to identify the best surviving stands of Beech in Denmark. The method has since been extended to other countries.

The Ainsworth list: deadwood fungi of Beech

Scientific name	Proposed common name	Tree associates
Flammulaster limulatus	Golden Powdercap	Beech, also oak, birch, pine
Flammulaster muricatus	Toothed Powdercap	Beech
Hohenbuehelia auriscalpium	Spatula Oyster	Beech, oak, Ash
Hohenbuehelia mastrucata	Woolly Oyster	Beech, Hazel
Lentinellus ursinus	Bear Cockleshell	Beech, willow
Lentinellus vulpinus	Fox Cockleshell	Elm, Beech, pine
Phyllotopsis nidulans	Orange Oyster	Beech, willow
Volvariella bombycina	Silky Rosegill	Elm, Beech etc
Phleogena faginea	Fenugreek Stalkball	Beech, oak, Alder, etc
Ossicaulis lignatilis	Mealy Oyster	Elm, Beech, etc
Camarops polysperma	Thick Tarcrust	Alder, Beech
Eutypa spinosa	Spiral Tarcrust	Beech, elm, Hazel, etc
Hericium cirrhatum	Tiered Tooth	Beech, birch, oak, etc
Hericium coralloides	Coral Tooth	Beech, Ash, elm
Hericium erinaceus	Bearded Tooth	Beech, oak, Sweet Chestnut
Gloeohypochnicium analogum	Fruity Crust	Beech, Acer
Mycoacia nothofagi	Fragrant Toothcrust	Beech, birch
Scytinostroma portentosum	Mothball Crust	Ash, Beech, Acer, Alder
Aurantiporus alborubescens	Pink Bracket	Beech
Aurantiporus fissilis	Greasy Bracket	Beech, birch, oak, Ash, etc
Ceriporiopsis gilvescens	Pink Porecrust	Beech, oak, birch, Ash, etc
Ceriporiopsis pannocincta	Green Porecrust	Beech, Acer, Alder, Ash, etc
Coriolopsis gallica	Brownflesh Bracket	Beech, Ash, elm, oak
Ganoderma pfeifferi	Beeswax Bracket	Beech, oak
Inonotus cuticularis	Clustered Bracket	Beech, Acer, oak, etc
Inonotus nodulosus	Silvery Porecrust	Beech
Phellinus cavicola	Cave Artist	Beech, oak
Spongipellis pachyodon	Toothed Mazegill	Beech, oak, Ash
Spongipellis delectans	Spongy Mazegill	Beech, Acer, Ash, etc
Oxyporus latemarginatus	Frothy Porecrust	Beech, Acer, Ash, etc

In Britain, this approach has been taken forward by Martyn Ainsworth (2005), currently Britain's first full-time fungal conservationist. By dint of long field experience and careful study of certain sites, most notably Windsor Forest, Ainsworth has produced a list of 30 species characteristic of old beechwoods, half of which are also on the Euro-list, which are both habitat sensitive and identifiable in the field. All of them grow on dead wood. Unfortunately, most of them are too rare to have acquired common names. Some, such as the mushroom-like *Ossicaulis lignatilis* or the shapeless bracket-like *Phellinus cavicola*, grow in the dark, damp recesses of hollow trees. Given their habitat, they would be unable to find a home in most managed woods. Others grow as brackets on the trunk, branches or roots of large trees; others still prefer fallen logs. Several of the 30 are distinguished by strong scents. The massed stalked balls of *Phleogena faginea* smell of curry powder, and the pinkish bracket *Aurantiporus alborubescens* and the toothcrust *Mycoacia nothofagi* share a strong sweet odour. Of the big *Ganoderma* bracket-fungi so characteristic of old Beech trees, Ainsworth selected just one, the Beeswax Bracket *G. pfeifferi*, whose growing surfaces become covered in a yellow deposit similar to beeswax. He also included two species of *Hohenbuehelia* or oysterlings, neat, shell-like brackets that resemble miniature Oyster Mushrooms.

▲ **Fox Cockleshell**
Lentinellus vulpinus, confined to decaying wood on Beech trees.

Ainsworth's list consists mainly of bracket fungi and their relatives, and includes relatively few mushrooms. However, he suspects that at least one mushroom genus may contain a whole suite of old-wood indicators, in the same way as waxcaps indicate old grassland. This is *Pluteus*, also known as 'shields', a genus of small to medium-sized mushrooms with neat round caps and pink spores, which grow on damp, decaying wood. The reason for their exclusion is that, although it is easy to recognise a *Pluteus* as such, not all the species can be reliably identified in the field. They also tend to have a short season, peaking in late summer. Hence, even if their ecology is right, there are practical problems limiting their use as indicator species.

Few of Ainsworth's potential indicators are seen regularly on fungus forays, and some do not appear in field guides either (the best, from this point of view, is Sterry & Hughes' *Complete Guide* (2009), which gives unusual weight to deadwood fungi). On the other hand, deadwood (saproxylic) species tend to fruit more regularly than other woodland fungi, perhaps because their environment is more stable and rarely dries out. And where you find them at all, several listed species can share the same log. It seems that one species of wood-rotting fungus prepares the way for another, in a kind of pathway of decay. Hence, their distribution is patchy, even within the right kind of wood: small hotspots of biodiversity, perhaps represented by only a few logs, or a particular giant tree.

The Ainsworth list has been field-tested in a range of beechwoods in southern England. Thirteen sites that might be expected to score well were each visited three times over the course of a year. The results were interesting. All of them yielded between 11 and 19 of the 30 indicators, the best site being Denny Wood, in the New Forest. These are high scores by European standards, suggesting that Britain's old beechwoods are comparable to the best sites in France, Denmark, Slovakia or the Czech Republic. Perhaps it is a consequence of our relatively clean Atlantic air, but it certainly also reflects the fortunate survival of large wooded commons and parks in England, most notably the New Forest and Windsor Forest and Great Park. And the best sites are not confined to the countryside. Andy Overall has recently found an impressive list of deadwood fungi, including some of the Ainsworth species, in the royal parks of London, notably Richmond Park and Bushy Park. They represent, in a dreadful pun Martyn Ainsworth borrowed from bathing beaches, our 'blue flag beeches'.

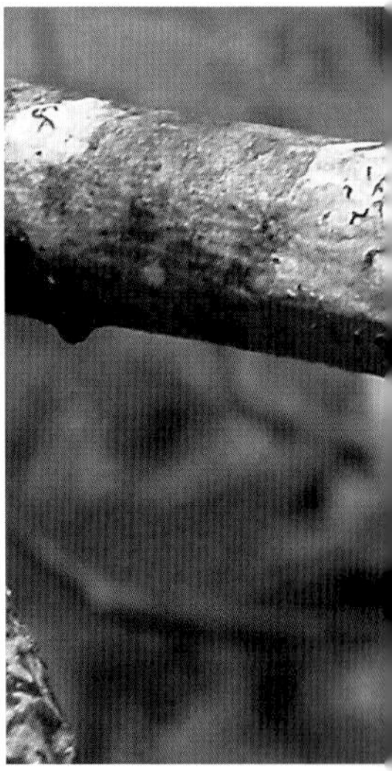

Case-study: life in the tree-tops

Hazel Gloves *Hypocreopsis rhododendri* (so-named because it was originally described on Rhododendron in the United States) is in several ways a remarkable fungus. It looks more like a lichen than a mushroom, with its thick, rubbery, orange rosettes. Its English name refers to the way projecting fingers of the fungus can clasp and fold around

▶ **Glue Crust**
Hymenochaete corrugata sticking twigs together.

small twigs, especially of Hazel, like a goblin glove. Although it is quite large and unmistakable, Hazel Gloves was not discovered in Britain until 1973. The reason, no doubt, is that it grows on bushes and trees. Mycologists tend to look down, not up. Unsurprisingly, it was discovered not by a mycologist but by a lichenologist. Because of its remarkable appearance – and because it was adopted as a kind of honorary lichen – Hazel Gloves has become quite well known. It seems to be most at home in undisturbed Hazel woods, which, in parts of western Scotland, is the natural woodland cover. Moreover, it is a fairly reliable indicator of the *best* Hazel woods, the ones that positively drip with lichens. It is perhaps a signpost to woods that date back hundreds of

▼ **Hazel Gloves**
Hypocreopsis rhododendri, a charismatic fungus of old Hazels.

years, and perhaps even into prehistory in a habitat that, 30 years ago, we hardly knew existed.

Moreover, Hazel Gloves is at the centre of a curious mini-ecosystem that must have evolved over a long time. It associates with another fungus, a bracket called Glue Crust *Hymenochaete corrugata*, so-called because its grey-brown folds bridge small gaps in adjacent twigs and stick them together. Recent research suggests that Hazel Gloves is either a parasite or a partner of Glue Crust. Together, they weave a kind of fungal net in the boughs of Hazel bushes that traps food in the form of woody debris. The *Hymenochaete* then rots down the twigs, and, it is believed, the Hazel Gloves lives off the flesh of its partner. It seems a wonderfully thrifty way of adapting to life in the treetops. As ever, there is so much more to these seemingly passive organisms than meets the eye.

Hazel Gloves has a much rarer congener, Willow Gloves *Hypocreopsis lichenoides*. It, too, has an apparent partner in the form of another 'glue crust', *Hymenochaete tabacina*. But something seems to have injured the partnership, for this once fairly widespread species has declined to the point where, so far as we know, it was reduced to clinging to a single old willow situated in mid-Wales. In its case, a third fungus has joined the act, a little rust-coloured disc-fungus, *Encoelia fimbriata*. Neither partner, fortunately for them, is entirely dependent on the survival of Willow Gloves. It would be a shame to lose so fascinating a species, just as we are getting to know it (both of the Gloves are 'priority species' in the Biodiversity Action Plan). We must hope there are more of them out there somewhere, perhaps deep in the undergrowth where willow twigs cluster close together in the humid shadows.

Fungal hedgehogs

Which are the most glamorous fungi of all? Everyone might have a different answer, but for me it would have to be the strange, forest-dwelling 'hedgehogs' that have spines where their gills should be. Hedgehogs, which are boringly called 'tooths' or 'stipitate hydnoids' (stalked hedgehogs) by mycologists, tick all the boxes. They come in a variety of colours and shapes, some with unearthly tints of orange, blue or pink, and are formed like children's spinning-tops or elfin picnic tables. Some are attractively tiled with soft scales, and a few weep drops of fluid as they grow, which in one case is the colour of blood. If we could watch them grow under time-lapse photography we would see them pour out of the ground like lava, often fusing together, and engulfing grass blades and twigs as they expand. Hedgehogs are a joy to find. They are quite rare, but can be common in the right habitat. They live in some of the most attractive woods in Britain, from the old oaks and Beeches of the New Forest to the ancient Scots Pine forests of the Highlands. And they are, perhaps surprisingly, often hard to name.

▲ **Scaly Tooth** *Sarcodon squamosus*, a fleshy pinewood hedgehog.

There are, or so we thought until very recently, around 20 species in Britain, shared between the genera *Hydnellum*, *Phellodon*, *Sarcodon* and *Bankera*. They came into prominence in the 1990s when most of them were added to the provisional Red Data List of fungi in Britain. Evidence from European countries indicate that, as a group, they are in rapid and disconcerting decline. In the Netherlands, some have disappeared altogether.

Experiments in the Netherlands suggest that these fungal hedgehogs are abnormally sensitive to chemical fertiliser, and need substantial areas of undisturbed forests. All of them are mycorrhizal fungi of trees, especially oaks, Sweet Chestnut and Scots Pine. They share a need for well-drained, often sandy soils, and open ground where root competition with grasses and other aggressive plants is minimal. Mossy woodland banks are one of their micro-habitats, but another, more curiously, is by the sides of paths and the disturbed soil around quarries and pits. Perhaps such superficial disturbance stimulates them to produce fruit bodies, which is, of course, the only time when we can see them.

▼ **Blue Tooth** *Hydnellum caeruleum*. The beautiful blue colour fades as the fungus matures.

There are different groups of hedgehogs in the north and the south. Those found in the Scottish pinewoods are similar to those of conifer forests in Scandinavia. The commonest one is the Scaly Tooth *Sarcodon squamosus* (better known by its former name of *S. imbricatum*), a large, fleshy species that is strongly associated with pine. It often occurs with the unkindly-

▲ **Devil's Tooth** *Hydnellum peckii*, which exudes blood-like droplets when young.

named Drab Tooth *Bankera fuligineoalba*, and three beautifully coloured *Hydnellums*, the foxy-red Orange Tooth *Hydnellum aurantiacum*, the unlikely Blue Tooth *H. caeruleum* and the best of them all, Devil's Tooth *H. peckii*, which is the one that exudes bright red droplets, hence its nickname of 'strawberries-and-cream', and its more memorable synonym *H. diabolus*, the Devil's Hedgehog.

In the woods and parks of Hampshire, Berkshire and Kent, by contrast, the commonest ones are Zoned Tooth *Hydnellum concrescens* and Grey Tooth *Phellodon melaleucus*, which have concentric tones of brown or dark grey, with a pale margin. They are commonly associated with oak on woodland banks, although they also grow under Sweet Chestnut and Beech. Other species which sometimes occur on the same patch of ground include Velvet Tooth *Hydnellum spongiosipes*, which looks a little like a miniature boxing glove, Black Tooth *Phellodon niger*, Fused Tooth *P. confluens* and, less commonly, Bitter Tooth *Sarcodon scabrosus*. The best English sites can contain between four and six species, often in more or less the same place.

▶ **Zoned Tooth** *Hydnellum concrescens* growing among moss on an earthbank in the New Forest.

With their well-documented sensitivities and predilection for growing together on the same bank, the hedgehogs seem to be an ideal group to study, fascinating in their own right but also hinting at the wider mycological value of the place. Unfortunately, there is a catch. They ought to be easy to name, but they are not. Some will match the characters in the book well enough, but others may not. The *Phellodon* species, in particular, seem ill defined. One kind tends to blend into another, without obvious distinction. One species, *Hydnellum scrobiculatum*, has been misidentified for a long time and may not be British at all.

DNA should help to sort out the situation, but first results produced a shock. Research at Cardiff University suggests that things are in a real mess. The good news is that we evidently have more species than we thought. For example, there are two species of 'Grey Tooth', one of which is widespread and the other more restricted. The same is true of 'Zoned Tooth' and 'Black Tooth'. Having digested this unexpected discovery, hedgehog specialists started to peer more closely at these species and realised, belatedly, that they are not quite the same after all. One form of Grey Tooth has lilac tones when young, whilst the other has more of a yellow tint. Similarly, one form of Zoned Tooth is fulvous when fresh, but another is distinctly pinkish. Both forms of Black Tooth, on the other hand, look equally black, despite their differences in DNA sequencing.

Hence, at the time of writing, the hedgehog pack is being reshuffled. The DNA sequencing suggests that we have several unsuspected new hedgehogs, a mixture of known species new to Britain, and unknown, undescribed taxa. As an example of the former, there have been two recent collections of *Hydnellum gracilipes*, a new addition to the exceptionally rich hedgehog mycota of Abernethy pine forest. All this new mixing and matching will take a while to settle down, and, unfortunately, it renders the excellent Kew monograph on hedgehog fungi out of date at a stroke. Rare and wonderful though they are, and undoubtedly indicative of natural soils in ancient woods, the taxonomists have a job to do first.

Or perhaps they are not all rare. Perhaps they are more plentiful among the roots, but appear above ground only occasionally. Or maybe they are just badly recorded. The next chapter looks at this thorny question of scarcity and plenty among fungi. How much do we really know?

chapter nine

Scarcity and plenty:

why some mushrooms are common and others rare

Maurice Rotheroe had a nice explanation of why a species of fungus may seem to be rare. The one he had in mind was Robust Bracket *Phellinus robustus*. As its name implies, it is a big, tough, woody bracket that can grow to the size of a cushion. It occurs mainly on the trunk and branches of old oak trees, and is considered by some to be an indicator species of old forest and parkland. The Robust Bracket briefly came into wider prominence in the mid-1990s, when the Crown Estate decided to tidy up parts of Windsor Great Park by felling certain old oaks that were spoiling the neat appearance of the avenues visible from Windsor Castle. One of those trees was home to the Robust Bracket. Quite a lot of Robust Brackets, in fact: they amounted to 25% of the total number of *P. robustus* known in Britain at that time. Some of them, it was said, were used as a handy natural step-up for a protester who took to the trees in an attempt to stop the felling.

Was this tree really so exceptional? Almost certainly not. With bracket fungi, we are dealing not with 'knowns', as Donald Rumsfeld might have expressed it, but with 'known unknowns'. Bracket fungi are poorly recorded at the best of times, and especially ones that grow high up on trees. As Maurice put it, 'The reasons for its rarity are becoming more obvious. To begin with, 275-year-old oak trees are rare. Secondly, mycologists are rare. Rarer still are mycologists who can spot a bracket fungus 20 feet up a tree. Rarest of all are mycologists who are still young and fit enough to climb an oak tree to identify the fungus.' It might not be too much of an exaggeration to suggest that *P. robustus* was on that particular tree because that was where the expert happened to look.

◀ **One of our commonest fungi, Sulphur Tuft** *Hypholoma fasciculare* grows on stumps and logs.

▲ **Pig's Ear** *Gomphus clavatus*, a most distinctive fungus of northern woods, has not been recorded from Britain for 80 years.

A great many fungi have been recorded only once or twice. Indeed, nearly half (40%) of all micro-fungi have just one record – the original one! Even among the agarics there are scores of species with only one or two British records. A random sample from the *Checklist* (Legon & Henrici 2005) produces *Coprinopsis ochraceolanata* – 'A single collection from Buckinghamshire'; *Lentinellus laurocerasi* – 'Known only from the type' (i.e. the specimen from which the original description was made); and *Marasmius pseudocaricis* – 'Known only from the type collection from Scotland'. Hardly anyone would know these species. They may be rare, they may be quite common. Unlike better-known groups, you can describe a fungus as 'rarely reported but apparently widespread', or 'rarely reported but rather frequent'. It is not necessarily the fungus that is rare, but, in Maurice's words, the person that could spot them is a real rarity.

With vascular plants, around 300 native species are sufficiently rare to qualify for the Red Data Book – about one sixth of our flora. With fungi, even if we restrict ourselves to the basidiomycetes, the proportion, on the basis of actual records, is far higher – more than half. It might be truer to say that at least half of the species in the *Checklist* are *unfamiliar*: that is, they are not included in currently used field guides. Alick Henrici tested this idea by selecting 50 species from the list at random. Of these, only 20 were reasonably well known. The Pan guide (Phillips 2008) illustrates only 11 of them, and that by Courtecuisse & Duhem (up to 2011, the most inclusive field guide yet published), just 18. Henrici had seen less than half of them in the field (and, I admit with shame, I remember seeing only eight of the 50).

Geoffrey Kibby tried out a different approach. By ploughing through the 3,200 species on the list, he reckoned to have seen about 1,700 of them (53%) in 40 years of foraying. Kibby is one of the most experienced field mycologists in Britain. On that basis alone, more than half of our basidiomycete fungi could be described as rarely seen, if not genuinely rare.

New species of larger fungi are discovered every year. Once the word gets round, perhaps from an article and a colour picture in *Field Mycology*, people look out and often start to find it, especially if it is a large and distinctive species. Such was the case with *Boletus ripariellus*. Although it is easy enough to spot, this deep red bolete of willow margins and damp streamsides was, until 1997, considered to be a no more than a colour form of the widespread and variable Red Cracking Bolete *B. chrysenteron*. Now that we know better, we can see that *B. ripariellus* was with us all along. For example, a painting of the 1860s purporting to be *B. chrysenteron* is almost certainly the new species.

▲ **Candelabra Coral** *Clavicorona pyxidata*, pretty and distinctive, yet known in Britain only from a painting.

To find the genuinely rare fungi we must look among a more select band of species that are too large and distinctive to be overlooked. In Britain, the unfortunately named Pig's Ear fungus *Gomphus clavatus* might be such a candidate, for it is attractive and quite unmistakable. Despite being quite common at British latitudes in continental Europe and North America, it has been recorded only a few times in the British Isles, the last in 1927. Refinding Pig's Ear would be a great event. Is it really extinct? Or was it perhaps never well established here in the first place?

Another candidate for the rarest of the rare is *Clavicorona pyxidata*, the Candelabra Coral, whose clustered coralline branches blossom into a pretty circle, like plastic candle-holders on a birthday cake. Its claim to be British rests not on preserved material but on a single painting, a watercolour by Carleton Rea, of a collection he made on 20th October 1896 in Shrawley Wood, Worcestershire. The wood is still there, albeit much knocked about by inappropriate planting, and there is no doubt about the identity of the painting or of Rea's bona fides. But the fact remains that no one else has set eyes on a Candelabra Coral in Britain before or since (even though, being attractive, it sometimes turns up in books). It is widespread in Europe, though nowhere common. I was once shown a specimen in Poland, growing on a fallen Aspen trunk. There it is regarded as an equal in conservation terms to any rare plant.

Nor is the Candelabra Coral the only fungus known from a portrait alone. Similar mystery surrounds *Pluteus violarius*, a small but very distinctive mushroom with a cap of Tyrian purple. In this case, the painting is by the great Victorian mycologist M C Cooke and is accompanied by a brief description by Kew's George Massee. Cooke's painting is the type specimen of this mystery fungus. So far, it has been found nowhere else in the whole world. Is it a true species? Will anyone refind it? Why ever not?

Another British endemic is *Hohenbuehelia leightonii*, known only from the type collection and two subsequent ones, all from 'the boards of an old hovel' near Shrewsbury, back in 1841. A more glamorous endemic is *Sarcodon regalis*, a hedgehog fungus new to science when it was discovered in pinewoods near Bracknell, Berkshire, in the 1960s. It was named after the royal estate at Windsor, but that did not prevent its site from being destroyed for housing. That species, if it is a species, has not so far resurfaced either.

▲ **Oakbug Milkcap** *Lactarius quietus*, an abundant woodland mushroom smelling of carrots or bedbugs, depending on which book you read.

Tremella versicolor, a little orange jelly fungus, was not recorded at all for a full century, between 1895 and 1996. We have many such 'lost' fungi, in the sense that no one has found them lately, but in this case we seem to have forgotten that we ever had it. Hence, when the tiny fruit bodies turned up growing parasitically on their usual host, a crust fungus *Peniophora*, it was thought to be a new species. Had someone traced those old records and revisited the localities they would probably have found it. But this is not a fungus one would expect to find without deliberately looking for it.

► **Sulphur Tuft** *Hypholoma fasciculare*, the commonest mushroom in Britain, according to site-based fungus records.

► (inset) **Fly Agaric** *Amanita muscaria* is listed as one of the top 100 species most likely to be found in Britain.

So much for rare species, real or apparent. What about common ones? There are species that one finds on practically every foray. These are so common that you tend to find them even in those hopeless seasons when there is nothing else about. It would be hard to enter a deciduous wood without coming across Ochre Brittlegill *Russula ochroleuca* or False Deathcap *Amanita citrina*, or a pinewood without Bovine Bolete *Suillus bovinus* or Rufous Milkcap *Lactarius rufus*. In my local woods, practically every oak tree seems to have Oakbug Milkcap *L. quietus* growing under it, every drift of leaves its quietly chewing armies of Russet Toughshank *Collybia dryophila*. Sooner or later, one develops a blind eye for these commonest of the common, in the search for the less than universal species growing among the crowd of fungal *hoi polloi*. On the basis of the fruit bodies one sees in an average wood, most of the general decay must be in the hands of a few dozen very common species.

Some fungi, then, are very common indeed. And, unlike rare fungi, there are some objective data on common fungi. The British Mycological Society has extrapolated a list of species with more than 1,000 records each, based on foray records and preserved material. There

are 162 in all, and they form a very handy aide-memoir of the species every foray leader needs to know. The commonest of the lot, with 6,023 records, is the Sulphur Tuft *Hypholoma fasciculare*, a mushroom that seems to grow everywhere there are decayed stumps, or even buried bits of wood. As its name suggests, it grows in tufts (*fasciculare* comes from the word 'fascicle' – a bunch or bundle). It is a shame, from the kitchen point of view, that this easily recognisable sulphur-yellow mushroom with black spores is completely inedible; it has an intensely bitter taste, like quinine.

Almost as common are three more fungi that grow on dead wood: Turkeytail *Trametes versicolor*, Hairy Curtain Crust *Stereum hirsutum* and Candlesnuff Fungus *Xylaria hypoxylon*, species we could regard as deadwood weeds (one of the drawbacks of garden woodpiles as fungal habitats is that they tend to get taken over by Turkeytails). That the top four commonest fungi all need dead wood might suggest a bias towards woodland as places where most forays take place. But it also emphasises the importance of wood as a fungal resource. In an earlier version of the list, the commonest species was the Stinkhorn *Phallus impudicus*, yet another fungus associated with dead wood, and an indication of how effective it is at drawing attention to itself.

But such statistics need to be taken with a pinch of salt. Species records among the fungi are still in their infancy. The Sulphur Tuft, for example, ought to be present in most of the 3,500 10km-grid squares in the United Kingdom. But, instead, its map shows an odd distribution, with dense aggregations of dots in Northern Ireland, the Lake District, Suffolk, Cornwall, the London area and parts of the West Midlands. In Wiltshire, where I can hardly go out of doors in the autumn without tripping over a Sulphur Tuft, the record is a blank. Clearly, the map says more about the nature of recording than it does about the real distribution of Sulphur Tuft. An even more telling case is the fungus that caused Dutch elm disease, *Ophiostoma novo-ulmi*. It must be present everywhere there are diseased elms, that is, over much of England and Wales, yet there are only 131 records on the fungal database. This is because only pathologists go to the trouble of isolating the fungus, identifying it, and recording its whereabouts. The rest of us simply see a dead elm and continue on our way. On the whole, the published distribution maps of fungi are not very meaningful. The dots tend to record the mycologists, not the mushrooms. The data are not yet sufficient to reveal the true picture.

Increasing and declining fungi

Given the right conditions, fungi can spread with great rapidity. The most notorious example in history is the Irish potato famine, caused by a hitherto little-known fungus that, in one damp, rainy year in the mid-19th century wiped out the potato crop on which so many depended (it had already caused a famine in the Hebrides the year before). More recently, Dutch elm disease wiped out most of Britain's elm trees within a decade.

Fungi with this sort of invasive potential are almost invariably newcomers that, lacking the normal checks and balances of established species, spread rapidly and in enormous numbers. Some of these are species of rusts and smuts, parasitic fungi that are usually host-specific, that is, they are restricted to a single host plant, or at least a family of host plants. One of them, familiar to long-suffering gardeners the world over, is the Pelargonium Rust *Puccinia pelargonii-zonalis*. Once its brown or yellow spots and pustules appear on the cherished pelargoniums, the most prudent action is to burn the lot and start again. It originates from South Africa, home of wild pelargoniums, and was unknown in Britain before 1965. It attacks only standard pelargoniums; the ivy-leaved ones are ignored.

Another newcomer is the Cineraria Rust *Puccinia lagenophorae*, a native of Australia, which made a landfall here by 1961 when it was found on Groundsel at Dungeness. In just two years it had colonised the whole of mainland Britain, and by 1966 had reached the Hebrides. The rust is now sweeping through the United States. It is reported to have reduced populations of Groundsel in Europe, with all the knock-on effects that might have on dependent game birds such as the Grey Partridge. A closely related species is the Daisy Rust *P. distincta*, whose distinctive spots and circles started to appear on wild and garden daisies in the 1990s. It does not seem to have harmed the wild population, but can impair the growth of ornamental kinds. Other new rusts we might have preferred to do without include the Hollyhock Rust *P. malvacearum*, which attacks wild mallows as well as garden hollyhocks, and Snapdragon Rust *P. antirrhini*, which stunts the growth of garden snapdragons but seems to leave its wild relatives alone. Out of around 260 British species of rust, 14 are species that have appeared here since 1966.

Our native fungi have been augmented by foreign species that have arrived and settled, in most cases without doing any visible harm.

▲ **Salmon Salad**
Guepinia helvelloides, a striking jelly-fungus, once rare, is now increasing in England.

An early example is the Larch Bolete *Suillus grevillei*, which was first recorded under (non-native) European Larch on the Atholl Estate of Scotland in 1830, and is now found almost everywhere that larch is grown. In the same way, we have acquired suites of species associated with various other imported conifers, and, more recently, with eucalypts. There is even a fungus confined to that imported Chinese endemic, Maidenhair Tree *Ginko biloba*.

Species of fungi that have appeared in the past decade or so and are now locally common include a jelly fungus, *Calocera pallidospathulata*, which abounds on fallen conifer branches, a bright orange truffle, *Paurocotylis pila*, and Stubble Rosegill *Volvariella gloiocephala*, one of the few fungi to thrive in the aftermath of the harvest in today's ultra-fertilised cornfields. Modern agriculture has also provided a new home for the Splitgill *Schizophyllum commune* on silage bags (and a potential health hazard for any farm worker who breaths in its spores).

Splitgill is not the only fungus to find new opportunities through the activities of humankind. The little navel fungus *Omphalina pyxidata*, for example, was once found mainly on sand dunes but has unexpectedly become common in fields of winter-sown wheat. Certain mushrooms formerly found in coastal grassland, among them Bernard's Mushroom *Agaricus bernardii*, are now increasingly at home on road verges splashed by the de-icing salt used on the roads in much the same way as are coastal plants such as Danish Scurvygrass.

Perhaps the best-recorded increase of an established species is the jelly fungus *Guepinia helvelloides* (formerly *Tremella helvelloides*), now unhappily called the Salmon Salad (or, in America, the Candied Red Jelly Fungus). Its very distinctive pinkish-orange goblets were first found at Sandsend in the East Riding of Yorkshire in 1914, and subsequently spread along rides where sawdust had been mixed with soil. It has turned up on buried woody debris over much of England, and also in Wales, where it appears to prefer quarries. By 2000, Salmon Salad had been spotted in central Scotland 'on the edge of a willow invasion front on disturbed soil in old gravel workings' (Watling 2001). Since it still occurs mainly in conifer forests, Salmon Salad seemed at first to be another introduction, a fungus that followed the forester. More recently, it has been suggested that it is in fact a native upland species that has descended the hill, just as Rosebay Willowherb did in the 19th century (Henrici 2008).

► **Wrinkled Peach**
Rhodotus palmatus, another unmistakable mushroom that became common in the aftermath of Dutch elm disease.

As for decreasing species, for the most part we lack the kind of detailed recording that allows conservationists to measure the changing status of fungi, and place them confidently into exact categories: rare, vulnerable or endangered. There *are* such data for certain species from just across the North Sea, in the Netherlands, where species such as the Chanterelle and mycorrhizal species in general have certainly declined. The main cause in their case is believed to be soil pollution from chemical fertilisers, and perhaps traffic fumes. Although we have made no such methodical surveys in Britain, there is every reason to suppose that we share this slow, insidious, fretting away of fungal diversity. Everyone knows that Field Mushrooms are not so common as they once were. Grassland fungi must have declined as natural grassland has declined. Those who forayed for fungi a generation ago will also tell you that the woods are nothing like as productive as they used to be.

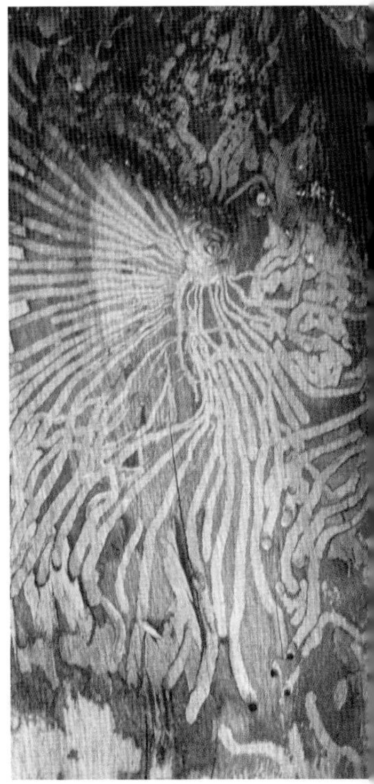

▲ **Galleries made by the beetle that causes Dutch elm disease.** But it is a fungus, a species of vascular wilt, and not the beetle, that fells the tree.

Certain parasitic fungi, notably some of the rusts and smuts, are confined to rare and declining host plants, and cannot therefore be anything but rare and declining themselves. They include such improbable hosts as Spring Gentian, Moon Carrot, Maidenhair Fern, Frogbit, Jacob's-ladder and the Cornish Bladderseed. Perhaps the least likely species to succeed is the tiny smut *Ustilago marina*, which infects the roots of Dwarf Spike-rush *Eleocharis parvula*, a diminutive little plant confined to the mud of a few river estuaries. Not surprisingly, perhaps, no one has set eyes on it for years, and digging up quantities of its very rare host to find it might, in the circumstances, be counter-productive, as well as illegal! The first Red Data List of British fungi, published in 1992, included no fewer than 63 species of rust and smut, some of which lacked any recent records. But they are not necessarily extinct; indeed, in several cases they have since been found alive and well on their host plants. It is the rust and smut specialists that are the real rarities. Even so, dependence on a scarce and vulnerable host plant does seem to be a risky strategy.

Fungal decline can also be inferred from the decline of their habitat. Elm wood, for example, had a rich and distinctive fungus flora. In the decades that followed Dutch elm disease there was a superabundance of dead elm, in

▲ Branching Oyster *Pleurotus cornucopiae*, a bracket-like mushroom that became briefly abundant on elm stumps in the wake of Dutch elm disease.

which some of these fungi were commoner than perhaps any time in recent history. But today, when most of the dead wood has been cleared away, they have become harder to find.

One of these is *Rhodotus palmatus*, now known as the Wrinkled Peach. It is unmistakable, a pinkish-orange mushroom with apricot-coloured gills and a curious rubbery texture, whose cap becomes increasingly wrinkled as it dries. For a time, in the 1980s and early 1990s, it was quite common in woods and hedges in the southern half of England, wherever there were logs or fallen branches of elm. Possibly the only reason why the Wrinkled Peach hangs on is that it is not confined to elm, and has various alternative, if less favoured, habitat in the dead wood of maples, Sycamore, Ash and other trees. Even so, by 2003, it was rare enough to be added to the European Red List of endangered species. And then, just when its fortunes seemed to be at their lowest ebb, the wet autumn of 2007 produced many new records, many of them from stacked log piles of elm.

Other distinctive fungi with a preference for elm that have suffered a similar fate include the beautiful Silky Rosegill *Volvariella bombycina*, the Branching Oyster *Pleurotus cornucopiae* (abundant on elm stumps in my neighbourhood in the 1980s) and several attractive species of *Pluteus*. We can only guess at the fate of smaller elm specialists. Elm was a noted habitat for tiny jelly fungi, such as the bright yellow *Filobasidiella lutea*, which grew parasitically on a corticoid fungus, itself confined largely to elm.

Elm also played host to what was billed, in the *Guinness Book of Records*, as the world's largest fungal fruit body. This is, or was, *Rigidiporus ulmarius* (although not rare, it has somehow avoided being given a common name). I saw it once, or what remained of it: a table-top of overlapping brackets, now mildewed with green, on the rotted remains of an elm stump. In its heyday, this specimen measured 490cm across, with an estimated weight of 316kg. By a strange coincidence, it grew close to the old International Mycological Institute building at Kew, not far from the main gate. It is, alas, long gone, along with its stump, as indeed is the handsome building nearby, which was summarily bulldozed to make way for a new wing.

Another group that may be declining *en masse* is truffles. Admittedly, the recent interest in cultivating and finding truffles has led to finds of large caches of Summer Truffles *Tuber aestivum*, which have made press headlines. Summer Truffles are not as rare as people believe, and probably lie unnoticed and undisturbed in many back gardens. But many other species of truffle, or 'hypogeous fungi' as some mycologists prefer to call them, are rarely found. A few are confined to a single record. Most discoveries of truffles are made by chance, for example when digging in the garden. The British Mycological Society used to run an annual 'truffle hunt', but stopped because the disturbance to the habitat was considered inappropriate in these conservation-conscious times. Unfortunately, the consequence is that we know very little about the present-day status of British truffles.

In Poland, truffles are considered to be threatened, and fully half of them – 62 species in all – are on the Polish Red List. Some 25 species of truffle have died out in at least one European country (Lawrynowicz 2001). One of the reasons suggested for the decline is soil compaction: truffles seem to have a habit of growing by woodland paths. One means of protecting them is to fence off certain sections of path to give the fungi time to recover. Whether collection harms them is uncertain. Digging and raking can actually stimulate fruiting, presumably by aerating the soil (the Summer Truffle fruited abundantly in the grounds of Bristol University after the soil had been dug). Even

▼ **What was the world's largest bracket fungus**, a mature *Rigidiporus ulmarius* on an elm stump at Kew Gardens, photographed in 1989.

so, in truffle-hunting countries there are rules to enforce the conservation of the stock. More fundamentally, truffles are mycorrhizal fungi and no doubt share in the general decline of such species that has been observed in countries such as the Netherlands and Germany.

Those 'honorary fungi', the slime moulds, may also be a group in decline. Perhaps we should make more fuss about them because Britain is a world stronghold for slime moulds. Uniquely among our wildlife, we are home to half the world's known species, accounting for about 380 out of 720 species. And of those 380, no fewer than 62 species are considered to be endangered. Some are known from only a few collections. Many more are restricted to habitats in decline. Yet the conservation industry, which pays reasonable attention to lichens and bryophytes, and even occasionally pays lip-service to larger fungi, virtually ignores them. There is only a single Site of Special Scientific Interest that specifically includes slime moulds in its value statement. This is Afon Pumrhyd, in north-west Wales, the type locality of certain ravine-dwelling species. Perhaps our prejudice against organisms that are small, slimy and slow outweighs any notion of conserving the whole living environment, and not just favoured bits of it.

A golden age of discovery

We know, more or less exactly, how many species of flowering plant are native to Britain. Newly discovered species are added to the list now and again, such as the Saltmarsh Sedge *Carex salina*, discovered in 2004, or a batch of new whitebeam micro-species announced to the world in 2010. But we can be sure that new discoveries will be few, and confined to species that are critical, that is, identifiable only by experienced botanists. We still find new bryophytes and lichens, but it is more of a trickle than a flood.

With fungi, it *is* a flood. The British list is mushrooming. New British species are being discovered all the time, in many cases by forayers, and among the micro-fungi the discovery rate is determined more by the scarcity of specialists than any inherent difficulty in finding new species. Among larger fungi, the present surge of species began in 1960 with the publication of a checklist of British agarics by Orton, Dennis and Hora. Peter Orton, who probably did most of the research, was a music teacher and amateur specialist based at Rannoch, Perthshire. He introduced 120 species new to Britain which, at the time, was thought excessive (Orton *did* tend to cut the cloth finely, and some of his new species have since been reduced to synonyms). But between then and 2001, an average of 17 new species of boletes and agarics have been added each year – that is, a total of nearly 700 new species since 1960. In more recent years the rate has, if anything, increased.

The last two decades have been an exciting time for fungal recording in Britain. The publication of *British puffballs, earthstars and stinkhorns* (Pegler *et al.*1995) drew attention to a group of attractive fungi that were poorly served by field guides at the time. There were no recent records for many species, but most of them have since been refound. They include the chalk-white Fen Puffball *Bovista paludosa*, found growing on a footpath at Buxton Heath, Norfolk, and a whole constellation of absent earthstars, culminating in the rediscovery of Berkeley's Earthstar *Geastrum berkeleyi* among the old stamping grounds of the Woolhope Society, in Herefordshire.

One of the most exciting finds of the decade was the pretty red oysterling, *Crepidotus cinnabarinus*, which probably owed its rediscovery to its inclusion in the popular field guide by Marcel Bon (1987). Another was the Marsh Honey Fungus *Armillaria ectypa*, perhaps overlooked because its habitat, alkaline fen, is not one where mycologists go foraying very often. The turn of the Millennium produced the rediscovery of three lost northern species: Scarlet Splash *Cytidia salicina*, Black Falsebolete *Boletopsis leucomelaena* (since redetermined as *Boletopsis perplexa*) and Roothole Rosette *Stereopsis vitellina*. Even more surprising was the discovery of Aspen Bracket *Phellinus tremulae*, which is the size of a horse's hoof and turned out, once people started looking, to be locally common on old Aspen trees in Deeside and Speyside, in Scotland. This new interest in Aspen trees produced other notable species, including a new porecrust, *Ceriporiopsis aneirina*. Among the new species discovered by the revitalised Grampian Fungus Group were *Cortinarius phaeopygmaeus*, found high up on the Cairngorms plateau, and no fewer than three new brittlegills, *Russula vinosobrunnea*, *R. font-queri* and *R. fusconigra*, all among native pines in the Cairngorms area (Holden 2006).

New species, not all of them dull and obscure, continued to be found in every year of the new Millennium. A legendary foray in 2000 by the British Mycological Society in County Fermanagh produced an astounding 167 species new to Ireland, and helped to revitalise field mycology in the Emerald Isle. A truffle presumed to be extinct since 1845, *Melanogaster intermedius*, turned up alive and well in Essex in

▶ **The long-lost Pepperpot Earthstar** *Myriostoma coliforme*, distinguished by its multiple pores.

▶ **Pepperpot Earthstar** *Myriostoma coliforme* painted by James Sowerby in 1797, when it was still widespread in south-east England.

2004, having drawn attention to itself by a stench compared with a mixture of rotting onions and burning rubber. That same year also saw the discovery of a new poroid fungus, *Ceriporiopsis herbicola*, on a wintering stem of Lesser Burdock *Arctium minus* by the palaeontologist, Richard Fortey, and a new bolete, *Boletus subappendiculatus*, at two sites in Scotland.

The year 2006 saw the discovery of a new tooth fungus, *Denticollis fragilis*, which is distinguished by long hedgehog spines. It turned up on the underside of a Hornbeam log in Putt Wood, Kent, a site noted for rare fungi that had already produced several new species. The following year, despite a poor autumn season in many places, produced a bonanza of newly discovered fungi: a new rollrim to add to our mere three species of *Paxillus*, a new scalycap, *Pholiota squarrosoides*, and an attractive new webcap, *Cortinarius arcuatorum*. The most celebrated find was yet another new bolete, *Xerocomus silwoodensis*, judged to be one of the top ten wildlife discoveries of the year by the Arizona-based International Institute for Species Exploration.

A further crop of new fungi followed in 2008, despite this being the second poor season in a row. Among them were a stocky grey Amanita, *Amanita simulans*, a large, heavy funnel mushroom, *Leucopaxillus tricolor*, the inevitable new bolete, *Boletus depilatus*, this time with a curiously 'hammered' cap, a colourful milkcap, *Lactarius picinus*, a duo of Highland webcaps, *Cortinarius diosmus* and *C. poppyzon*, and a member of a new genus to Britain, *Callistosporium luteo-olivaceum*, a troop of which olive-brown agarics was found on the inside surface of a rotten stump at Ebbor Rocks, in Somerset. The year 2009 included an inkcap new to Europe, *Coprinopsis tectispora*, found on the garden path of our leading boletologist, Alan Hills. And 2010 turned out to be the best year of the whole decade for new species, with at least 36 recorded at the time of writing.

Resurrection: from beyond the brink

On the morning of 19th February 2006, someone walking his dog through an oakwood near Ipswich noticed an unusual fungus. Where the path passed a steep sandy bank, he found an unusual kind of puffball shaped like a star and perforated with numerous holes. Leaving it *in situ*, he looked it up on his return home in his copy of *Mushrooms and other fungi* by Roger Phillips and found what he was looking for on page 252: *Myriostoma coliforme*, the Pepperpot Earthstar, a species that had

not been seen in mainland Britain since 1880, and which was assumed to be extinct. 'It is hoped that the publication of an illustration of this interesting fungus', the percipient Phillips had added, 'will lead to its rediscovery.'

He reported the discovery to the landowner, Chris Povey, who duly searched the spot and eventually found it, or rather several fungal Pepperpots. He did all the right things. He photographed a specimen in its natural state, and picked one for confirmation. But then he left it, sprinkling spores very like pepper, in the back of his car for a week until he was able to purchase a good field guide and confirm its identity. He thereupon emailed the website of the British Mycological Society. His modest message asking whether anyone might be interested in the rediscovery of *Myriostoma* was picked up by the Society's then conservation officer, Shelley Evans, who, by coincidence, was one of the authors of the field guide Povey had just used. The details checked out, and, in Shelley's words, a 'vicarious adrenaline rush set in'.

The Pepperpot Earthstar is no ordinary fungus. It differs from other British earthstars in having a ball perforated with many pores, rather than a single, central one. Moreover, the ball is supported by a set of little stalks, like the portico of an ancient temple (its scientific name means 'many pores, like a column'). It was first discovered in Britain as long ago as 1695, when it was new to science. It was sufficiently noteworthy for Samuel Doody, one of the local helpers of the great naturalist John Ray to describe the exact locality 'in the Lane that leads from Crayford to Bexley-Common in Kent'. Fungal pepperpots turned up over the years in other places, usually on dry soils, often among nettles, but mostly in East Anglia and the London area; it even once turned up in the well-trodden grounds of Hampton Court. The last specimen outside the Channel Islands was collected near Hillingdon, Norfolk, in 1880. I have held this last Pepperpot in my hand: feather-light, like a dead leaf, and seemingly as much a relic as a fossil bone in a museum drawer.

Was it with us all the time, unnoticed, producing little puffs of spores every time it rains, or has it recolonised Britain from across the sea (for it still grows on the dunes of the Netherlands)? Spotting an ephemeral fungus is always a matter of chance: the haphazard and, on the whole, unlikely conjunction of a shy fruit body with an eagle-eyed naturalist. The latest version of Britain's Red List of fungi includes a long list of apparently extinct species – though the fact that they are still listed suggests doubt on that point. Given the uncertain appearances of fungi, it might be premature to write off any of them too soon. Take *Puccinia polemonii*, a rust that parasitises wild Jacob's-ladder *Polemonium caeruleum*. No one had found it in Britain for many years, but that may have been because no one had looked for it; the standard illustrated work on rusts and smuts is long out of print. When Malcolm Storey decided to examine the colony of Jacob's-ladders at Lathkill Dale, in the Peak District, he quickly found the telltale spots and smudges of the missing rust. Claiming rediscoverer's rights, he proposes to rename it Rusty Ladders.

At least Rusty Ladders can be relied upon to show itself regularly. Many large fungi are more unpredictable in their appearances. Some of the large, colourful species of *Cortinarius* and the beautiful coral fungi in the genus *Ramaria* are notorious for their fleeting appearances. They may not appear for year after year, but then suddenly burst into a brief and glorious mass fruiting (as some large species of *Cortinarius* did in the autumn of 2010). We can be fairly sure a green plant such as the Summer Lady's-tresses *Spiranthes aestivalis* is extinct, for it appeared annually, its sites were known, and orchid-hunting is very popular. Moreover, we have plausible reasons for its extinction: over-collecting and the drainage or over-shading of all its known sites. But fungi are transient by nature. We do not know whether they are genuinely rare, or simply that they are stimulated to fruit only now and again.

The growth of local fungus groups and the great increase in amateur activity generally has slightly narrowed the odds against a rare fungus being spotted. Several long-lost fungi turned up alive and well around the turn of the Millennium. One, which made its way into the national newspapers and prompted a little homily on the importance of fungi in the editorial pages of *The Times*, was *Cytidia salicina* or the Scarlet Splash (perhaps a pun on the splash it made in the papers?). Since it forms unmistakable bright red blotches on dead sallow sticks that are still attached to the tree, it might seem surprising that *Cytidia* was overlooked for so long. At any rate, it was a retired forester, Gordon Simpson, who spotted what he thought at first were dabs of red paint as he walked through Kielder Forest, Northumberland, on 30th September 1999. Curious, he sent a sample to an expert, Alan Legg, who identified it and sent the sample on to Kew. The

▼ **Scarlet Splash** *Cytidia salicina* made a splash in the press when it was rediscovered in Britain after nearly a century.

rediscovery made mycologists wandering through humid sallow thickets more *Cytidia*-conscious, and they were soon finding Scarlet Splashes in various other parts of the Borders and the Scottish Highlands.

Another wonderful rediscovery was the Black Falsebolete *Boletopsis perplexa*, a species otherwise known only from North America (until recently it was thought to be a related species, *B. leucomelaena*, found in Northern Europe). It is called 'falsebolete' because, although it looks superficially like a bolete, it is more closely related to the polypores. It seems to be excessively shy at fruiting in Britain. First found under native Scots Pines at Loch an Eilean, near Aviemore, in 1876, it was collected from the same locality at long intervals until 1963. The story goes that on that last occasion, the late Derek Reid was enjoying a picnic lunch in the forest, while simultaneously going through the specimens in his basket. Dismissing the bun-sized black object as 'an old something else', he skimmed it into the heather. It had not hit the ground before Reid suddenly realised what it might have been. There followed an anxious 20 minutes as the whole party scrambled about on their hands and knees (the Frisbee-shape of the falsebolete could have propelled it a good distance). Fortunately, falseboletes are tough, and

▼ **The Zoned Rosette** *Podoscypha multizonata* is perhaps commoner in English parks than anywhere else in the world.

the specimen was reunited, not much the worse for wear, with Reid's basket. No further specimens have come to light in the original place, but in September 2001 Liz Holden found it on the opposite side of the Cairngorms in Deeside, in a pinewood near Braemar. Since then it has turned up in at least two other places, both among pines on sandy ground. It is officially listed as 'vulnerable', but that is only a guess. In America, where the Black Falsebolete is more common, its complex biochemistry is being investigated for its medicinal potential.

The third of this trio of fungi rediscovered around the time of the Millennium was *Stereopsis vitellina*. This yellowish, fan-shaped species, like a small bracket cut adrift from its parent tree, was new to science when first recorded at the Boat of Garten, Speyside, in 1900. It is the only British species of a mainly tropical genus, and evidently has a penchant for the diggings of Moles and other small mammals. Its new English name, the Roothole Rosette, combines its micro-habitat of holes and hollows with its floral shape. It, too, became a missing fungus. Many decades passed without a sighting until, in October 1999, it was refound by the late Peter Orton, not far from its original locality. Once the field guides get around to illustrating it, I predict a sudden expansion of its range.

Stereopsis is one of a small family of 'rosettes' that have attracted attention because of their rarity and unusual appearance. The largest, Zoned Rosette *Podoscypha multizonata*, is a near-British endemic with few records elsewhere. Most British endemics are recently evolved and barely distinguishable from their relatives, but Zoned Rosette is a most distinctive fungus with densely packed, frilly-edged lobes rising from a short thick stem, rather like a dahlia. It is usually found under mature oaks or Beech in park-like settings, and can be locally common in places such as the New Forest. It is one of the fungi (the Pink Waxcap is another) for which Britain is envied. Another scarce rosette, Woolly Rosette *Cotylidia pannosa*, has recently been added to the Biodiversity Action Plan list. Its pink-edged frilly lobes arise from separate stems, but are often bunched together in an attractive way. It is widespread but rare in England and Wales, for reasons still not understood.

These are just a few of the interesting fungi that have been discovered or re-discovered in the past few years. With more knowledgeable field mycologists about than ever before, many of them specialising in certain groups or particular habitats, there are sure to be many more.

Stars of the sand

Among the most distinct and unusual fungi – ones that might stop anyone in their tracks – are the earthstars. They are a kind of puff-ball that has two layers of skin, the outer one of which curls outwards and backwards, like segments of an orange, to reveal a little ball in the middle. Depending on the species, this inner ball may nestle within a collar, be raised aloft on a pedestal or suspended on backward-pointing rays. Some earthstars are 'weather stars', which curl up in dry weather and unroll again when it rains. Altogether, they are a fascinating group.

Perhaps it is not surprising, therefore, that earthstars have a following that resembles a cult. Those in the know guard the whereabouts of rare earthstars as jealously as any orchid. The 'gastros', as earthstar fans are known, are said to be so secretive about some sites that they are not known outside the fraternity. Unfortunately, secrecy offers no kind of protection. Ignorance means danger, and that this is true even in our premier botanic gardens at Kew was demonstrated recently, when certain flowerbeds noted for their earthstars were buried under several inches of woodchip mulch.

Until 1995, when Kew Gardens brought out an excellent field guide to earthstars and other 'gastroids' (Peglar *et al.*1995), earthstars were poorly known. So much so that recent records were lacking for no fewer than six out of our 17 species, leading to the sad conclusion that they were probably extinct. But the reason there were no records was that no one was specifically looking for them. Once the Kew guide drew attention to earthstars, it seems to have become a challenge to the field mycology community to rediscover them. And so they did, and in short order. One of the lost earthstars was the magnificent Berkeley's Earthstar *Geastrum berkeleyi*, which has a rough-textured inner ball surmounted by a conical peristome, a collection of bristles that regulates the release of its spores. It was named after the great Reverend Miles Joseph Berkeley, grandfather of field mycology in Britain, and, fortuitously, it turned up on ground that he would have known, not far from Woolhope, Herefordshire, where the first 'forays amongst the funguses' took place (see Chapter 10). Another lost species, the Field Earthstar *G. campestre*, formerly known mainly from flowerbeds in the Director's garden at Kew, recently turned up in a much wilder place on a National Nature Reserve in Norfolk, changing its status from an apparent introduction to an apparent native species in the process.

Every single one of the lost earthstars has now been refound, and the naturalist and photographer Paul Sterry was able, with a little inside help, to photograph all but one of them in a single season.

Earthstars seem to occur mainly in dry places, such as well-drained banks, on vegetated dunes and on sandy ground inland, above all in the Breckland of East Anglia. They are, in a sense, our desert fungi. None of them can be said to be common, although one of the largest, the Collared Earthstar *Geastrum triplex*, quite often turns up on forays (as the scientific name implies, it has a third layer that forms a cup or collar beneath the ball of spores). Finding an earthstar of any kind is always a highlight, but to find a full circle of tiny, rare stars on some far-off dune is, as Wordsworth might have said, the very heaven. The least one can do is enter the circle with a foolish smile and make a wish.

▼ **Rosy Earthstar**
Geastrum rufescens, an earthstar of sandy soils in woodland, heath and occasionally sand dunes, distinguished by the slight rosy or reddish-brown hue in the inner lining of its outer skin.

chapter ten

Forays amongst the funguses

A walk in search of fungi is traditionally known as a foray. This is a happy choice of word, with its layered meanings of issuing forth, wandering, searching and (in its piratical sense) raiding. It captures the nature of the field excursion with rare economy. That foray also begins with the same letter as fungus is a bonus. The word has long since crossed national boundaries, not to mention the Atlantic, and is now widely used throughout the world wherever fungi are sought and gathered.

It was first used in 1868, when the Woolhope Naturalists' Field Club of Herefordshire decided to hold a novel 'Foray amongst the Funguses'. 'The Woolhope', as it was known, was more than a mere local society. Many luminaries of the natural world were members, including the cream of the first generation of field mycologists: M C Cooke, author of *The Plain and Easy Account of British Fungi*, was one, George Worthington Smith, a book illustrator and amateur archaeologist, another, while the presiding spirit was Henry Graves Bull, one of the first Britons to take a serious interest in eating wild fungi. With Worthington Smith as the invited expert, the foray was followed by a memorable 'fungus dinner' at the Mitre Hotel, in Hereford. Smith designed the special menu card, which became a keepsake of the event. It was, by all accounts, a great success, and forays became a fixture in the club's autumn calendar. That The Woolhope's doings became quite well known was thanks to Smith, who made regular and amusing reports to the *Gardeners' Chronicle*, illustrated with his cartoons of mycologists making merry. They continued to foray among the funguses at least once a year, until Bull's death in 1885.

◄ **A touch of violet among the fallen leaves** is likely to be this beautiful, common species, the Amethyst Deceiver *Laccaria amethystina*. In dry weather it turns brown.

▲ **Mordecai Cubitt Cooke (1825-1914),** the first great populariser of fungi, an ardent forayer, collector, author and artist.

By that time, other field clubs had started running fungus forays, notably the Essex Field Club, where M C Cooke was again the leading light, and, above all, in the woods and vales of northern England with the Yorkshire Naturalists' Union. The latter decided to form a special mycological committee in 1892, which, four years later, morphed into a national society, the British Mycological Society (BMS), with the purpose of co-ordinating mycological activity in Britain. Ever since then, the BMS has represented British mycologists, both amateur and professional, at home and abroad, and promotes their work through publications and regular meetings. These have long included two major forays a year, one in spring and the other in autumn. More recently, an overseas foray and a truffle hunt (now, alas, abandoned for conservation reasons) were added.

From the start, the Society was served by leading mycologists of the day. G E Massee, the full-time mycologist at Kew, was its first president, chosen because he had written more papers than anyone else. He was assisted by the tireless Carleton Rea, who served as treasurer, secretary or editor for 34 years, as well as being one of the most active and well-travelled field mycologists of his time (and a talented artist to boot). The BMS has always been quite small. In 1900 it had about 100 members; today there are about 2,000, at home and abroad. Its leanings have become more international, and, perhaps inevitably, weighted towards fundamental research of only marginal interest to most forayers. The Society held its first international congress at Exeter University in 1971, and took a rather belated plunge into conservation matters in 1988. Its international symposium on conservation, held in 1999, was written up in book form as *Fungal Conservation: Issues and Solutions* (Moore *et al.* 2001).

From the 1990s onwards there has also been an explosion in foraying at a local level. It has led to the formation of many local and county-based fungus groups. The stimulus for their formation was often a local enthusiast and expert, around whom a gallant band of keen beginners coalesced. Alan Outen is at the heart of activities in Hertfordshire, Derek Schafer in neighbouring Buckinghamshire, and Andy Overall in the London area. Further afield, Liz Holden in Grampian region and David Mitchel in Northern Ireland have revolutionised foraying in their respective regions. Upwards of 30 fungus groups now operate over much of England, Wales and Northern Ireland; in Scotland they are spread more thinly, though with pockets of dense activity. My own local group is the very busy Cotswold Fungus Group, led by Dave Shorten, which forays over a broad area stretching from Gloucester in the west to the Marlborough Downs in the east. Fungus groups pay meticulous attention to identification, and a great many of the exciting finds of recent years have been theirs. Some regularly visited sites now have lists running to hundreds, or even a thousand or more species. Many fungus groups are represented by the Association of British Fungus Groups (ABFG), now a registered charity with its own journal, *The Forayer*, edited by Michael Jordan. Others are affiliated to the British Mycological Society.

▲ **A Green Dragon menu** designed and illustrated by George Worthington Smith, wood engraver and book illustrator, and regular attendee of the Woolhope Club 'forays amongst the funguses'.

Fungus forays are also run by field centres, among them Slapton Ley, in Devon, and Kindrogan, in Scotland, which alternate field excursions with classroom studies and sessions at the microscope. The hinterlands of these centres are, not unnaturally, among the best recorded for fungi. In addition, some county wildlife trusts and other local natural history societies run forays, where the accent is often more on education and entertainment than serious recording (though there is some of that, too). And there are also popular forays which are better described as forages, where the idea is to find edible mushrooms to cook and eat. I would mention some examples, but they have a habit of becoming out of date very quickly!

Foray leaders need to arrange permission to enter someone's land, and also to pick specimens, for wild fungi are technically the landowner's property. Picking is often necessary since many species are not identifiable in the field, and require confirmatory work in the lab. Permission is rarely withheld, although there have been occasions when public bodies have tried, rather counter-productively, to impose restrictions on collecting (they are better informed now). In these health-and-safety conscious times, Public Liability insurance is necessary in case of accidents; cautionary tales go the rounds of someone slipping on wet leaves and suing the organisers (for, we are encouraged to believe, it must be *somebody's* fault). Individual insurance would be beyond the pockets of most fungus groups, but fortunately both the BMS and the ABFG can provide groups with a joint cover that indemnifies them against accidents.

▲ **A successful foray!** Liz Holden and Andy Taylor surveying fungi in Sweden.

We are also encouraged to make a risk assessment before leading a foray. This is not a legal requirement but it is considered to be good practice to point out possible hazards, including the unfortunate fact that some fungi are poisonous. Most people know about poisonous mushrooms already, but with children in the party it is a commonsense reminder as well as potentially entertaining in its own right (kids love the idea that some mushrooms are dangerous and thrillingly 'evil'). We remind people that there are no short cuts in telling edible from poisonous species, and that there are small risks of allergic reaction, even from some edible mushrooms. In some circumstances, it might also be prudent to remind people that a few fungi are protected by law from picking, and that, technically, we are not supposed to pick any fungus that could fall foul of the Dangerous Drugs Act as amended in 2005. It has even become necessary to point this out in books, and to assert that the authors are not responsible for the consequences of gastronomic experiments that go wrong (I am not responsible, by the way).

The perfect foray

There is a small pinewood between the road and the River Dee at Inverey, near Braemar, which has a legendary reputation among field mycologists. I visited it for the first time with Roy Watling and a party from his course at Kindrogan Field Centre. Roy had gone ahead, and by the time we arrived on the scene he had a look on his face that I recognised as mycological ecstasy. 'Look!' he cried. 'Here is *Russula paludosa*! And', he added, skipping a few feet to the left, 'there is *Lactarius helvus*! Over here', he hopped over to a tuft of blaeberry he had marked with a twig, 'is *Pleurotellus porrigens*,' indicating the tiers of translucent, pure white half-moons projecting from a sprig of pine. 'And, best till last, right over here', he cried, *fortissimo*, with what I can only describe as a look of absolute adoration, 'is *Cortinarius mucosus*!'

Cortinarius mucosus or Orange Webcap, I should explain, is one of a group of robust-looking webcap mushrooms that possess sticky foxy-brown caps. The glossy coat of this one positively drips with slime. It is rarely encountered outside the native pinewoods of Scotland, as are many other fungi found in this wonderful wood, including no fewer than 12 listed on the Biological Action Plan. On a fine day in early autumn – fine for fungi, that is – you can hardly avoid finding a rarity. On one of my subsequent visits, I photographed a reddish-brown brittlegill that I thought was *Russula vinosa*, the Darkening Brittlegill, one of a colourful range of *Russula* found in these mountain woods. I even brought one back in a basket to make sure, and took a photograph. Looking at it again now, I believe it could be Naked Brittlegill *R. vinosobrunnea*, a species unknown in Britain at the time I found it. Had I bothered to examine the specimen's spores and microstructure, carefully dried it inside a little customised oven, and then consulted the British *Russula* expert, the glory of discovery might have been mine. Instead, I probably ate it.

This small wood, no more than 10ha, is one of the best places for pinewood fungi in all of Scotland. (With Roy's support, I tried, but failed, to get it notified as a Site of Special Scientific Interest). But there is a puzzle: this is a not a native wood but an old plantation. It is natural looking, and is close to real native pines, but was planted by the hand of man on open ground about 150 years ago. So why is it so rich in rare fungi? Well, to begin with, it is well recorded. The wood is close to the road, and is open to walkers. It is also visited by Red Deer as they descend the hill in the autumn and they graze it pretty tight. As a result the ground is open and mossy, and the warmth of the early autumn sun penetrates the upper layers of the soil. Furthermore, at this altitude the season is short and the fungi tend to appear all at once. It may well be that most or all of its rare species also occur in other pinewoods nearby. But its lucky combination of circumstances makes this wood an exceptional and exciting place for a foray.

Fungal treasurehouses

There are many other sites with exciting lists of fungi, some of them running into a thousand-plus species. About this number (plus 130 lichens and 44 slime moulds) have been recorded from Roydon Woods, in Hampshire, for instance, while the list from Savernake Forest, Wiltshire, has long passed 1,000. At Dawyck Botanic Garden, in the Scottish Borders, where fungi have been recorded over the past 15 years, the list has reached nearly 1,000 and shows no sign of slackening. We might regard 1,000 species as a convenient benchmark for defining a 'good' site, but even with that number – more than half the British list of vascular plants – it is more of a reflection of recording effort than actual biodiversity.

Perhaps only four places in Britain are so well recorded that we may be close to knowing their real fungal diversity, and that makes them extraordinarily interesting. Yet none of them are pristine, A1 habitats. First of the four is the 380ha Esher Common, in Surrey, a favourite venue for Londoners since a railway station was built at nearby Oxshott in the 19th century. In recent years the list has been steadily expanded by Brian Spooner, who, until his retirement in 2011, was the senior mycologist at Kew Gardens. Over the past quarter-century he has used the Common as an outdoor laboratory, quietly poring over samples of soil, wood and dung to identify micro-fungi that are rarely seen in nature. Brian's concentration on ascomycetes means that the list is less biased towards mushrooms and toadstools than usual. Esher is the type locality of numerous fungi that were new to science when discovered there, and nearly every year Brian finds more. In 2001, some 19 newly discovered species were awaiting a scientific description. The list currently stands at 3,300 species and counting – more than the recorded fungi of most counties. We might conclude that something like 3,000 species may be the norm, rather than the exception, for large wild commons in south-east England. We will never know for sure because taxonomists like Brian, always rare, are dying out. Esher Common may be our best fungus site for a long time to come.

The next-best site is Slapton Ley, in south Devon. This 211ha expanse of shingle, freshwater and woodland, purchased by the Herbert Whitley Trust in 1917 to save it from development, is now a nature reserve with a flourishing 50-year-old field centre. Visits since 1969 by the likes of David Hawksworth and Frank Dobson have produced another astonishing list of around 2,500 species, including 30 that were new to science. Again, the site has been combed for tiny fungi normally missed on forays. Thirty-one species were found attached to Bramble, for example, another 20 on Gorse and 30 on Stinging Nettle. Interestingly, there is only a 40% overlap between the fungi of Slapton Ley and Esher Common. This suggests that, even now, both lists fall well short of the real total. Unfortunately, Slapton Ley in its current form will not exist for much longer; it is protected from the sea only by an eroding shingle barrier, and the current conservation philosophy is to allow nature to take its course.

Perhaps even richer, in terms of the density of different species, is Mickleham Common, Surrey. Here, some 1,300 species of fungi have been recorded from just 4ha and in only one principal habitat, chalk grassland. There is nothing to suggest that Mickleham Common is in any way exceptional, and we might expect many other chalk grassland sites to be just as rich.

The fourth exceptionally well-recorded site is the Royal Botanic Gardens, Kew. The herbarium at Kew contains the largest collection of preserved fungi in the world, but the garden outside has an equally astounding collection of living fungi on the lawns and woods, mulched flowerbeds and glasshouses. Altogether, 2,750 species of fungi have been recorded, many of them by mycologists based there or at the nearby International Mycological Institute – and often during a stroll through the garden. Kew's list contains a greater than usual number of exotic species recorded from the hothouses. In that sense, its fungus flora is truly cosmopolitan, with wild-growing mushrooms from all corners of the earth.

Genius loci: places defined by a mushroom

The Lodge, at Sandy, Bedfordshire, is the headquarters of the RSPB. As the village name suggests, The Lodge lies on an island of sand – the Bedfordshire greensand – with patches of heath, wild grassland and stands of pine reminiscent of the Breckland of East Anglia. Birders with an eye for fungi have discovered a good number of interesting species there, among them waxcaps, earthtongues, earthstars and *Volvariella caesiotincta*, a pretty rosegill with a distinctive blue-tinged cap, found on decaying elm stumps. But the mushroom they are most proud of is *Hygrophorus speciosus*, a relative of the waxcaps known as a woodwax, which has a handsome bright orange cap and a yellowish stipe. Since it is known from nowhere else in Britain, perhaps it should be named the Sandy Woodwax, or may be the Birder's Blessing. It grows under a belt of pines planted as a windbreak, and was perhaps introduced in the roots of the trees, for it is believed to be a native of North America (where it is known as the Red or Larch Waxy Cap and, incidentally, is gathered for food). Whether or not it is an alien, it is a beautiful and easily recognised mushroom that lends added distinction to an already special place.

The RSPB was quite properly concerned that the Sandy Woodwax should be preserved when, in a bid to restore more heathland, it decided the pines must go. Fortunately, it had the foresight to retain the trees where the woodwax grows, and thoughtfully planted some more around the periphery 'to act as a windbreak against desiccation' (Allison 2001). More ambitiously, its minders propose to transfer woodwax spores or mycelium to other wooded parts of the estate, thus 'encouraging mycorrhizal links with young planted conifers that will then be removed and transplanted elsewhere'. The RSPB calls this a 'non-avian biodiversity programme'. Never mind that any mycologist might retort that the RSPB's entire corpus of work is a misdirected 'non-fungal programme', aimed at preserving feathered creatures of no fundamental importance to the life systems of the planet. The point is that they care.

The magisterial *Checklist of the British & Irish Basidiomycota* (Legon & Henrici 2005) is rather sniffy about the RSPB's woodwax. It is relegated to the back of the book as 'not authentically British', for, the authors note, there is no voucher material in the national collection and so the record remains 'unsubstantiated'. As it normally grows under larch, not pine, the authors suspect a case of mistaken identity and suggest that it may be a mere colour form of the common *Hygrophorus hypothejus*, the Herald of Winter. Over to you, RSPB!

Just as the Sandy Woodwax helps to individualise The Lodge as a place of mycological interest, so other special fungi can help to define the *genius loci* of a place: the tiny details that separate one place from another. The nearest large wood to my home is Savernake Forest, an ancient tapestry of woodland and wood-pasture that has, frankly, seen better days. The 'saddle' oaks and organpipe Beeches and giant hawthorns that make historic Savernake what it is were in danger of being swallowed up in dull, dense woodland that, by contrast, could be anywhere. In recent years, the Forestry Commission has done its best to restore the place by clearing a breathing space for its elderly trees, and leaving the hulks of the dead ones to rot. It is in these localised spots, and also in the mysterious open 'greens' of the forest, that most of its fungal richness resides. Like many large forests, it consists of isolated fungal 'hotspots' within a jungle of mediocrity.

Nevertheless, there are mushrooms at Savernake that seem more common there than almost anywhere else. One of these is the Magpie Inkcap *Coprinopsis picacea*, a signature species of chalky beechwoods, which has an unmistakable conical black cap with white spots. Another is *Lepiota ignivolvata*, too rare to own an English name, with its distinctive fluffy orange cap and brown-edged stem-ring, which abounds in the grassy parts of the forest. Distantly related to it is a form of parasol mushroom with a star-shaped brown umbo at the centre of the cap that seems to be peculiar to Savernake. And, on a good day, the Forest provides some exotic mushrooms for supper – amethyst-coloured chanterelles, *Cantharellus amethysteus*, and brilliant saffron rockets of Orange Grisette *Amanita crocea*.

Sometimes it is a probable alien that becomes the highlight of a foray. At Newborough Forest, on Anglesey, one of the outstanding species is a stocky, dark-crimson-coloured brittlegill, *Russula torulosa*. It appears to be a mycorrhizal associate of Austrian Pine *Pinus nigra* and so was probably introduced to the forest with its host, but, if so, it is certainly well established now. The same may be true of a remarkable bolete discovered at Bedgebury Pinetum, Kent, during the hot summer of 1976. This is *Suillus placidus*, sometimes called the Bedgebury Bolete, and readily distinguished by its ivory-coloured cap and reddish-brown granules running down the stem. It is associated with Weymouth Pine *Pinus strobus*, one of the signature trees of Bedgebury, and so may be another introduction (although it looks wild on the other side of the Channel). Given the relationships they have with forest trees, these fungi could be commercially important (could Austrian Pine flourish on the Anglesey sand without *Russula torulosa* in its roots?).

▼ **Bearded Amanita** *Amanita ovoidea*, a huge mushroom resembling a half-buried ostrich egg when young, is now firmly established in the Isle of Wight.

One of the mushrooms I would be willing to make a special trip to see is *Amanita ovoidea*, lately dubbed the Bearded Amanita, although 'Ostrich-egg Amanita' would be more descriptive of its remarkable appearance. Apart from a few stray records, it is confined to the hottest, sunniest part of the Isle of Wight, where it was discovered by Colin Pope in 1989, under the deep late-summer shade of Holm Oaks. Graham Mattock, who sought it out in 2005, found its bald white domes bursting through bone-dry soil 'like scattered ostrich eggs' (Mattock 2006). As the great caps break through from their protective membranes, rags of veil cling to the cap like a tattered beard. This is by any standards a magnificent fungus, up to 20cm across the cap, and it grows in the strangest of settings, a hot wood of Mediterranean trees that cling to perhaps the steepest down in Britain. Where has it come from? As a southern European species associated with Holm Oak, it might be an introduction. But equally it could be a natural coloniser, part of a whole new ecosystem of plants, fungi and insects associated with Holm Oak. *Amanita ovoidea* is a natural wonder. It has not yet been recognised by conservation bodies, but its portrait is on prominent display at the Heritage Centre in Ventnor.

Some places are outstanding for a whole genus of fungi. Anyone who has forayed widely will know places that, for whatever reason, are outstanding for boletes or coral fungi or webcaps, as though conditions that suit one species suit many more. One of my favourite spots for boletes is a small wood on the calcareous marl clay in the southern part of the New Forest. It has a pitted surface where marl diggers removed the clay to fertilise their fields a century ago, and is also full of springs, each of which creates a small boggy glade. I was lucky enough to visit this wood back in August 1997, when the prevailing hot muggy weather made it feel like a rain forest. I had hardly taken a step before I came across a robust bolete with a khaki cap flushed with rose-pink, a stumpy yellow stipe and red pores that turn inky blue when touched. It was one of the rarities of the Forest, a bolete seen so seldom that mycologists have struggled to give it a name. The currently correct one is *Boletus rhodopurpureus*, the Oldrose Bolete – and that day I saw hundreds. The wood was bursting with other rarely encountered species, too, such as the glorious *Boletus legaliae* with its pink-flushed cap and bright red stem net like a devilish body stocking, and a spicy smell like cheap coffee. (And why do the authorities always adopt the most boring name from their self-created synonymy? Its former names were *B. satanoides* or *B. splendidus*). There was also plenty of *Leccinum carpini*, a lanky, rough-stemmed bolete with a wrinkled grey cap that has been compared with the skin of a toad. There were troops of the Ruby Bolete *Xerocomus rubellus*, with their round, raspberry-pink caps, like toadstools in a fairytale. There were others with beige-brown caps and bright lemon pores: *Boletus impolitus*, the Iodine Bolete, so-named from its eye-watering puff of chemical when you cut the stalk. I wandered through the wood, glassy-eyed and gasping beneath the steamy boughs. Even now, I wonder whether I dreamt it. I have been back many times since, and each time saw nothing out of the ordinary. That vast quantity of fungal energy lies dormant and out of sight, unsuspected, except during occasional, unpredictable irruptions when an apparently ordinary wood suddenly turns into a stage for fungal magic.

Kings Wood, near Bedford, is not, on the face of it, a promising wood either. Much overgrown by bramble, it is close to a large town and has become a handy dump for locals to empty their dogs. Yet it is an outstanding place for one genus: the fibrecaps, or *Inocybe*, and has furnished Alan Outen, the expert in the genus, with a wealth of material for study, including rarely found species. And they grow not in the depths of the trees but on the edges of the paths, among the litter and dog excrement. In a good year, this is *Inocybe* heaven – clusters of noticeably smelly brown mushrooms, each with its own distinct set of fibrils, prickles and bulbs. One of the best years was 2008, but unfortunately, not even the dogs of Bedford could reach its paths that autumn. The police had closed the wood. Apparently, terrorists had earmarked it as a place to bury explosives!

Floras and mycotas

A tradition in British botany that dates back more than 300 years is that of compiling lists of wild plants growing in a particular place. These have become known as floras. They usually include accounts of the geography of the area, the places where plants are to be found and detailed notes on the distribution of each species. Recent county floras include maps based either on the hectad (10km square) or, increasingly, the tetrad (2km square), and lavish colour images on glossy paper.

Floras are traditionally confined to vascular plants, although some have extended the range to include bryophytes and stoneworts. A few, such as *The Flora of Dorset* (Bowen 2000) and *The Flora of Berkshire* (Crawley 2005), have strained the definition of a plant to include fungi. But mushrooms sit rather uneasily among flowers, trees and ferns; fungi are not, of course, plants. That is why mycologists prefer the word 'mycota' to 'flora', even if that may mean little to the wider public. Mycota means an assemblage of fungi, just as a flora means an accumulation of flowers. In an ideal world, every county flora would have a county mycota as a companion volume.

In this less than ideal world, local mycotas are few and far between. The only recent examples in book form are *Fungi of the New Forest – A Mycota* by Gordon Dickson and Ann Leonard (1996) and *Fungi of Northwest Wales* (2005) by Charles Aron, both heroic, self published tomes in A4 format. They include records of around 2,500 species and have some welcome colour photographs, as well as relevant background material in the manner of a county flora.

There have been others. The very oldest dates all the way back to 1788, when a local naturalist in Yorkshire called James Bolton published *An*

History of Fungusses growing about Halifax, thus beginning a Yorkshire tradition of foraying that goes on to this day. Bolton was a gifted and accurate draftsman who knew how to use the simple brass microscope of his day. He described 231 species of fungus from the Halifax area, and thanks to him we know that the now nearly extinct Nail Fungus *Poronia punctata* was then common there in fields used by horses. Bolton found two more now-rare species, the hot-tasting milkcap *Lactarius acris* and Dusky Bolete *Porphyrellus porphyrosporus*, both in a particular, identifiable wood, and they were still there (perhaps were even the same genetic individuals) when the young Roy Watling visited it 150 years later. James Bolton is not forgotten in Yorkshire. In 1996, the Halifax Scientific Society held an exhibition of his work in which Roy made a tribute to his forerunner.

Comprehensive records of Yorkshire fungi were published in the journal of the Yorkshire Naturalists' Union from the late 19th century onwards, most recently in 2004, with a local list from the Scarborough area. Other century-old lists of fungi were published in the Victorian county 'histories', notably one for Shropshire by William Phillip, which included lichens and slime moulds, and another for Essex by M C Cooke.

The first county mycota of modern times was *A Fungus Flora of Warwickshire* (1980), edited by Malcolm Clark. It was remarkable for the proportion of micro-fungi included; only one-third of the 2,600 species listed were agarics and boletes, and of the 1,200 species of micro-fungi, 29 were new to science. The survey group has added a total of nine supplements since then, published among the *Proceedings of the Birmingham Natural History Society*, and is still going strong 30 years later, a glowing tribute to stamina and staying power in the heart of England.

Richard Dennis, a Kew mycologist who helped to produce the first two checklists of British Basidiomycete fungi, also published a pair of local fungus floras, *Fungi of the Hebrides* (Dennis 1986) and *Fungi of South East England* (Dennis 1995). Reflecting the author's wide interests and expertise as a plant pathologist, they too are less biased towards larger fungi than one might expect, with mushrooms and boletes comprising only 29% and 31% respectively. Remarkably, 2,905 species of fungi had been found in the Hebrides by that date. And even this impressive list barely touches the untold legions of other micro-fungi that must exist there.

The fungi of the Scottish islands are surprisingly well recorded, thanks mainly to the work of Roy Watling and his associates. He published a checklist of fungi on the island of Mull in 1985 as a continuation of a survey of the flora and environment of that island, and then followed it up with two more island studies, *The Fungus Flora of Shetland* (1992) and, with Tom Eggeling and Evelyn Turnbull, *The Fungus Flora of Orkney* (1999). These listed around 1,000 and 1,500 species respectively, including, in the case of Orkney, 26 species new to Britain.

Hence, published mycotas are like county floras standing on their head – weightiest in the far north and sparse in the south. Above all, it is the northern islands (and Anglesey) that have been probed and forayed most assiduously. Being isolated and self-contained, islands are scientifically intriguing as well as exciting places to visit – and it is that, as much as their potential interest, that explains their attraction. In recent years, the bias towards the northern isles and Hebrides has been countered by the frenetic activities of some fungus groups. The fungi of areas such as Kent, Bedfordshire, the Cotswolds, the Lake District and the London area are being uncovered year by year, although nowadays the results are more likely to appear online than in book form.

It is thanks to fungus forays and surveys such as these, large and small, that we know as much as we do about where fungi live and how they are distributed. We also have a much better idea about which species are common and which ones rare. But, with fungi, we have to bear in mind that what we are seeing is only the fruiting parts of organisms that for most of the time live out of sight. Now and again, species that are normally rare suddenly decide to have an *annus mirabilis* and briefly become quite common, at least locally. Such a year was 2010 when, for a short time in September, the woods were full of colourful and rarely seen webcaps *Cortinarius*. And strangely, it was the same over much of the country, as though the fungi had put their heads together and decided to act in concert. We can only speculate how they do it.

Most field mycologists foray for fungi for their own sake. But many more do it for a purpose – eating them. Searching for wild mushrooms is a rewarding but scary activity: unless you know them well, the dark image of the Death Cap and its fellow poisoners peer over your shoulder as you fill the basket with goodies. Let us take a closer look at these delicious and deadly offerings, and ask ourselves how safe this increasingly popular activity really is. And, in the chapter after that, we ask whether mushroom picking is sustainable, and whether regulation might be the answer.

chapter eleven

The good, the bad and the crazy

'Can you eat it?' This is the question you hear most often on fungus forays. The expected answer is either yes, you can, or no, you can't, it is poisonous – that is, one or the other. People often look rather disappointed when you tell them that most fungi are of no culinary interest. You could technically eat a bracket fungus, say, or a little brown mushroom, providing you had identified it correctly, but you would probably find it either completely tasteless (or tasting unpleasant) or impossibly chewy. Like flowering plants, only a minority of wild mushrooms are worth eating. This chapter is about the ones that interest most of us the most: the 'good' kinds that taste delicious, the 'bad' kinds that will cause severe upsets or even kill us, and the 'crazy' ones that cause hallucinations and other mind-altering experiences.

Kitchen mushrooms

The British and Irish have traditionally played safe with wild mushrooms. Even today, when 'wild mushrooms' appear on every pub menu, the UK mushroom industry is dominated by a single species, the commercial Cultivated Mushroom *Agaricus bisporus*. The reason why you rarely find the common wild Field Mushroom *A. campestris* in supermarkets is because it is difficult to cultivate. The larger Horse Mushroom *A. arvensis* was once cultivated in beds of dungy soil and sold at market. But today the less tasty Cultivated Mushroom has swept aside every rival. The industry is still experimenting with other species, but the only one to show much promise in a mass market is the 'chestnut mushroom', and that may be just a brown-scaled form of *A. bisporus*. The largest producer of shop-bought mushrooms is based at Bradford-on-Avon, where caverns that once were quarried for Bath stone are

◀ **Oyster Mushrooms** *Pleurotus ostreatus* makes excellent eating.

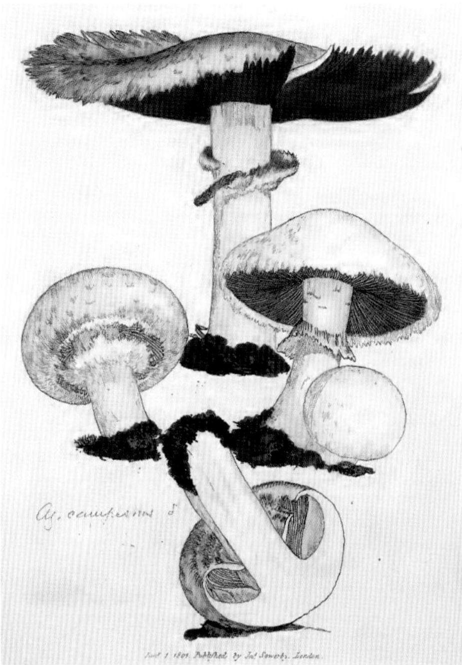

▲ **Field Mushroom**
Agaricus campestris, painted by James Sowerby in 1797, and among the first accurate drawings of fungi in the English-speaking world.

now full of little button mushrooms, grown in a controlled environment on compost bags of straw, mixed with chicken manure and gypsum. No wonder they do not taste of much.

'Wild mushrooms' came into fashion from the 1980s onwards on the back of the organic movement, aided by media shows such as Michael Jordan's Channel 4 series *Mushroom Magic*, and celebrity chefs such as Antonio Carlucci. A sizable trade has since built up, focused on perhaps a dozen species. It has so far been impossible to cultivate boletes and chanterelles, and so every one of these species sold worldwide comes from the wild. Fortunately, those that grow on dead wood, such as Oyster Mushrooms *Pleurotus ostreatus* and the oriental Paddystraw Mushrooms *Volvariella volvacea*, are easy to cultivate, even in the garden. Many of the more exotic 'wild' mushrooms sold in specialist outlets are imported from Europe or America, even though they may grow commonly in a wood near you.

About 100 wild British mushrooms are both edible and easy to recognise. Those who take to the woods each autumn in search of them soon get to know where certain species appear in quantity. We gather them with a basic toolkit of a flat-bottomed trug or wicker basket (never a polythene bag) and a sharp knife, or better still, a custom-made mushroom knife with a curved blade and a handy little brush attached. We gather only firm, fresh specimens, we take only a portion of the crop, and we don't pick too many (a basketful is enough). We never pick mushrooms from polluted ground, such as landfill sites or busy roadsides. Having nice manners and a respect for the country code, we obtain permission before picking on private land. And we never collect what we cannot identify.

Over time we learn to be better cooks, to know what goes with what, and which species one can dry or preserve. Not all wild mushrooms give of their best by simply being fried in a pan. The tastes of the wild are subtle and sometimes delicate, and need coaxing forth. Some species, notably the strong-flavoured ceps, are worth drying (they make excellent mushroom soup). Morels go well with eggs or pasta. Milkcaps are helped by parsley and tomato, the slightly peppery girolles are perfect with steak, parasols lend themselves to sage and onion. Certain little brown mushrooms come into their own as flavourings. Few would bother with the stringy-looking Deceiver *Laccaria laccata* on its own, but added to a casserole it brings a surprising richness. The experience of gathering, preparing and cooking wild fungi is best shared. A foray followed by a feast of mushrooms is more than a meal: it is an autumn festival, a communion with nature, an expression of the joy we take in hunter-gathering from the wild and in sharing a quiet passion.

▲ **Parasol mushrooms** *Macrolepiota procera* – good with parsley or sage.

Many of our best edible mushrooms look appropriately wholesome. Egg-yolk yellow Chanterelles or the plump forms of boletes nestling in the basket are a visual delight. So, too, is a smallish Giant Puffball *Calvatia gigantea*, with its skin like the finest calf leather, or the shaggy yet elegant drumsticks of young Parasols *Macrolepiota procera*. Some also have appetising scents, not only of mushrooms but also of freshly ground flour, aniseed, or the perfumed floral bouquet of the blewits. Colourful *Russulas*, the brittlegills, brighten up any mushroom dish and add a bit of crunch.

Just because a mushroom is certifiably edible, it does not mean you will necessarily enjoy it. Personally, I love brittlegills, which are seldom picked in Britain (although they are among the most popular mushrooms in Catalonia), and elevate morels and cauliflower mushrooms to culinary heaven. But I can happily leave inkcaps and the smaller puffballs. I have heard people sing the praises of little-known mushrooms such as The Gypsy *Cortinarius caperatus*, or enthuse about such dubious delights as Stinkhorn 'eggs'.

There are probably more edible mushrooms than we know. Some common species are rarely gathered but are, in fact, excellent. One of these is Oakbug Milkcap *Lactarius quietus*, championed by John Wright in his mushroom-gatherer's Bible, *Mushrooms* (Wright 2007). No doubt people were put off by its English name and oft-repeated statement that it 'smells of bedbugs'. Wright points out that a more obvious, and infinitely more tempting, comparison is with fresh carrots. With that in mind, I tried a few on a poor day for fungi and found them perfectly acceptable, with a mild, mushroomy taste and pleasant crunchy texture.

▲ Dryad's Saddle
Polyporus squamosus is said to be edible when young.

Another of John Wright's 'new edible' mushrooms, the Porcelain Fungus *Oudemansiella mucida*, may take longer to become established. This is the pure white mushroom with the polish of finest bone china that grows in tufts on the branches, standing or fallen, of Beech. Its agreeable shine comes from a thick coating of slime, which has to be washed off first (and also means they have to be kept away from other mushrooms in the basket). Apparently, cleaned and then sautéed, it has a rich, pleasant flavour; most books, noting its abundance of slime, dismiss it out of hand as 'inedible'.

People eat some funny things. I have never been brave enough to try a Stinkhorn 'egg' (apparently, they taste like a sort of jellied hazelnut). I have tried some young bracket fungi, but cannot recommend them. Yet others have enjoyed young, relatively tender specimens of Dryad's Saddle *Polyporus squamosus*. Another bracket, the multi-tiered Hen of the Woods *Grifola frondosa* (not to be confused with Chicken of the Woods *Laetiporus sulphureus*) was once sold in Norwich market as 'morels', surely a case for the Trade Description Act, had it existed then.

▲ Edible in Finland, 'poisonous' in Britain: Woolly Milkcap
Lactarius torminosus.

Even stranger things are eaten in other countries. It is not unusual to find fungi, especially boletes, completely covered in a powdery mould called *Hypomyces*. One form of this is bright red, and infects certain species of brittlegill and milkcap in such a way as to resemble the flesh of a cooked lobster – red on the outside, white on the inside. These blood-red fungal corpses are marketed in North America (and very expen-

▲ **Porcelain Fungus** *Oudemansiella mucida*, regarded as inedible until tried and given the thumbs-up by the *River Cottage Handbook*.

sively) as 'lobster fungus'. There is a growing taste for them in Britain, too.

▲ **Popular all over the world – Chanterelle** *Cantharellus cibarius.*

Mushrooms that are not much eaten at home can be favourites overseas. The Honey Fungus *Armillaria mellea* gets a poor press here but is popular in Poland. The Velvet Shank or Winter Fungus *Flammulina velutipes*, a common mushroom found on willow logs at the end of the season, is cultivated in Japan but practically ignored in Britain (although there was some recent commercial interest in *Flammulina* extract to lengthen the shelf-life of fresh tuna and to stabilise the natural colour of beef). No one except, perhaps, psychotropic thrill-seekers, would even think about eating a brittlestem *Psathyrella*, but one species is part of a national dish in Haiti. Woolly Milkcap *Lactarius torminosus* has a burning hot taste and is sometimes described as poisonous (the name *torminosus* means 'griping' or 'fretting of the guts'), but it is eaten with relish in Finland.

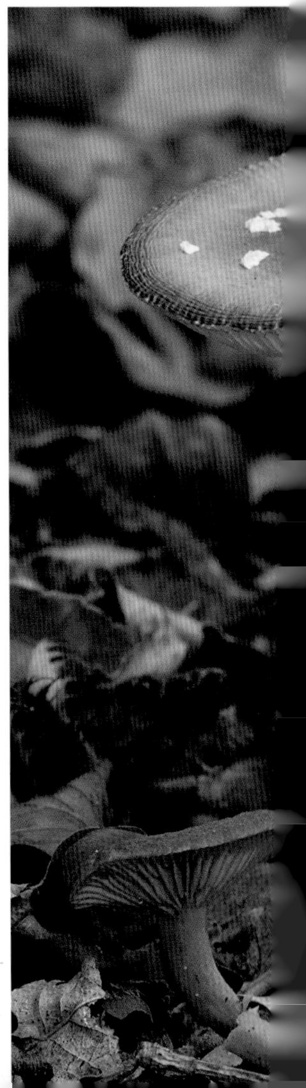

In the Far East, where fungi are valued for their medicinal properties as much as their food value, fungi not regarded as edible over here are sold at market, in some cases at exorbitant prices. One of them is *Cordyceps* (see the next chapter), a club-shaped parasite of buried insects. Orientals also have a taste for bracket fungi, including the common Turkeytail *Trametes versicolor* and the glossy, colourful, but tender-as-a-gatepost Lacquered Bracket *Ganoderma lucidum*. Perhaps the least likely species on the market is the plasmodial stage of *Fuligo septica*, a slime mould that bears the apt nickname of 'dog-vomit'.

The most famously expensive edible fungi are, of course, truffles. Neither of the two most desirable ones, the white Piedmont Truffle *Tuber magnatum* and the black Périgord Truffle *T. melanosporum*, are found wild in Britain. But we do have a less sensational black truffle, the Summer Truffle *T. aestivum*, a pale imitation of the Périgord Truffle but which is nonetheless strong enough to impart an earthy flavour to any dish (keep one in the fridge overnight unwrapped, and, by morning, everything will taste of truffle). A smaller British species, the Winter Truffle *T. brumale*, is also edible, and around Bristol and Bath the Red Truffle *T. rufum* was once sold at market as 'Bath Truffle'.

In the past, British truffles were gathered mainly by professional hunt-

ers, using double-twined truffle forks and either a trained pig or a breed of hound known as the English truffle-dog. Sussex, Kent, Wiltshire and Hampshire were the main centres, with Winterslow, in Wiltshire, once boasting no fewer than 12 families in the trade (the art of truffling was passed from father to son for generations). By the early 1900s, however, this richly bucolic way of life was already dying out: it was hard work finding enough truffles to sustain it, especially as they were sold for the equivalent of only 12-20p per pound. The last full-time truffle hunter, Alfred Collins of Winterslow, downed his truffle fork for good in 1936. Until recently, the art had passed out of memory, and many people might now be surprised to learn that England has any truffles at all. But they have latterly come back into fashion in a small way. A company based in Dorset, having mastered the art of cultivating truffles using small, planted trees, offers weekend dog-training courses. And there are

▲ **Not poisonous, but not nice either – False Chanterelle** *Hygrophoropsis aurantiaca.*

▼ **Panthercap** *Amanita pantherina,* a beautiful but dangerously poisonous mushroom.

small bands of truffle hunters who are understandably secretive about the special places where, towards the end of summer, they pass their hands over the earth to find black English truffles, dark as Badger poo, smelly as old socks, and there for the taking.

One of the best-known urban legends on fungi is that every delicious mushroom has a poisonous look-alike. Unfortunately, this legend is true in part. The Chanterelle, for instance, is the same colour and basic shape as the False Chanterelle *Hygrophoropsis aurantiaca*, once regarded as poisonous (it isn't, but it certainly cannot compete in taste with the real thing). Another ill-starred pairing is the eatable (when you can beat the slugs) Blusher *Amanita rubescens* and its poisonous counterpart, the Panthercap *A. pantherina*. They are not really alike, but if you cannot tell the difference you should avoid eating Blushers! Perhaps the most dangerous pairing is two medium-sized brown mushrooms, the Sheathed Woodtuft *Kuehneromyces mutabilis* and the ominously named Funeral Bell *Galerina marginata* (or, in America, the Autumn Skullcap). Both are common, both are the same nondescript shade of brown, and both grow on stumps. And the very modest culinary potential of the one is scarcely worth the risk of serious poisoning by the other. For the same reason, few of us would be inclined to take risks with genera such as *Cortinarius*, where every edible one is surrounded by up to a dozen look-alikes that are at best doubtful and at worst virulently poisonous.

The skull and crossbones

Falling in love, they say, is like eating mushrooms. You never know when it's the real thing until it's too late (there is another saying that goes: All mushrooms are edible – once). Poisonous mushrooms are real and they are also part of folklore. They are the dark yang to the mushroom's yin. Living in dark, dank places, they were the opposite of light-loving flowers and fruits. At one time, most mushrooms were thought to be poisonous. There was a theory that they absorbed poisons from the ground, perhaps from rusty nails or rotting fabrics and other buried rubbish. You could tell a really dangerous mushroom, thought Pliny the Younger, from its 'livid' colour (he also thought that the safest mushrooms were those with red skins). Another ancient scholar, Nicander, contended that fungi somehow imbibed the toxic breath of serpents. They could be made safer by cooking with the stalks of pears. It was all rubbish – just as much as the prevailing belief that poisonous mushrooms tarnish silver.

The poet Robert Graves had a theory that our wariness of wild fungi was a hangover from a time when 'magic mushrooms' were the prerogative of a priestly elite. Richard Mabey argued that, on the contrary, it is part of our cultural estrangement from woodland, as keen and methodical de-foresters. Our ambivalence towards them seems to be peculiar to north-west Europe. Britain, Ireland and the Netherlands are the traditionally mycophobic countries. Everywhere else, from Sweden and Finland to Italy, Spain and the Balkans, wild mushrooms are gathered and eaten with great enthusiasm.

But there is some justification for our reticence. Some fungi are indeed poisonous, and a few can do serious damage. Fatal poisonings are rare in Britain, not because poisonous mushrooms are rare but because, until recently, we have generally stuck to two or three easily recognisable kinds. In Europe, where many more species are gathered as food, poisonings are much more frequent. In France, there were 300 fatalities in one year alone, 1885, an annual toll that had been brought down to 100 or so by 1912 (cited in Findlay 1982). That is why, at least until recently, every corner pharmacy in France provided a mushroom identification service (in Russia, where wild mushrooms are gathered with equal enthusiasm, poisonings seem in contrast to be few).

▼ **Deathcap** *Amanita phalloides* – the greatest poisoner of them all.

Among the more celebrated victims (or supposed victims) of mushroom poisoning are Emperor Claudius (as seen in the final episode of *I Claudius*), Pope Clement VII and the Holy Roman Emperor Charles VI, whose sudden collapse after enjoying a dish of sautéed Deathcaps led to the War of Austrian Succession. In France, a serial killer called Girard poisoned his many victims with deadly mushrooms in order to pocket their life insurances. Mushrooms also made a gruesome murder weapon in an episode of *Midsomer Murders* with the suggestive title of 'Destroying Angel'.

Poisonous mushrooms definitely have glamour. When I was a boy, I had a set of triangular postage stamps from Poland featuring fungi, among which were the Deathcap *Amanita phalloides* and the Fly Agaric *A. muscaria*. Both were labelled 'trujacy', or poisonous. I thought it wonderful that a country should wish to celebrate its deadliest mushrooms, especially on cool three-cornered stamps. Primacy was given to the Deathcap, too, in everyone's first mushroom book, *The Observer's Book of Common Fungi* (Wakefield 1957) – its baleful olive-green presence formed the first colour picture in the book.

The Deathcap is, famously, 'the most poisonous mushroom in the world' (whether or not that is strictly true, it has certainly chalked up the most known victims). It contains a powerful cocktail of dangerous biochemicals called amatoxins which destroy the human body's cells, especially those in the liver and kidneys, and inhibit the synthesis of proteins. Their deadliness does not take effect right away, so that, by the time you begin to feel seriously unwell, it is far too late for a stomach pump. In times gone by, the victim used to expire after enduring a sweaty, painful and deeply worrying nine days or so. Nowadays, drugs, dialysis and liver transplants have reduced fatalities to around 20%, but a survivor may still be crippled for life. The Deathcap is, indeed, fabulously poisonous: the lethal dose is 30g, or half a cap. There is no imaginable advantage to the mushroom in being so, and it is, in any case, eaten with apparent impunity by slugs and snails. Its ability to poison human beings is presumably an accidental and biologically irrelevant aspect of biochemistry. It apparently tastes quite nice.

The deadliness of the Deathcap has probably been common knowledge throughout human history. The 10th-century Arab physician Avicenna evidently knew of it when he counselled patients not to eat mushrooms that are green. It was among the first mushrooms to be described scientifically. In 1727, a young Frenchman called Sebastien Vaillant was struck by the phallic shape of the young fruit body as it emerged from a membranous bag or volva – hence its scientific name, *phalloides*, 'like a penis' (or alternatively, 'like *Phallus impudicus*', the Stinkhorn, which also emerges from an 'egg'). The Deathcap is easy to identify from the combination of this bag and its silky greenish cap, suggestive of a Granny Smith apple. It is quite common in woodland under oak or Beech, especially in southern England. Dozens of them appear every year on a bank half a mile from my home. It is a stately and rather attractive mushroom that initially smells faintly of rose petals, though later on it turns sickly-sweet.

This pretty, sweet-scented mushroom was responsible for all but one of the 39 fatal mushroom poisonings recorded in Britain between 1920 and 1950. Since then, the death rate has fallen. There were just 11 reported cases between 1973 and 1981, of which only one was fatal. One unlucky victim had tucked into a dish that contained not only Deathcap but also its much rarer and equally poisonous relative, Destroying Angel *Amanita virosa*. He survived, after emergency treatment, but the experience left him with malfunctioning kidneys. The most recent casualty was a resident of the Isle of Wight, who died in September 2008. Her younger companion, who had shared the meal, survived. Two years later, 12-year-old Lucy Adcock ate two of them raw, thinking they were Field Mushrooms. She too survived.

These deaths were not caused by eating them intentionally but from eating what were thought to be edible mushrooms. Quite possibly some of the victims were gulled by the old wives' tale that a mushroom is edible if you can peel off the skin, and especially if it has a ring round the stem. This nonsense is still widely believed – witness its reiteration by that normally wise old journalist, Bill Deedes, in his *Daily Telegraph* column in 2006. In point of fact, the Deathcap peels readily, as do many other poisonous mushrooms, and it has a prominent stem-ring. It is another reminder that the only way to be sure that a mushroom is edible is to identify it correctly.

▼ **Destroying Angel** *Amanita virosa*, just as toxic as the Deathcap, but much rarer.

▲ **'Beware: Deathcaps about'.** A warning sign at Canberra, Australia.

The Deathcap is more dangerous abroad than at home. In Poznan, in Poland, in 1918, 31 children died after taking part in a mushroom feast prepared by their school that contained some Deathcaps. There were around 100 fatalities (out of 5,000 reported cases of poisoning) in the Berlin and Brandenburg areas of Germany in the lean post-war years, when hungry families combed the local woods to supplement their rations. The danger has since been exported to far-away countries. The Deathcap now thrives in the San Francisco Bay area, where it is thought to have been introduced with nursery Cork Oaks. It has appeared under imported chestnuts and oaks in New York State, and under pines and other trees in South Africa. Around Canberra, Australia, it is so common that they put up warning signs. Those most at risk are immigrant populations from the Far East who have picked Deathcaps in mistake for the Paddystraw Mushroom, a staple of Oriental cuisine. Both have a distinctive bag at the base of the stem and, since the Deathcap does not occur in South-east Asia, they have not learned to tell the difference. In Oregon, four members of a Korean family were poisoned by Deathcaps, one of them fatally. Of seven victims in the Canberra area of Australia, during the 1980s, three were from Laos and had been picking Paddystraws. When, in the 1980s, the image of the Deathcap was accidentally transposed among the edible mushrooms in a popular book, the book was, understandably, withdrawn from sale.

The genus *Amanita* is famous for its incongruous mixture of the delicious and the deadly. These are charismatic mushrooms, many of them attractively coloured – orange, green, red, warm brown, dove-grey – and bearing a rich assortment of rings, veils, bags and leopard 'spots' (the spots are fragments of the veil which have stuck to the cap and shrivelled). Sharing the Deathcap's pedestal as the world's most dangerous mushroom are its close relatives, the Destroying Angel and the Fool's Mushroom *A. verna*. Both have white caps and, since they could therefore be mistaken for the Field Mushroom, would be even more dangerous were it not that they are rare in Britain. Indeed, *A. verna*, as it is currently understood, is probably not British at all; all the preserved material examined turned out to be a white form of the Deathcap. But Fool's Mushroom is common in America, where it is said to poison cattle.

Apart from the Deathcap, the only wild British mushroom to have caused a death is *Inocybe erubescens* (formerly *I. patouillardii*), lately

▲ **Deadly Fibrecap** *Inocybe erubescens* is the most toxic of the fibrecaps.

dubbed the Deadly Fibrecap. The victim, who died in 1937, was from Surrey. In 1963, there was a mass poisoning in a Gurkha camp in Hampshire, which was also traced to the Deadly Fibrecap, although in this case they all survived. This is a whitish mushroom that stains pink and turns brown with age, and could conceivably be confused with small Field Mushrooms (although it has brown spores). Fibrecaps in general, and this one in particular, contain muscarine, a substance first found in the Fly Agaric, but is present in greater amounts in *Inocybe*. Victims can expect to endure a lot of sweating, salivating and crying. In America, they have an acronym for it: SLUDGE, that is, salivation, lacrymation (crying), urination, defecation, gastrointestinal upsets and emesis (vomiting). In some cases, there may be hallucinations to look forward to as well. The victims usually stagger back to their feet after a day or two.

Many poisonous fungi are 'little brown mushrooms' (LBMs) that few would think of eating, with the significant exception of toddlers who sometimes inquisitively graze small fungi growing on the lawn. One larger species is more dangerous because it has been mistaken for the edible Chanterelles. This is *Cortinarius rubellus* (formerly *C. speciosissimus*), the Deadly Webcap, an uncommon species found mainly in Scottish pinewoods. So long as you know your fungi, there are hardly any points of resemblance between the two, for chanterelles are yellow, not reddish-brown, and have folds instead of gills, and pale yellow, not brown spores. But the Deadly Webcap is not a well-known species, and if one was not examining them too closely, if one was chatting to friends and enjoying the day out, you can imagine how they could end up in the same basket, and then blend in equally well with the delicious

▼ **Dangerously bland, the Deadly Webcap,** *Cortinarius rubellus*.

yellow trumpets as they sizzle in the pan. Deadly Webcap causes what is known as orellanine poisoning. Like the Deathcap, its effects are dangerously delayed while the toxin homes in on the kidneys. The first known case of *Cortinarius* poisoning was in Poland in the 1950s, when more than 100 villagers were taken ill at a fungus feast, and 19 of them subsequently died. In Britain, where *C. rubellus* was little known, three holidaymakers at a Scottish campsite were taken ill in autumn 1979 after eating mushrooms growing nearby, and Roy Watling was able to identify the remains of Deadly Webcap in their stomach contents. Two required kidney transplants. Its most celebrated victim was Nicholas Evans, author of *The Horse Whisperer*, along with his wife, her brother and sister-in-law. The webcap, gathered from a pinewood on his brother-in-law's estate and eaten with parsley and butter in 'a momentary suspension of doubt', nearly killed them; their sufferings were horrendous, and three of them were left dependent on regular dialysis and in need of kidney transplants (for which there is a long queue) (Levin 2010). Perhaps the first best-selling novel about mushroom poisoning is just around the corner.

▼ Livid Pinkgill
Entoloma sinuatum, the 'grand poisoner of the Cote d'Or'.

Deadly Webcap is not the only poisonous *Cortinarius*. Orellanine has also been found in several related species (being fluorescent, it is easy to detect) and, on the Continent, several people have fallen victim to another species, the rather callously named Fool's Webcap *C. orellanus*. The presence of such dangerous species casts doubt over the whole of this very large genus, especially as by no means all the species have been tested. Some species of *Cortinarius* are certainly edible; the giant of the group, Goliath Webcap *C. praestans*, is highly prized in Europe. But eating an unknown *Cortinarius* is akin to playing chicken with a loaded revolver.

Another poisonous species that is better known in Europe than over here is the Livid Pinkgill *Entoloma sinuatum*, also known as the Livid Entoloma, the Leaden Entoloma, or, best of all, the Lead Poisoner (livid and lead are both translations of its former species name, *lividum*, which originally meant pale or

ashen coloured, not red in the face). Yet another name was the Miller's Purge, a reference to yet another edible look-alike, The Miller *Clitopilus prunulus*, which shares the same mealy scent. Here is one account of *Entoloma* poisoning from the 19th century: 'I was so continually and fearfully purged', wrote the victim, 'and suffered so much from headache and swimming of the brain, that I really thought that every moment would be my last,' (Smith 1867).

▲ **Brown Rollrim**
Paxillus involutus – death by slow poisoning.

On the Continent, the Livid Pinkgill is said to be responsible for 10% of all mushroom poisonings. In the vineyards around Dijon, they called it *Le Grand Empoissonneur de la Cote d'Or.* In 1983, in Geneva, some 70 people who had eaten it were admitted to hospital with severe gastric upsets. Delicious to relate, the man who first placed the fungus into its correct genus, the French mycologist Lucien Quelet, was himself a victim. Since other species of *Entoloma* are known or thought to be poisonous, and are quite difficult to identify, this is clearly another genus to avoid.

Some toxic fungi are more subtle. Brown Rollrim *Paxillus involutus* is an unprepossessing mushroom with a sticky brown cap skin which rolls round and tucks in under the gills, like the crust of a pie. What it lacks in beauty, it makes up for in abundance, for this is among our commonest large toadstools. One often finds it in quantity when edible

▲ **Don't touch! False Morels** *Gyromitra esculenta* on sale at a market in Helsinki, Finland.

mushrooms are thin on the ground. At one time, 'poor peasants on the continent made large use of it' (Hay 1887). The late F Bayard Hora, the British author of the famous Collins field guide, acquired a taste for *Paxillus*, and is said to have eaten immoderate quantities of it throughout his surprisingly long life. He presumably did not know that a fellow mycologist, Julius Schaffer, had developed renal failure after overindulging on rollrim, which eventually killed him in October 1944. The effects of what is now known as the 'Paxillus syndrome' are slow and accumulative, but potentially fatal. In 1980, an antigen was discovered in the Brown Rollrim that stimulates an autoimmune reaction, causing the body's immune cells to consider its own red blood cells as enemies and attack them. In susceptible people, this can lead to severe haemolytic anaemia and death. Hence, the Brown Rollrim is another mushroom no longer on the menu.

There is at least one poisonous mushroom that is widely eaten, especially in Scandinavian countries, fresh, dried or canned. This is the False Morel or Gyromitra *Gyromitra esculenta*, a relative of the morels with an intricately folded cap that has lent it such alternate names as Turban Fungus and Brain Mushroom (the genus name means 'round hat', while the species name reminds us that it is an esculent, that is, fit for food). The False Morel is hugely popular in some countries, despite its known toxicity; like the Japanese *fugu* fish, it needs careful preparation, in this case by parboiling, to make it safe. Unfortunately, heating does not necessarily destroy Gyromitra's unique and lethal toxin, gyromitrin, which is broken down in the stomach into a dangerous chemical better known as 'rocket fuel'. And yet they go on eating it. Now that its lethal potential is better understood, False Morel is prohibited from sale in Spain, Switzerland and Germany. In Sweden, sales are restricted to the restaurant trade, whilst in Finland, where it is close to being a national dish, it is sold under warning signs, including one asking you not to risk touching it. The deadly sting of *G. esculenta* casts a shadow over the so-called false morels in the genus *Helvella*, and even over the hugely popular *Morchella* or true morels. There are, Brian Spooner relates, stories of nouvelle cuisine chefs ruining receptions by serving elegant but toxic dishes containing raw morel.

▲ **Yellow Knight**
Tricholoma equestre, once highly regarded, now suspect.

Gyromitra is eaten, even though it is known to be poisonous. More often, we eat mushrooms that we think are edible but are not. One of these is the large and beautiful *Phaeolepiota aurea*, known by the unflattering name of Golden Bootleg. This is a large and striking golden-brown mushroom with yellow spores and a scent of bitter almonds. Far too rare in Britain to attract attention, it is gathered in France and America, where it has been praised for its wholesome mushroomy smell and rich, pleasing taste. But when, back in 1942, a Belgian mycologist decided to analyse it, he was surprised to find quantities of highly toxic hydrocyanic acid – the source of its pleasantly almondy smell. Admittedly, other mushrooms, including the Fairy Ring Champignon, also contain small amounts of this substance. It is supposedly broken down and rendered harmless by heating. But this is not so with *Phaeolepiota*, and, to make matters worse, it also accumulates the toxic heavy metal cadmium. So, it is time to kick the Golden Bootleg out of the kitchen.

Another dubious mushroom is Yellow Knight *Tricholoma equestre*, also known as Man on Horseback. This is an all-yellow species, sometimes with tints of olive or brown, and with small brownish scales in the middle of the cap. In France, where it is, or was, greatly esteemed, it is known as *canari*, the canary. As legend has it, people of the knightly (seigniorial) class would reserve this handsome mushroom for themselves, while assigning an inferior one, the Cow Bolete, to the peasantry. But people from south-west France were recently taken ill after consuming this species, complaining of weakness and muscle pain, accompanied by nausea and sweating. According to reports, one of them actually died. Researchers in Japan have now identified a unique toxin in this supposedly edible mushroom that would fully explain why they were ill. It may be that some Yellow Knights are fine to eat and others not, perhaps because a group of mini-species are sheltering behind the name. If so, the trouble is that it is impossible to tell the difference.

There are also mushrooms which, while not dangerously poisonous, can cause severe stomach-aches and ruin any dish of mixed fungi. Two of these are actually *Agaricus* mushrooms, close relatives of the Field Mushroom. The Yellow Stainer *A. xanthodermus* is common in woods and gardens, indeed, nowadays is more common than the Field Mushroom. It, and its less common, scaly relative, Inky Mushroom *A. moelleri* (or *A. placomyces*), are easily mistaken for edible mushrooms, but they have a nasty smell of ink and bruise a bright chrome yellow at the base of the stalk. The smell comes from phenol, which is not destroyed by cooking. Two people who accidentally ate the Yellow Stainer in mistake for the Field Mushroom reported headaches, stomach-aches, dry mouths and a general sense of weakness. Others, apparently, can digest them unscathed, although they taste nasty. It is said to be the commonest cause of poisoning through mistaken identity.

Some mushrooms, while technically not poisonous, react with alcohol, causing instant nausea, purple faces, hot flushes and worse, so for most of us they might as well be. The effect is similar to that of 'antabuse', used in the treatment of alcoholics. The Common Inkcap *Coprinopsis atramentaria* is the best known, but there are others, including the Lurid Bolete *Boletus luridus* and the Club Foot *Clitocybe clavipes.* Yet another group, which includes many species of milkcaps and brittlegills, has burning hot tastes. For those who like hot dishes, this might not be a turn-off, although species such as Woolly Milkcap *Lactarius torminosus* 'agony milk' and Sickener *Russula emetica* irritate the bowel lining and so can cause gastric upsets.

Lastly, there are mushrooms of good repute that sometimes misbehave. The demand in the 1990s for the sulphur-yellow bracket Chicken of the Woods *Laetiporus sulphureus* was such that it fetched high prices at market. In texture it resembles chicken breast, a kind of vegetarian poultry. I have eaten it, with no ill effects, although I did wonder what all the fuss was about. But there are also reports of dinner-party guests falling out of their chairs, retching and gasping for breath, whilst the host dialled 999. Some people can eat it with impunity, while others suffer mild reactions such as swollen lips and giddiness. The effect may be an allergy, or perhaps this bracket fungus, which can grow on trees such as Yew, may absorb toxins from the wood. The advice is that one should begin with a cautious nibble, and eat only fresh young specimens.

One could extend this list of inconstant esculents. Honey Fungus *Armillaria mellea*, a handy pot mushroom when there is nothing else about, can produce allergic reactions in perhaps one in five of us. Slippery Jack *Suillus luteus*, a common bolete of pinewoods, can also cause trouble if the slimy cap skin is not removed first. Shaggy Parasol *Chlorophyllum rhacodes*, long considered edible, includes strains that are, apparently, mildly toxic. Weeping Widow *Lacrymaria lacrymabunda*, another very common mushroom that is sometimes gathered when there is nothing more tempting to hand, has a dark relative, *L. glareosa*, found in Scottish gardens, which has recently been implicated in cases of poisoning. A question mark hangs over Weeping Widow, too, since it has been known to cause stomach upsets.

If you have read thus far, dear reader, you might wish to endorse the remarks of mushroom-hunter, John Wright, that picking for the pot is a perilous pursuit and that there is a fine line to draw between encouragement and frightening you to death (Wright 2007). Nor is this a complete list. Those who tell you there are only a few poisonous toadstools to learn and avoid, are mistaken. There are hundreds of them, and more are being added to the list all the time. Great swathes of *Cortinarius*, *Amanita*, *Entoloma*, *Inocybe*, *Galerina*, *Hebeloma*, *Lepiota* and *Clitocybe* carry the skull-and-crossbones symbol. There are malign morels, evil-natured boletes, fatal funnelcaps and treacherous *Tricholoma*s. If you ate every fungus you found, you would be in a hospital ward before sundown. So what? There are plenty of poisonous berries, but that doesn't stop us picking blackberries. One cuts the coat according to the cloth. Limit yourself to species you can identify with confidence and eating wild mushrooms is safer than walking down the street. I have gathered and eaten Greasy Green Brittlegills *Russula heterophylla* growing among Deathcaps, which match their colour exactly. To me, they are as different as chalk and cheese. But I would avoid any Little Brown Mushroom, even if they were said to taste like caviar. As generations of Poles, Spaniards, Frenchmen and Slovenes can tell us, mushroom-hunting is one of the greatest pleasures the countryside can offer. The fact that so many of them are poisonous adds to, rather than detracts from, the fun.

Pink elephants and magic mushrooms

Back in the 1980s, Michael Jordan presented a well-received television series called *Mushroom Magic*. It celebrated the world of fungi for its mystery, its sensual engagement, its capricious nature and its universal appeal. Mushrooms somehow seem more magical than other living things. Delicate-looking fungi can lift asphalt and force holes through concrete. There are fungi that live on jet fuel, toenails, tennis balls, even CD discs. Some fungi are gone in a morning, others, if we can count a genetically uniform clone as an individual, live for hundreds, even thousands of years. They come in every colour of the rainbow, and they smell of everything from gas-tar and creosote to fresh radishes and cheap scent. A single giant puffball could populate the earth, given a chance.

Mushroom magic is timeless, but magic mushrooms are a recent discovery. Perhaps we should say rediscovery, because there is nothing new about the peculiar effect that certain fungi have on the human senses. Everyone knows that Viking 'berserkers' went wild on the sense-distorting effects of the Fly Agaric (whether the story is true is another matter; it seems to be an early urban legend). Fly Agarics were certainly eaten by the shamans of certain tribes in Siberia. Apparently, its effects are most potent after having passed through one's guts, so that one ate the mushroom and then drank one's urine, or persuaded a co-operative reindeer to eat one, and then drank *its* urine. Essence of Fly Agaric gave the shaman a sense of flying, which, some say, is the origin of the legend of Santa Claus, in his red-and-white uniform and his team of flying deer.

In Britain, it seems we stopped using fungi as mind-altering recreational drugs a long time ago, only to rediscover them again during the hippie culture of the early 1970s. The fungus now called the Magic Mushroom was, until then, known as the Liberty Cap *Psilocybe semilanceata*, from a vague resemblance to the pointed hats worn by French revolutionaries (the 'p' in *Psilocybe* is silent, as in psychic). Its interesting properties first came to light in the 1950s when an American banker-turned-anthropologist, Gordon Wasson, became convinced that a little mushroom, known by the natives as Angelico, the little angel *P. mexicana*, had played an important role in the evolution of human culture and religion. Wasson experimented with it and other species, cultured it in his laboratory and, with the help of a French botanist, Roger Heim, isolated a chemical, psilocybin, whose active form,

psilocin, is chemically similar to the notorious 1960s drug, LSD (itself a derivative of a drug found in another fungus, ergot). Psilocin turns blue when exposed to the air. Hence, fungi that stain blue when bruised may contain it (but not always – the blue reaction of some boletes is related to copper compounds, and is quite innocent).

The effect of a sufficient quantity of Magic Mushrooms is said to be very similar to that of LSD. One of those who tried it was the novelist Arthur Koestler, who described the experience as 'quite spectacular'. 'For nearly an hour', he wrote, nothing at all happened...[But] when I closed my eyes, I saw luminous, moving patterns of great beauty, which was highly enjoyable. Then the patterns changed into worms, which had a tendency to change into dragons, which was less enjoyable.' It also gave him a heightened sense of music: 'I had never heard [chamber] music played like that before. I suddenly understood the very essence of music, the secret of music...' (Koestler 1968). This heightened intellectual sense, and the suddenness in which dreamy images could turn into nightmares, is exactly how I distantly remember my own experiments with Magic Mushrooms.

▲ **The notorious Magic Mushroom** *Psilocybe semilanceata*, also known as Liberty Cap from its resemblance to the bonnets worn by revolutionaries in France.

Despite the abundance of Liberty Caps on commons, parks, sheepwalks and road verges throughout Britain, the counterculture was late in discovering this bountiful source of free drugs. As late as the mid-1970s, a Sheffield mycologist, Rod Cooke, could report that, despite its distinctiveness, the Liberty Cap 'has never been used even as a casual inebriant' (Harding 2008). By the time I moved to Scotland in 1977, however, its hallucinogenic powers were widely known. They eventually became something of a youth cult north of the border. After a bumper season in 1981, no fewer than 44 people, mainly teenagers, ended up in the emergency department of the hospital in Dundee (Spooner & Roberts 2005). Newspapers picked up stories of confused teenagers who, under the impression that they had super-powers, had hurled themselves from upstairs windows. Today, a significant proportion of cases of poisoning by fungi involve Magic Mushrooms. For example, in Ireland, 62 of 114 referred enquiries between 1997 and 2000 were from young people overdosing on *Psilocybe*. Another 43 cases were as a result of toddlers grazing the lawn. Only five related to the traditional danger of mistakenly eating the wrong mushroom.

Magic Mushrooms are peculiarly revolting to eat, especially in their fresh state. Keep them in Tupperware overnight, as I once did, and you end up with a box full of maggots. When dry they look and taste like mouldy popcorn. In moderate doses, which were the limit of my own ambitions, they provided nothing more alarming than patterns dancing on the wall: no dancing elephants, alas, or illusions of flying. The experience lasts about three hours and recalls Alice's experiences in Wonderland, when several impossible things happened before breakfast. I do not remember any unpleasant kick-backs or after-effects, although, as I say, I am fairly cautious by nature.

Back then, it was not illegal to possess wild-gathered Magic Mushrooms (the law outlawed the chemical but not the mushroom). It was a moot point whether one could legally grow or prepare them, for instance by drying the mushrooms on a radiator. In 2002 the Home Office, in a sudden burst of liberalisation, decided to 'clarify' the law and informed the public that it was not, after all, an offence to possess, sell or consume fresh-picked Magic Mushrooms. The result was a brief explosion of websites and home-grown 'shroom shops' (which did, indeed, spring up like mushrooms). They sold grow-your-own kits, including potent species from the New World that left our Liberty Caps looking comparatively tame. The traffic in Magic Mushrooms doubled. Health officials panicked, and three years later the Government made an abrupt about-turn and, swerving violently in the opposite direction, re-classified Magic Mushrooms as Class A drugs, along with heroin and crack cocaine. It is now an offence 'to import, export, produce, supply, possess or possess with intent to supply' any fungus containing psilocin. Other countries, including the USA and the Netherlands, cracked down at about the same time, and for the same reasons.

The Home Office generously assured landowners that they would not be sent to prison if the said mushrooms grew wild on a bank or in a meadow on their property. Fungus forayers were placed in a more difficult position. With our eyes to the ground and our obvious interest in little brown fungi, we are easily mistaken for Magic Mushroom pickers. Should we wish to dry and preserve a specimen of a mushroom that happens to have psychotropic properties, we are technically in breach of the law and might face an awkward and very worrying interrogation by drug squad officials. The least one might expect is the confiscation of one's herbarium, with the contents mashed up and tested for banned substances in the Drug Squad's lab. The Home Office admitted that no one thought about field mycologists when the legislation was drawn up. Its suggestion was for us to 'destroy' the fungus after identification. (How? Stamp on it? Consume it in a bonfire?) Alternatively, properly labelled specimens could be 'delivered to a person who can lawfully take custody of them as soon as is reasonably practicable'. In practice, this boils down to the licensed national herbariums at Kew or Edinburgh. From the point of view of the fungus forayer, it is all very tiresome.

The new drugs act outlaws every species of fungus that contains 'psilocin or esters of psilocin'. The problem for forayers is that it is not only *Psilocybe semilanceata* that contains the proscribed substance. A great many other fungi do, or are suspected of doing so, among them species of *Inocybe*, *Conocybe*, *Panaeolus*, *Stropharia* and *Panaeolina*. There is even a (so far, non-British) psychotropic puffball. Indeed, there are probably more of them than we know. One of the largest mushrooms found on rotting logs is the Spectacular Rustgill *Gymnopilus junonius*. This beautiful orange species is rarely gathered for food in Europe and so its properties were unknown until samples were tested and found to contain psilocybin. This might explain why, in Japan, it is known as *waraitake* or 'the laughing mushroom'.

Since they had outlawed them in advance, the Home Office had to ask Kew's resident mycologist, Brian Spooner, to draw up a draft list of fungi known or suspected to contain psilocin. It was surprisingly long. By 2005, the substance had been detected in 31 British species, and was suspected of being present in another nine. Whilst red is the customary colour of danger, with fungi it seems to be green. Several green and slimy mushrooms are on the list, including, as 'possible but not confirmed', that delight of grassland forays, Parrot Waxcap *Hygrocybe psittacina*. Interestingly, it also includes at least one species usually considered to be edible, the Deer Shield *Pluteus cervinus*.

It is easy to see the reaction to Magic Mushrooms as a legal sledgehammer to crack a nut. The officers of the law seem to agree. So far as I know, no foray leader has yet had to answer questions at the local police station, or release his or her basket for inspection by the Drugs Squad. Having failed to register our existence in the first place, the Home Office seems to be happy to go on ignoring us.

chapter twelve

Picking for the pot

There has been a great deal of debate, but not a lot of evidence, about whether gathering mushrooms for food does any harm. Should we pick 'mushies' to our hearts' content, or should we hold back a bit? And, if the latter, is there a case for making that restraint compulsory? This is not, frankly, a question that greatly concerns professional mycologists. But it is undoubtedly a concern for conservationists, and, to judge from the tabloids, the general public too. That is understandable because more wild fungi are being picked in Britain than ever before, partly by people from countries in Eastern Europe where gathering mushrooms in the autumn is embedded in the rural culture, but also from the catering and restaurant trades. There is a huge demand for 'wild mushrooms', and companies have sprung up to supply it. Scotland, at least, has become a net exporter of wild fungi, with a seven-figure annual turnover in the late 1990s.

The number of mushrooms collected for commerce in Britain is still small in comparison with other countries – a mere dozen species or so, compared with scores in France, Finland or Croatia. But the demand for species such as the Chanterelle and the Cep is considerable. In the 1990s, up to 400 casual pickers gathered mushrooms and boletes in Scotland alone, mainly working for the supply trade but sometimes going freelance and selling their produce door-to-door. The incentive is the top prices paid for fresh, unblemished mushrooms, which can fetch as much as £100 a kilo. Pickers, working in a favourable locality at peak season, can earn as much as £2,000 a week. Among the pressure points are Deeside, Speyside and the Black Isle in Scotland, and the New Forest and the commons and woods around London in England. Everyone has their horror story of how a wood was picked bare of mushrooms,

◀ **John Wright cooking up a feast** after a successful foray in the New Forest.

of how they were sorted out later and the unwanted ones left to rot in the car park. Alarmist headlines appeared in the tabloids: 'Highlands plundered in fashion for fungus'; 'Why this fungus feast could turn into a last supper'; 'Mushroom pickers strip New Forest'. The impression given by such reporting is that picking mushrooms is like uprooting wild flowers or chopping down trees. Take them and they are gone.

Some public landowners responded by banning picking. The Forestry Commission, which manages the Crown woods of the New Forest on behalf of the state, banned commercial picking there (although it turns a blind eye to collecting by local restaurants). It has also tried to ban all collecting in certain areas for scientific reasons. In legal terms, they were perfectly entitled to do so. Wild fungi are considered to be property, and taking them without permission is therefore a form of trespass (though not, strictly speaking, theft). But the gatherer has rights, too. Where there is a right of public access, for example on registered public footpaths, the public has the right to pick 'the Four F's': fungi, foliage, fruit and flowers. Anyone who does so, says the common law, 'does not steal what he picks'. So, as long as we are on a public footpath we can gather mushrooms, just as we can pick blackberries, or holly and ivy for Christmas decorations, or sloes for making sloe gin – unless there is a bylaw to prevent us doing so. There is, however, an important proviso. Such collecting must be for personal use, and not for sale. The recent Countryside and Rights of Act (the 'CRoW Act') complicates matters a little. Basically, while we can continue to pick berries from the path, the Act does not confer any further rights. We may wander where we like off the footpath, but our political masters do not allow us to pick so much as a blackberry. This was probably not a considered policy. It seems that those who framed the law simply forgot.

Public concern about mushroom picking came to boiling point in 1996 when, at the British Mycological Society's centenary exhibition, Antonio Carluccio's cooking demonstration was interrupted noisily by green activists accusing him of 'pillaging the environment'. Others pitched in on their side. Entomologists have argued that the survival of various invertebrates depends on there being an adequate supply of fungi (they do not say what happens in a dry season when there are none). Amenity bodies consider that fungi form part of the beauty of the scene, and for that reason alone should not be removed. Conservation bodies suggested that, where there was doubt about its long-term effects, the activity should be regulated. This was referred to as 'the precautionary principle'. What no one produced was any evidence that collecting was actually damaging the resource, although some must have felt that it was only commonsense to assume that it did.

In 1998, an ebb tide of ripples led to a Code of Conduct, a 'recommendation of good practice' for picking fungi, issued jointly by the Government's countryside watchdog, English Nature (now Natural England), and the British Mycological Society (BMS), and endorsed by the National Trust and other public landowners. The Code was presented as moderate and reasonable, and so, for the most part, it is. It enjoins ignorant visitors to obey the country code and beware of poisonous mushrooms. It urges pickers to take no more than they need, and in any case not to take away more than half of what they find. It suggests a limit of 1.5kg per visit (and, as the Forestry Commission put it, 'if you find that much you're doing well!'). It was presented as a voluntary code, but that was hardly the case. Tucked away in the small print was a clause suggesting that 'if the land is SSSI or a protected area it will *probably be appropriate* [my italics] to limit picking to scientific collecting'. Over much of lowland England, at least, this would place many of the most productive sites out of bounds to the casual picker, as well as the commercial gatherer. It was, at the very least, a strong hint to landowners of Sites of Special Scientific Interest to refuse requests to gather mushies for the pot.

Behind the scenes, there had been a difference in opinion between the British Mycological Society and the more hardline spirits within English Nature. 'The scientific evidence shows that commercial picking is not in fact damaging the numbers of fungi', Roy Watling told *The Independent*, 'and we want the code to remain flexible and not be turned into a law.' But when poor Maurice Rotheroe, the Society's conservation officer, drafted a version that would not have outlawed picking on protected sites, he received a thundering rebuke from some jobsworth in English Nature reminding him that the Code as drafted was English Nature's 'intellectual property' and that 'you do not have our consent to use it'. Maurice, the most mild-mannered of men, was taken aback by this language, but he reacted with a reasoned article in *British Wildlife* that judged the pros and cons of mushroom-picking, while reminding us that the real threats to wild fungi are well documented, and are not, in fact, collecting but habitat loss and pollution (Rotheroe 1998).

Since the British Mycological Society was a signatory to the Code, it was in no position to object to parts of it. But it is hard to imagine any country where mushroom-picking is more engrained in the social calendar that would allow such an attack on personal freedom without enquiry or evidence. It seemed, at least to me, that a liberty we take for granted was being eroded by stealth. The English have a fine record of standing up to officious busybodies, and it was in that spirit that I wrote a letter to the British Mycological Society. In the event, although it was moderately worded, they decided it would be divisive to print it. So, I thought, to hell with them, and phoned Charles Clover, then the environment editor at the *Daily Telegraph*.

The result was an editorial worthy of the peasants' revolt, headed: 'Mushrooming Bureaucracy'. 'After Greenpeace, green police?' it continued. 'This week will see the publication of one of those increasingly familiar "codes of conduct" which tell you what to do in areas where we have managed well enough without rules. This one is to control mushroom picking, for heaven's sake, and it promises to provide splendid new opportunities for minor-league jobsworths whose hobby is bossing us about…Leave us to pick our mushrooms in peace,' concluded Charles, 'and if we wish to sell them, that is our own affair.'

Since then, things seem to have calmed down. I believe that the English Nature/BMS Code of Conduct was a formulaic response to an unfamiliar problem that had been whipped up out of all proportion. The pressure on English Nature to do something about it seemingly came from within; I know my friend, Ted Green, had been upset by bolete-stripping incidents at Windsor Forest and elsewhere. It was also an opportunity for the government agency to make some sort of statement on conserving fungi, an aspect of its statute and responsibility that it had so far neglected. Little has been heard about the Code since then, and English Nature and its successor body, Natural England, has subsequently made amends by funding conservation projects on rare fungi.

In Scotland, they went about things with greater tact. The Scottish law on trespass is impenetrably vague, but any restrictions on personal collecting would almost certainly be unenforceable. The Scottish Wild Mushrooms Forum, which included representatives of various conservation bodies, issued a moderately worded code of its own, simply asking landowners to 'be aware that your management activities may affect fungi', which kept everything nice and vague. It says nothing about weight limits or commercial picking, and troubles nobody.

The question remains, are there any circumstances in which collecting could harm wild mushrooms? The answer, it seems, is yes, in cases where an already scarce and habitat-sensitive species is being targetted. I review some of the evidence, such as it is, below.

The case for regulation

Fungi are beautiful, or if not exactly beautiful, at least magical, bizarre and interesting. The small print under many a welcome sign to a public amenity enjoins visitors to leave the mushrooms 'for others to enjoy'. There is no evidence of how many people 'enjoy' fungi in this way, but mushrooms and toadstools are obviously part of the general ambience of autumn. And who would not be outraged by piles of fungi wasted by pickers? Or bracket fungi mindlessly wrenched from a tree? On nature reserves, there is a reasonable assumption against picking or collecting *anything*, on the grounds that it is a protected place: one where nature should come first, at least in principle. The argument is not so much one of sustainability as of ethics and good behaviour.

We are not the only animals that enjoy fungi. They are a seasonal food source for slugs and snails, maggots and worms, woodlice and other small life, as well as voles and squirrels. For certain invertebrates they are a necessary food source. In seasons where mushrooms and boletes are scarce, they presumably subsist on bracket fungi. For most beasties, mushrooms must be a seasonal luxury food, nice when you can get it.

Objectors are on stronger ground when it comes to the means of collection. Raking and disturbing the soil can have a deleterious effect on fungi, which is exactly what one would expect, since it is in the upper layers of the soil that the fungal mycelium is often situated. This is why the British Mycological Society gave up its truffle hunts. There is also some evidence, for example in some city parks in Italy, that trampling can be harmful. This, again, is what we would expect, for compression alters the physical structure and properties of the soil. But it is a matter of degree. Mild disturbance can actually stimulate fungi to fruit, and the edges of paths are often marked by troops of mushrooms, almost as if they were put there as garden decorations. Also potentially damaging (though rarely mentioned) is picking bracket fungi for paper-making, for producing natural dyes, or for homemade potpourri. These are minority hobbies in Britain, and probably do little harm, but brackets are apparently collected in large numbers in parts of the United States.

Cautionary tales

So far as we know, collection has not in itself caused lasting damage to any species of fungus in Britain. But in other areas, and in certain rare circumstances, commercial collecting has been shown to be unsustainable. Here are three well-documented examples.

▲ **The mighty *Pleurotus nebrodensis*,** a rare and highly regarded Mediterranean mushroom.

In the northern mountains of Sicily grows a remarkable white mushroom known to the locals as *funcia di basiliscu* but to scientists as *Pleurotus nebrodensis*. It is a relative of our Oyster Mushroom, but bigger, far more massive, and is creamy white when fresh. It grows on the roots of those giant fennels *Cachys ferulacea* that are so common in the central Mediterranean, the fat, cup-like fungi appearing beneath the plants as the ground warms up in the Sicilian spring. Mushrooms have been eagerly gathered as food in Sicily for centuries, and *funcia di basiliscu* is the most desirable and expensive one of them all. It is famed not only for its delicious taste but also as a health food, rich in amino acids and trace elements. It is said to be particularly effective against rickets, bone disease and cancer.

The trouble nowadays is that demand exceeds supply, for while the demand has grown, the mushroom's habitat has shrunk. Today, it is confined mainly to the Madonie National Park, where collecting fungi is regulated by rules such as a ban on picking young specimens. But the regulation does not seem to be enforced and the mushroom is now listed internationally as critically endangered. The mycologist Guiseppe Venturella has persuaded the Park authorities to create a sanctuary with a total ban on picking to give the mushroom space to recover its numbers. But regulation may not count for much in a traditional rural society with long-held customs and beliefs.

The long-term solution, since everyone wants to go on eating the wonderful *funcia di basiliscu*, is cultivation. In China, where the same species is known as the White Sanctity Mushroom, it has been cultivated successfully on cottonweed hulls, maize cobs and even sawdust. This technique has been taken up recently in Poland. The cultivated form is now sold fresh or canned for as little as $10 a kilo (or even $5 in China), compared with 50 times that for fresh, wild *funcia* from Sicily. But, as with farmed salmon, connoisseurs may be unconvinced that cultivated *funcia* tastes anything like as good as the wild mushroom. Nor will taking a can from the shelf at the Palermo deli approach the fun and community of a day in the forest. Whether Sicilian *Pleurotus nebrodensis* survives as a wild species, only time will tell.

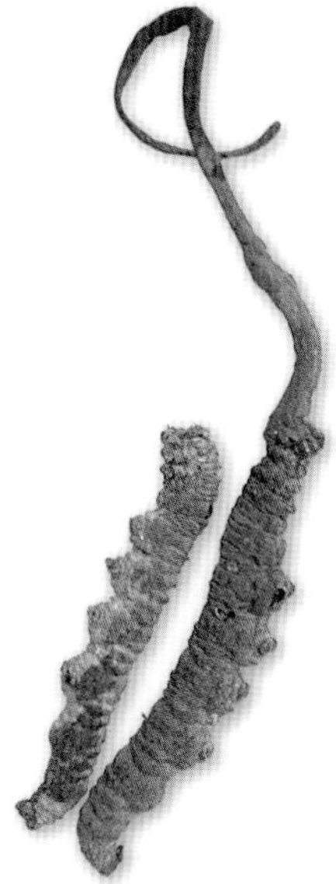

▲ **Bu** or *Cordyceps sinensis*, a parasite of caterpillars shown dried as it is sold in street markets in China and Japan.

In the Himalayas, where mushroom gathering is as much part of rural life as in Sicily, the greatest demand is for a matchstick-like fungus that grows on dying caterpillars. This is *Cordyceps sinensis*, a gruesome, worm-like growth known there as the *bu* (which means 'worm') or *yartsa gunhu*, the 'summer-grass winter-worm'. The 'worm' is the warty brownish fruit body of the fungus that pokes through the alpine turf, its nether end remaining attached to the gutted remains of a caterpillar – usually, and fittingly, the larva of the Ghost Moth. It is this mystical union of worm and fungus that lends *Cordyceps* its peculiar allure and status. Its power in overcoming and drawing forth the life of a caterpillar can, traditionalists believe, be transferred to human beings. A regular supply of *Cordyceps* is said to keep the body's defences strong, and so helps to alleviate ailments. The *bu*'s finest hour arrived in 1993, when three Chinese athletes, all women, broke a series of track records at the world athletics championships in Stuttgart. Later, their coach admitted that they had all taken *Cordyceps* (oh, and turtle blood), which, apart from helping athletes to run like hares, provides Viagra-like sexual potency, at least for believers. Scientists sifting through its biochemical secrets have isolated unique substances from *Cordyceps* which, when tested on mice, did seem to have positive effects, with possible applications in anti-cancer and anti-viral treatment. Britain has several smaller species of *Cordyceps*, of which the Scarlet Caterpillarclub *C. militaris* is the best known. It can be found popping up like little toy soldiers on lawns and well-grazed paddocks. But the stolid British have never been tempted to explore its nutritional potential.

Like *funcia di basiliscu*, the demand for *bu* is enormous, while the supply is limited. So far (and there have been many attempts), it has been impossible to cultivate. Instead, villagers gather the wild fungi from pastures during its short season in May and June. It is considered important to gather the whole fungus, dead caterpillar and all, by lifting it from the soil with a narrow trowel resembling a dandelion digger. The collectors pitch their tents on the high meadows and systematically work the hillsides for the tiny spurts of brownish-orange in the turf. They are scarce and hard to spot, but the work is lucrative, bringing in three times the average annual income in Tibet (the middle men, of course, make far more). Prices have risen steeply in recent years: four-fold between 1997 and 2004, and by 20% in each successive year. This reflects rising demand from the increasingly affluent Chinese markets, but it also indicates growing rarity. Where there were 100 *bu* clubs 25 years ago, today you would be lucky to find ten. Currently *bu* is, quite literally, worth its weight in gold, at $900 an ounce. Do such extravagant prices spell doom for the fungus? It is argued that some fruit bodies, at least, will have discharged their spores by the time they are found. But some form of conservation policy seems needed. Yet people see things differently in the Himalayas. '*Bu* is different,' remarked one collector. '*Bu* will always be growing,' (Winkler 2010).

In Britain, hardly anyone eats *Tricholoma*. We have nearly 50 species of these fleshy, white-spored woodland mushrooms, some smelling ominously of gas, soap or cheap scent. The only species formerly gathered for the pot, the Yellow Knight or Man on Horseback *T. equestre*, turned out to have a nasty kick in its tail. Yet the mushroom in greatest demand worldwide is a *Tricholoma*, a solid-looking white mushroom with soft brown scales. This is *T. magnivelare*, better known by its Japanese name, *matsutake*. This is an American species, but it has an Asian relative, the 'real' *T. matsutake*, which is reputedly the most expensive mushroom in the world after the truffle (and, presumably, the *bu*). *Matsutake* has a spicy fragrance that is said to recall the earthy scents of pine groves, just as wild bilberries somehow capture the essence of the moor. The Japanese value beauty in their food as much as taste, and perfect young specimens of *matsutake* are given as gifts inside carved wooden boxes – expensive gifts, for they will pay as much as $200 for a single piece. The trade in *matsutake* is phenomenal: worldwide, it is said to be worth $3-5 billion, more than twice as much as the next most popular mushroom, the Chanterelle (Arora 2001). Consumption on this scale has created mushroom boomtowns in places as far afield as Guatemala, Bulgaria, Zimbabwe and Tibet. The houses built on the proceeds are known as 'matsutake mansions'. The autumn rush to the hills to collect the *matsutake* has been called the 'white gold rush' (Spooner & Roberts 2005).

Matsutake is always sold fresh; there is no market for the dried product. In the Pacific Northwest of America, mushroom-hunters sell their produce to local depots, which rush it to the airports. Having crossed the Pacific Ocean to Japan in a matter of a few hours, the valuable cargo is briskly unloaded and rushed by lorry straight to market. The

▲ **Matsutake** *Tricholoma matsutake*, 'the most expensive mushroom in the world'.

reason why they go to such trouble and expense is that local Japanese stocks of *Tricholoma matsutake* have all but disappeared. In 1950, over 6,000 tonnes were harvested, but by 1984 this had fallen to just 180 tonnes. Unfortunately, like other mycorrhizal mushrooms, *matsutake* does not respond well to farming techniques, and most of the crop is taken from the wild. Moreover, the greatest demand is for mushrooms at the button stage, which are taken before the spores can ripen. And collecting the half-buried buttons involves digging and raking, which also damages the mycelium of the fungus.

In Japan, the species is threatened with extinction. The collecting, we can assume, has contributed to the decline, but whether it is the main cause of it is debatable. A more proximate cause, which is shared by other Japanese fungi, is from a combination of pollution, changes in forest management and infestations by a certain nematode worm. The shortfall, meanwhile, has been taken up by imports from Korea, China and Tibet, where the stock is now falling in turn.

In America, the substitute *matsutake*, *Tricholoma magnivelare*, is currently worth more than the timber of the forests in which it grows. Hence, this species has been a force for conservation, a strictly fiscal argument against intensive logging. On the other hand, digging and raking are just as damaging to the fungus here as in Asia. The answer has been regulation and a ban on practices that damage the resource. One means of achieving this has been to regulate the harvesting period through licensing. Another is to rotate the harvesting areas to allow time for the forest floor to recover. More fundamentally, the Federal Government is trying hard to persuade local consumers and Asian customers that mature *matsutake* tastes just as good as the buttons. Regulation is difficult, since *matsutake* picking is a fiercely independent form of life; turf wars are not unknown. But, from a British perspective, what comes across from the American experience is a much more mature and intelligent way of approaching the problem than our clumsy, home-grown attempts at banning commercial picking altogether.

The case against regulation

Chanterelles are in demand as food throughout the world (recent DNA evidence indicates that chanterelles from North America are different to the common European species, *Cantharellus cibarius*). Everyone, everywhere, seems to enjoy them, as much for their wholesome appearance as their taste. Coloured like egg-yolks, and with a delicate fruity scent, sometimes likened to fresh apricots, they are indeed very appealing. The scientific name of the common British species fittingly means 'cup of food'. And, unlike some mushrooms, chanterelles are hardly ever infested with maggots. The reason may be their high concentrations of Vitamin D, which protect the fungus from slug and insect attack while raising its status as a health food. Chanterelles also contain unusually low levels of toxic or radioactive metals, the latter being a more than usually pertinent cause of anxiety after the Chernobyl incident in 1987. The fruit bodies appear in the same spot, year on year, and whilst most mushrooms last only a few days, chanterelles may persist for several weeks. The search for them takes us to pleasant wild places: Highland birch woods, banks and leafy glades under the spreading boughs of Beech, and mature pinewoods, where the orange trumpets peer through heather and blaeberry. No wonder we love them.

Every chanterelle, of any species, sold in the world has been picked from the wild. That is a lot of chanterelles. In 1992, some 14,765 tonnes from Eastern Europe and Turkey were supplied to Western Europe, where demand outstrips local supply. Another 515 tonnes are exported from the Pacific Northwest of the United States. Britain is an exporter of wild chanterelles, picked mainly in Scotland. How has all this picking affected the resource? The answer, judging from the scientific evidence, is: hardly at all. Thirteen years of monitoring data from the USA showed that heavy picking has, if anything, produced a slight improvement in numbers. Cutting, instead of picking, seems to depress numbers slightly. Of course, 13 years is not very long, and would not necessarily reveal any long-term effect (and chanterelles seem to be long-lived). But, so far as we know, the current rate of exploitation of wild chanterelles is fully sustainable. In any case, probably far more of them are eaten by squirrels, sheep, deer and pigs than by people.

Is the chanterelle an exception? Probably not. In 1987, Eef Arnolds, the influential Dutch expert on mushrooms, reviewed the data thoroughly and found no evidence whatever that mushrooms are threatened by overpicking (Moore *et al.* 2001). The Danish mycologist, Thomas Laessoe, came to the same conclusion. He noted that the city parks of Copenhagen have been looted by morel-seekers every spring for the past 80 years, and every one of them still has healthy populations of morels.

Both men cited examples from other parts of Europe where fungi have been picked intensively over many years without, apparently, having any long-term effect on the crop. Maurice Rotheroe quoted some statistics from Serbia, where a staggering five million kilograms of wild mushrooms were exported in 1996, a figure he described as 'only the tip of the iceberg' because it excludes illegal exports, dried mushrooms and, of course, the considerable tonnage consumed within that country. These are levels of exploitation far outstripping anything in Britain, and yet there is no evidence that the mushroom crop is permanently affected. Their numbers vary with the seasons, but each year seems to be as bountiful as the previous one.

All this seems counter-intuitive to those whose experience is with plants rather than fungi. We tend to forget that the visible part of the fungus, the bit that we eat, is only the organism's fruit body, closer in concept to an apple on a tree than the whole plant. No one has ever suggested that picking apples will spoil the following year's crop, but those are the grounds on which those who wish to restrict picking seem to base their argument.

Fungi, as a whole, are indeed declining. The evidence from Britain is circumstantial at best, but there is a great deal of evidence from the Netherlands and the Black Forest, in Germany, where mushroom species have been mapped and documented in detail. But the decline is common to all fungi, especially mycorrhizal mushrooms, edible and inedible alike. In the case of the (European) Chanterelle, there is strong evidence that atmospheric pollution (and its consequent effect on the soil) is the main cause, at least in the Netherlands.

Some argue that picking will reduce spore production, and hence reduce the recruitment of fungi in the future. Again, the evidence does not bear this out, or at least not for long-lived fungi, which most of the edible ones are. Mycorrhizal fungi such as chanterelles and ceps are 'K-strategists', which depend on vegetative growth as their chief means of growth and dispersal. Their spores are more of a long-term life insurance policy than a means of recruitment.

On all these grounds the scientific case against picking fails to stand up to testing. Those who argue for the 'precautionary principle' (that is, that the mere risk of harm is, in the lack of sufficient scientific evidence, enough to warrant regulation) should bear in mind the words of the UK Strategy for Sustainable Development, that action must be based 'on fact, not fantasy, using the best scientific information…Precipitate action on the basis of inadequate information is the wrong response' (Rotheroe 1998).

The final argument against regulation is, in the words of the *Daily Telegraph*, that picking mushrooms is no one else's business. Anywhere else, the puffing and blowing of small-time scientific agencies and societies would have been sent packing in a gale of public mirth. Perhaps, I thought, we have become so wedded to regulation and petty restrictions in this country that the authorities can get away with anything.

Then someone decided otherwise.

The legal challenge

In November 2002, a 60-year-old lady was picking mushrooms in the New Forest. She was apprehended by an employee of the Forestry Commission who told her that she was breaking the law. No one was allowed to gather mushrooms for sale, he said, and especially not in places where all picking had been banned. He contacted the police, who confiscated her basket of 'brown chanterelles worth £27', and put her on a charge for theft.

Mrs Tee-Hillman ran a small business, Mrs Tee's Wild Mushrooms, which supplied top restaurants, at home and abroad, with wild mushrooms. She also cooked them at her guesthouse near Lymington, noted for the quality of its cuisine. She had received a written warning from the Forestry Commission the previous year, but refused to heed it since, in her view, the Commission had no right to stop her. Her case was that picking mushrooms was as much a right as using a public footpath, and that she had earned that right by practising it for 30 years. Neither the Commission nor the Government *owns* wild fungi, she maintained. If they belong to anybody, they belong to the person that picked them. Her line, essentially, was that the Commission had gone beyond what the law allowed. The Forestry Commission's contrary view was that taking products from the Forest was like stealing apples from someone's garden. It was theft, plain and simple.

To cut a long story short, Mrs Tee eventually appeared before a Crown Court judge on trial for theft, a criminal offence. But things took an unexpected turn when the judge, John Boggis QC, told the Commission's lawyers in no uncertain terms that they were wasting his time. He was there, he said, to try serious criminal cases, not 'little old ladies' who pick mushrooms. If the Commission wished to sue the defendant, he said, they should do so in a civil, not a criminal court. He threw out the case and made the FC pay costs, which, by now, were well into six figures. The Commission saved face by awarding Mrs Tee a special licence for life to pick mushrooms in the Forest, which avoided having to concede their powerlessness to prevent others doing the same. There have, so far, been no more prosecutions.

Mrs Tee's arguments are exactly those used to protect fungi from over-exploitation in the United States and other countries. 'I pick the brown chanterelles every ten days from the same place', she explained to a reporter. 'By making sure I don't damage their root system, I can get a new crop every ten days for up to three months.' Research supports her claim that picking actually encourages mushrooms to fruit more often. Experience suggests that in this, as in other cases where mushroom picking has been arbitrarily banned, public authorities acted precipitately, and unwisely. Eco-foraging, as it is now called, is now considered to be good for us and harms nobody. Perhaps we should assert our rural freedoms more often, as Mrs Tee did. In a world distressingly full of power-barons and obedience junkies, I think she is a hero.

chapter thirteen

Saving mushrooms

Mycology and nature conservation make uneasy bedfellows. Until recently, they did not share the same bed at all. Nature reserves and other protected sites have existed for the best part of a century, but not until the 1990s was one designated to protect a mushroom (a 70m length of protected verge). For a half-century we have had a large network of Sites of Special Scientific Interest, currently with about 6,000 sites covering an area the size of Wales, but the scientific interest did not, apparently, include mycology. Nor did the Nature Conservancy Council or its successors find room for a proper mycologist among its hundreds of staff. The first full-time post for a conservation mycologist was created in 2010, just in time to celebrate the 60th anniversary of organised nature conservation in Britain.

To some extent, the mycologists have themselves to blame for this shameless neglect of the third kingdom. The British Mycological Society (BMS) did not include conservation among its functions until 1985, and even then it seemed rather half-hearted about it. Unlike the Botanical Society of the British Isles (BSBI), it had no organised scheme of biological records until very late in the day. Unlike the RSPB, it has no nature reserves. As a small, learned society it did not even have staff or an office. Even today, the BMS struggles to make much impact in the conservation world, and would, I suspect, be happier sticking to its core strengths of fundamental science and fungus forays. And there is another problem. Mycologists are themselves becoming an endangered species. Professional taxonomy is in free-fall, and the pool of academe is drying out.

◀ **Bearded Tooth** *Hericium erinaceum*, a mass of miniature stalactites within the hollow of a lightning-damaged Beech, found by the author and photographed in fading light by Bob Gibbons.

Perhaps there is also something more fundamental at work here. The microbiologist James Staley, of Washington University, argued that, as a society, we do not care about all species equally. We care most about the species that are closest to us and engage our sympathies and emotions. Who would not be moved by images of endangered monkeys or embattled birds of paradise? Who could care less if some mildew or mould died out? There are almost certainly species of micro-fungi that are endangered. Ditto microbes: the ones that live in the stomachs of whales, for instance. But in our perception these organisms invoke negative reactions. They are 'germs' associated with disease and spoilage. Because they rank so low on the kinship scale, 'the demise of a microbial species is not an emotional issue for humans,' says David Moore, editor of *Fungal Conservation* (Moore *et al.* 2001). The fundamental role of fungi and microbes in the systems of the planet pale in comparison with the damage which they can cause to one's prize chrysanthemum or the nasty marks they can make on the lawn.

Nevertheless, several parties are championing the cause of fungi. The BMS is represented on liaison groups and forums in Europe and at home, and has a part-time conservation officer and conservation committee (now the Field Mycology and Conservation Committee). The Association of British Fungus Groups (ABFG) represents the interests of local bands of forayers. The Royal Botanic Gardens at Kew and Edinburgh have a strong interest in conservation, backed by their world-class libraries and herbaria (or 'fungaria', as some mycologists prefer). CABI Bioscience brings mycological expertise to bear on problems in agriculture and the environment. The charity Plantlife, set up 'to do for plants what the RSPB does for birds', includes fungi as honorary plants. Also loosely attached, since lichens are, after all, modified fungi, is the British Lichen Society, a small but highly focused society with an excellent mapping scheme. Until 2009, representatives from all these bodies met at a Fungus Conservation Forum, administered by Plantlife, to share experiences, pool their knowledge and identify priorities for action. Among the issues supported by the Forum over the years were booklets on preserving grassland fungi, an assessment of the most important areas for fungi and, at some cost to its morale and energies, a grand conservation strategy, *Saving the Forgotten Kingdom* (see below). The Forum, in its informal way, offered a focus as well as a meeting ground, and got mycologists talking to conservationists.

Nonetheless, field mycology faces great problems, both externally and internally. The external problem is lack of influence, with the result that the protection of fungi tends to be all talk and little action, beyond compiling lists and plans. Internally, there are serious divisions between what might be called the establishment, represented by a learned society such as the BMS, and the 'new kids on the block', the forayers, represented by Michael Jordan's ABFG. In an ideal world, they would sit at the same table and share the work, each party contributing its strengths, just as the popular RSPB and the scientific BTO (British Trust for Ornithology) manage to do. In practice, they barely speak to one another. The result is duplication of effort: rival databases and rival periodicals. From the productions of the BMS you seldom find any mention of the ABFG. In those of the Association, the BMS is also rarely mentioned.

The trouble is that there is no one willing and able to bang their heads together. From the standpoint of 2011, the positions seem entrenched. The government bodies are reluctant to get involved, saying it is an internal matter among mycologists. Most forayers I know would rather keep right out of it. It seems that one result of the lack of cooperation was the breakdown of the Conservation Forum in 2009. British fungi deserve better than this. One senses reluctance among mycologists to become involved in such disputes. For us, fungi are a welcome form of escape, not an engagement with struggle and argument.

Even so, the conservation of fungi has not been without its small achievements. There is a loose network of people acting as ambassadors for fungi and lichens in the regions. Natural England now has several people who have managed to squeeze more time for fungi into their packed schedules. Until recently, Plantlife had a specialist (Ray Woods) working mainly on fungi and 'lower plants', and mainly in Wales, by organising surveys and defending good sites from roadworks and development. At Kew, the new 'Senior Specialist, Fungi', Martyn Ainsworth, maintains dossiers on our BAP species (now known officially as 'Section 41 species'), surveying their known sites and finding new ones. And in Scotland, a much tighter ship, the formal links between forayers, charity workers and conservation agencies seem to work well.

The last pages of the BMS's book, *Fungal Conservation* (Moore *et al.* 2001), are taken up by the views of mycologists around Britain, Europe and the world on the future of our fungi. Most of them claim to be optimists, none more so than the Chinese professor who is confident that 'the Chinese people will definitely guard, protect and explore the native fungal diversity'. They point out, surely rightly, that more attention is paid to fungi today, and that the role of fungi in ecosystems is more widely understood and appreciated. Current research in molecular systematics and the role of pathogens in the wild is providing exciting new insights into the natural world. Current trends in conservation offer some possibility of remedial action. In some ways, it is a good time to be a mycologist.

On the other hand, most mycologists are less confident about the future of fungi and their habitats than the Chinese professor. As Paul Cannon of CABI Bioscience put it, 'Sustainable exploitation is aspiration rather than the reality.' Professional, field-based mycology is in decline across Europe, and without experts, Eef Arnolds reminded us, 'we shall simply not know what happens to the mycota'. Few believe that the erosion of natural habitats by mismanagement and pollution will not continue. Yet it is human nature to accentuate the positive. As Vincent Fleming of the Joint Nature Conservation Committee (JNCC) put it, 'Optimism does not guarantee success, but to be pessimistic is not to try.'

The protected list

British fungi have two grades of official protection: the Biodiversity Action Plan (BAP) and legal protection under the Wildlife and Countryside Act and its various amendments. Formal protection is the route taken by many European countries to safeguard rare flowers and fungi. It means that they cannot be picked, collected or physically harmed. In Britain, we took the view that fungi are rarely threatened by collecting. It is fungi's habitats that are in the greatest danger, and simply protecting a species is seldom enough since it does not guarantee the protection of their ecosystem or immediate surroundings. Hence, we have turned to the Biodiversity Action Plan as the main tool for conserving rare species *and* their habitats. Planning allows for a much more dynamic approach, although, in practice, some of the plans amount to little more than a call to find out more!

Nevertheless, we did protect formally four species, and their stories are worth telling. At the time, the four were so little known to the public that English names had to be manufactured for them. They were: the Sandy Stiltball *Battarrea phalloides*, the Royal Bolete *Boletus regius*, the

Oak Polypore *Piptoporus quercinus* (under its former name, *Buglossoporus pulvinus*) and the Bearded Tooth *Hericium erinaceus*. Why these and not others? The main points in their favour are that they are easy to identify (or so it was thought) and they all occur in habitats that are under threat. Three of the four grow in parks or open woods with veteran trees, while the fourth occurs on inland sandy commons and waysides. Since they are all large, striking species it seemed unlikely that they had been overlooked. There was some evidence that they had declined, and that protection would help to put things right. For example, it was thought that the edible Royal Bolete and the Bearded Tooth were being targeted by collectors.

Even so, there was obviously a strong element of tokenism about the exercise. It was politically necessary to add a few fungi to the protected list, if only to demonstrate that the Government was carrying out its international commitments. But since its wildlife agencies had no mycologists on their staff, they depended on the advice of the expert body, the BMS. Its then conservation officer, Bruce Ing, told me that the Society had produced a list of 20 or so species for consideration. The decision to whittle it down to just four was taken internally, without any further discussion with mycologists. In other words, it was not a scientific decision but a political one.

Whether official protection made the slightest difference to the fortunes of even these four is debatable. In the one case of proven deliberate damage – the action the law is supposedly there to prevent or punish – the law fell flat on its face (see below, under Sandy Stiltball). Protection did not engender a generous funding of research, nor did it result in better protection for their habitats. If it achieved anything, it was to focus attention, through these particular species, to the plight of fungi generally. In other words, the law in practice is not so much punitive as broadly educational: it reminds people that rare fungi exist, that they too interact with their environment, and that action may be needed in some cases to save them from extinction. That mere protection is not enough to achieve this is now generally acknowledged.

Even so, the Big Four, as we can call them, tell their own tale. Each, in their different ways, is an object lesson on the hazards of choosing species on imperfect evidence. But it also shows the political benefit of drawing attention to a particular fungus, especially when it is of showy and dramatic appearance.

▲ **Sandy Stiltball** *Battarrea phalloides*, a bizarre stalked puffball found on dry banks, sometimes in association with decaying elm stumps.

Sandy Stiltball *Battarrea phalloides*

This is one of our stand-out fungi, a foot-long drumstick of shaggy mycelium bearing a roundish, soon browning, puffball at the top end, and a membranous cup or volva half-buried in the soil at the other. It is the largest of a select group of stalked puffballs, all of which are characteristic of sandy or stony ground (except *Queletia mirabilis*, a probable alien which is known only from heaps of 'spent' bark used by the tanning industry). The recommended English name is now Sandy Stiltball, although the original name, Sandy Stilt Puffball, is retained in law. Because it grows mainly on sandy road verges and banks, this is one of the few species that can be spotted from a car (one new colony, by the busy A12 near Marlesford, Suffolk, was indeed spotted by a driver while waiting at the traffic lights).

When the Sandy Stiltball was first found, on a bank near Bungay, Suffolk, in 1782, what was called 'this extraordinary vegetable production' was new to science. Until it was unhappily renamed *Battarrea* after a now obscure Italian botanist, and so rendered almost impossible to spell, it was known as *Bungea*. The Sandy Stiltball has been found in odd places across southern and eastern England, nearly always on open, dry, sandy soil, often near decaying elm stumps or even inside the crumbling hollow of an elm trunk. There are currently some 30 known sites, nearly half of them in Norfolk or Suffolk. The same species occurs over much of Europe, including the Mediterranean where it may or may not be the same species as the 'donkey fungus' *Battarrea stevenii*. In places, the Sandy Stiltball fruits regularly in the spring as well as late summer and autumn. And since its shaggy stalks are tough and persistent, it can be detected out of season.

As a rare and spectacular 'fungal freak', *Battarrea* was a natural choice when it came to legal protection. This in turn represented a challenge to find out more about it. The Sandy Stiltball now has a 'lead partner' or champion in the Suffolk Wildlife Trust, where Peter Lawson, in particular, has been active in monitoring the known sites and discovering new ones. Exceptionally, it even has its own protected site, dubbed 'Roadside nature reserve no. 162', a section of bank backed by an elm hedge near Melton, and administered by the Suffolk Wildlife Trust.

Alas, the protection offered to the Sandy Stiltball was soon to be tested, and found wanting. One cold November day in 2001, a digger driver set to work on a roadside bank that supported one of the best *Battarrea* colonies in Norfolk. The owner, who wanted to erect a new fence, had made all the right moves. He contacted English Nature, co-operated in drawing up a plan, surrounded the sensitive area with temporary fencing and was careful to brief both the contractor and the driver. Yet despite all that, the digger driver removed the protective fence and proceeded to demolish the site, soil, roots and all. Incriminating photographs were taken and the police informed. It seemed like an open and shut case for prosecution. Unfortunately, the law as it is phrased seems to require proof of a deliberate and malicious attempt to damage the fungus, for example, for financial gain, or through a burning desire to destroy Sandy Stiltballs! Since it was impossible to prove that this was anything other than a case of careless absent-mindedness, a prosecution was unlikely to succeed. The case was therefore dropped. Ignorance, in such cases, seems a perfectly good defence.

However, we do at least know quite a lot about Sandy Stiltballs. It seems to be a rare but characteristic fungus of warm, open, arid places, notably sandy banks, with an overlay of humus. It might not be stretching things too far to characterise it as one of England's inland 'desert fungi'. It is an interesting species, counter-intuitive in its love of dry places, and it is always a thrill to come across a group of them, like crops of giant matchsticks, their dusty heads brown and peeling in the blinking light.

Royal Bolete *Boletus regius*

It is tempting to assume that this bolete was chosen for its good looks. It is gorgeously regal in its ostentatious colours – carmine-red and golden-yellow – and stately proportions. Appropriately, its best-known site had royal connections. What was believed to be the species grew near Windsor Great Park, with its great oaks and noble avenues. The Royal Bolete had appeared regularly since the 1960s around a mature (but not ancient) maiden oak on a bank by a lane in an area noted for rare fungi. There were scattered records elsewhere, all from southern England, including the New Forest, where it was associated with Sweet Chestnut. In central and southern Europe, this a widespread but scarce species associated with warm, open places within broadleaved woodland and parkland.

▼ **Royal Bolete** *Boletus regius*, a rare and beautiful central European species with only one confirmed British record.

There were stories that it was being targeted by mushroom collectors. Ted Green, its discoverer and unofficial guardian at Windsor, found only cut stalks one year, days after the mushroom showed signs of a rare mass fruiting.

As things turned out, the record of Royal Boletes was much confused. Shortly before it was added to the list of protected species, another very similar looking bolete was described from Europe. Its name is *Boletus pseudoregius* – the 'false-royal' bolete, and this fake royal has since been found in England, too. Indeed, it is turning up in more and more places, and seems to be quite widespread in the south. It differs from the Royal Bolete in various details: a cap colour of 'old rose' (that is, a smoky pinkish-brown) instead of carmine, and by a bluing reaction when the flesh is bruised or cut (the true Royal Bolete blues only faintly, if at all). It also occurs in a wider range of habitats, including woods, parks, hedgebanks and, once, a hotel lawn. When I investigated the pair in 1998, on behalf of Plantlife and English Nature, I nicknamed *B. pseudoregius* 'The Pretender', a name that has stuck and now become official.

It was soon apparent that there were far more Pretenders than true Royals. The bulk of the British material named as *Boletus regius*, including the Windsor specimens, has now been examined and redetermined as *B. pseudoregius*. For a while, it seemed questionable whether *B. regius* was a British species at all. However, a specimen collected from Ashurst, in the New Forest, by the Czech-born mycologist Milan Kratochvila, in 1987, was judged to be the real thing. But no one has set eyes on one since, and it is still an open question whether the species survives here.

Oak Polypore *Piptoporus quercinus*

The Oak Polypore has a much more substantial presence in the landscape than the Royal Bolete. It is a bracket fungus, sharing basically the same soft-fleshed, half-moon appearance of the better-known Birch Polypore *Piptoporus betulinus*, but in much richer colours. At first the Oak Polypore is pale and resembles a golf ball. It turns yellowish as the cap expands, and then chestnut brown, with dense white pores which darken with age. By then, in texture and shape, if not in colour, it more closely resembles the Beefsteak Fungus *Fistulina hepatica*, with which it often grows (but this species has red pores and flesh). The Oak Polypore is a summer species: the fruit bodies, appearing singly or in tiered clusters, can be found as early as June. By the time the foray season begins in September most of them are well past their best and have started to rot.

▲ **Oak Polypore**
Piptoporus quercinus, a bracket of over-mature oaks in woods and deer parks.

Early fruiting may be one reason why this fine fungus was rarely recorded. Another was its absence from field guides. Bracket fungi in general fare poorly in books, which have tended to be compiled by experts on agarics, not polypores. The Oak Polypore entered the conservation agenda as a classic species of ancient oak trees, the fungal equivalent of a Stag Beetle. They used to say it was no use looking for it on oaks less than 200 years old. Yet what Oak Polypore requires is not great age *per se*, but rather heartwood exposed or overlain by dead sapwood. Most such trees are, indeed, old and over-mature, but the fungus will fruit on younger trees that have been sawn or otherwise damaged to provide an escape route from the core to the outside. It also fruits on stumps and fallen branches, as well as on standing trunks.

The Oak Polypore was legally protected at a time of intense interest in ancient trees (it was listed under the cumbersome name *Buglossoporus pulvinus*, although taxonomists have since managed to rename it). Back in 1992, the Oak Polypore was regarded as rare and possibly endangered. The known localities were on the twisted spire-oaks of Sherwood Forest, and the plumper, lightning-blasted park oaks of Windsor. But when mycologists started to search for it elsewhere, they found it wherever there were large, open stands of old oak trees. It occurs on park oaks across England, although centred on the south-east and East Anglia. It has turned up as far north as Moffat, Dumfries, and on one

▲ **Bearded Tooth** *Hericium erinaceus*, one of the elegant spiny fungi growing on rotting wood on standing or fallen trees.

of the most famous trees in Wales, the ancient stump of the Curley Oak of Wentwood. Like the Sandy Stiltball, it is now possible to see the Oak Polypore in its true colours, as an old forest fungus that may play an important role in the biology of over-mature oaks. If it is rare, it is only because over-mature oaks themselves are rare.

Bearded Tooth *Hericium erinaceus*

The fourth of our protected species is a strange and beautiful 'toothed bracket', one of the hedgehog fungi that bears its spores on spines instead of pores or gills. In the case of Bearded Tooth, these are very long and resemble stalactites, although they have the texture of cooked bean sprouts. It too grows on over-mature trees and logs, appearing first as a cricket-ball-sized swelling, before taking on the lineaments of a cauliflower and finally sprouting spines. And then the spines grow and grow, becoming longer and thinner until the object it most resembles, as someone pointed out, is the paw of a Polar Bear! The fruit bodies linger several weeks, changing from waxy white to yellowish, like old ivory, in the process. They appear mainly on Beech and oaks, with plenty of dead and rotting wood in their structure. Probably, like Oak Polypore, the fruit bodies appear when an exit route occurs, linking the core of the tree with the outside. Some trees go on producing its fruit bodies year on year for decades, and become known as 'Hericium trees', after the fungus's generic name. It sometimes appears high up on the trunk, requiring binoculars to confirm its identity, but a characteristic micro-habitat is a fissure that exposes the core of the trunk or branch.

The Bearded Tooth was an obvious candidate for protection. It is rare and occurs exclusively on over-mature trees. It looks the part of a relic from the primeval past and so offers some good PR for ancient woodland. Being so large and conspicuous, it could not be wholly overlooked. It ticks most of the right boxes. Yet an even better candidate might have been its relative, the Coral Tooth *Hericium coralloides*, which is even rarer, even more beautiful, and just as closely associated with ancient timbers.

Perhaps the Bearded Tooth's place on the list was also influenced by stories, hard to confirm, that it was being targeted as wild food. It is edible and has the kind of texture that goes well with Chinese food. It has a good flavour, compared by some to chicken, by others to lobster. It is also said, with some biochemical justification, to be good for your health. But there is no need to collect it from the wild. Bearded Tooth is easy to cultivate and is sold in Asian grocery stores, and even in supermarkets. This is where it has acquired most of its many nicknames: 'pom poms', 'lion's mane', 'bear's head', 'old man's beard', and, at least in China, 'monkey head'. But, whether or not it was collected, it was certainly a victim of over-zealous tidying up. In the New Forest, one of its host trees near a busy car park was felled on safety grounds.

▼ **Coral tooth** *Hericium coralloides*, the rarest and most beautiful of our three *Hericium* species.

Table 1 Threatened European fungi
and their habitats proposed for listing under the Berne Convention

*Amanita friabilis** (Fragile Amanita)	Alluvial forest with Alder
Amylocystis lapponica (non-British)	Taiga
Antrodia albobrunnea (non-British)	Taiga and northern coniferous forest
*Armillaria ectypa** (Marsh Honey Fungus)	Alkaline fen and raised bogs
Boletopsis grisea (non-British, Black Falsebolete)	Taiga
*Boletus dupainii** (non-British)	Beech forest on limestone
Bovista paludosa (Fen Puffball)	Alkaline fen
Cantharellus melanoxeros (Blackening Chanterelle)	Beech forest
Cortinarius ionochlorus (non-British)	Holm Oak forest
Entoloma bloxamii (Big Blue Pinkgill)	Calcareous grassland and scrub
Geoglossum atropurpureum (Dark-purple Earthtongue)	Calcareous grassland and scrub
Gomphus clavatus (Pig's Ear)	Montane spruce and Beech forest
Hapalopilus croceus (non-British)	Oak or oak-Hornbeam forest
Hapalopilus odorus (non-British)	Taiga
Hericium erinaceus (Bearded Tooth)	Old oak or Beech forest
*Hohenbuehelia culmicola** (Marram Oyster)	Mobile dunes
Hygrocybe calyptriformis (Pink Waxcap)	Dry grassland and scrub
Hygrophorus purpurascens (non-British)	Montane spruce forest
*Laricifomes officinalis** (non-British, Agarikon)	Montane larch/*Pinus cembra* forest
Leucopaxillus compactus (non-British)	Beech/boreal broadleaved forest
*Lyophyllum favrei** (Gilded Domecap)	Beech forest
Myriostoma coliforme (Pepperpot)	Riparian mixed forest
Phylloporus pelletieri (Golden Gilled Bolete)	Beech or chestnut forest
Podoscypha multizonata (Zoned Rosette)	Beech or oak forest
*Pycnoporellus alboluteus** (non-British)	Herb-rich spruce forest
Sarcodon fuligineoviolaceus (non-British)	Taiga
Sarcosoma globosum (non-British)	Taiga
Sarcosphaera coronaria (Violet Crowncup)	Beech forest
Skeletocutis odora (non-British)	Herb-rich spruce forest
Suillus sibricus ssp. *helveticus* (non-British)	Alpine larch/*Pinus cembra* forest
Torrendia pulchella (non-British)	Cork Oak forest
Tricholoma colossus (Giant Knight)	Pine forest
*Tulostoma niveum** (White Stalkball)	Stony calcareous grassland

▲ **Marsh Honey Fungus** *Armillaria ectypa*.

◀ **White Stalkball** *Tulostoma niveum*.

Subsequent surveys have established that Bearded Tooth is widespread, at a low density, in southern England, appearing most often, perhaps, in the New Forest. Even here, however, it is scarce. Martyn Ainsworth and Alan Lucas found only 12 'fruiting beeches' in the whole Forest during a recent survey. It is another 'old forest' species, rare, spectacular, and with the aura of a survivor from the distant past.

Once, while foraying in the New Forest with the nature photographer Bob Gibbons, I found a magnificent Bearded Tooth, like falling water frozen in ivory, framed by the hollow of a shattered trunk. It was dusk, and light was failing, but Bob was busy fussing around a log on which there was nothing but common fungi. He ignored my calls, and by the time he reached the Bearded Tooth he needed a flashlight. But Bob was right and I was wrong. His shot of *Hericium* was OK but not great (see the opening photograph to this chapter), whilst his fungussy log was a magnificent evocation of autumnal decay that has since appeared in several magazines and books. In the eternal quest for novelty, one should never overlook the commonplace.

The Berne Convention – a false start

Long before we started to protect species of fungi under British law, Britain became a signatory to the 1982 European Convention on Wildlife and Natural Habitats (usually abbreviated to the Berne Convention, from its place of origin). This piece of Euro-shtick obliges us to list threatened habitats and their species, and to promise to do something about them. Although the Berne Convention does not amount to much in practical terms, the list is at least of interest as a pan-European consensus of the species most in danger. Some 33 species were proposed for listing in 2003 (Table 1), but the proposal was unsuccessful. An asterisk indicates that the species is considered to be 'endangered' throughout Europe.

Reddening the data

Traditionally, red is the colour of danger. The boldest of primary colours, it was the obvious choice for post boxes, telephone boxes and road signs, all objects that need to stand out from a distance. By extension, red has also become the colour of danger for wildlife, species that are in the red, so to speak. These are tabulated on 'Red Data Lists' and in 'Red Data Books', which also include documentation of the plight of a species and the basis on which it is included. The ruling spirit of Red Data Lists around the world is the International Union for the

Conservation of Nature (IUCN), founded in 1948, with its headquarters in Geneva. The IUCN sets out the basic criteria of Red-listing, and divides its lists into various risk categories. The reddest of the reds is 'critically endangered', meaning 'on the very brink of catastrophe'. The other categories are, in diminishing order of danger, 'endangered', 'vulnerable' and 'least concern', with separate entries for 'extinct' or 'extinct in the wild' (meaning that the only living examples left are in zoos or gardens). A last category, 'data deficient', means that we have no idea how rare it is. This is the category most appropriate to fungi. Nearly every mushroom species is data deficient.

There are Red Data Lists on all sorts of scales: international, European, British (or English, Scottish, Welsh and Northern Irish), and even at local or county levels. The international Red List is a very gloomy document, full of wonderful animals that everyone knows – whales, elephants, rhinoceroses, big cats, eagles and crocodiles. The national Red Lists, on the other hand, are not widely known outside their parent country, and tend to include much less familiar species. The first British Red Data Book, for wild plants, was published in book form in 1977. It went through various updates, culminating in a magisterial third edition in 1999, which unfortunately went out of date very quickly after the IUCN decided to change the goalposts. Since then, Red Lists have also been published for British bryophytes, stoneworts and lichens.

Non-lichenised fungi are more problematical. Unlike flowering plants, we have only a very imperfect idea of their status and distribution, for field mycologists put most of their intellectual energies into identification. Only recently has there been a co-ordinated national scheme for recording fungi (or, rather, two schemes, since the British Mycological Society and the Association of British Fungus Groups run separate databases). Hence, it is difficult to assess which species are genuinely rare and perhaps declining, and which are merely poorly recorded. Moreover, in the case of fungi, a scarcity of records may mean that a species simply does not fruit very often; it might, for all we know, be quite common underground. Nevertheless, Britain has pledged to produce a Red Data List to assist conservation planning. Certain countries, most notably the Netherlands, West Germany and Poland, where the academic divide between fungi and plants is less absolute than in Britain, have made creditable stabs at producing them (although only the Dutch one has quantitative data to back it up). Elsewhere, the evidence is patchy. Finland, for example, has good data on the polypores, but not on agarics, while such knowledge in Greece and Estonia is restricted to a small number of species of special interest.

▲ **Bruce Ing**, author of the first Red Data List for fungi in Britain (left), and **Ian Evans** searching mossy limestone boulders for the rare White Stalkball *Tulostoma niveum* (see photo page 246).

In Britain, the work of drafting a Red Data List was given to the British Mycological Society, led by its then conservation officer, Bruce Ing. An effort had been made to gather together records of slime moulds ('honorary fungi'), gasteroid fungi and the Xylariacae (candlesnuff fungus and its relatives). Experts on other groups were consulted and the available knowledge pooled. Ing duly produced a long 'provisional list' of 583 species (Ing 1992). It reflected the evidence, in containing a disproportionate number of slime moulds and gasteroids. And it says something about our state of knowledge then that many of the species it tentatively listed as extinct have since turned up alive and well!

No one seemed very happy with this list, but producing a better one took a long time. It was not until 2007 that the BMS produced a revised list of *Threatened British Fungi*, prepared by an inner council of Bruce Ing, Alick Henrici and Shelley Evans (Evans *et al.* 2007). Still modestly described as 'a preliminary assessment', it represents a complete rethink about selection. While including such data as there were on apparent declines, its authors looked at larger fungi in the context of their habitats, reasoning that if the habitat is in trouble, so their dependent fungi must be too. For that reason, many species on this somewhat shorter list of 380 'taxa' are confined to the important and limited habitat of dead wood in mature woodland, especially native pinewoods and undisturbed beechwoods. Fungi confined to comparatively well-recorded habitats such as sand dunes or 'waxcap grasslands' are also well represented. Many of the larger fungi on the new list are conspicuous and easy to recognise, and so, it was reasoned, unlikely to be overlooked. It also includes a surprisingly large number of rusts

Table 2 Fungi for which action plans have been published (as at 2010)

Armillaria ectypa	Marsh Honey Fungus
Battarrea phalloides	Sandy Stiltball
Boletopsis perplexa	Black Falsebolete
Boletus regius	Royal Bolete
Buglossoporus pulvinus (now *Piptoporus quercinus*)	Oak Polypore
Hericium erinaceus	Bearded Tooth
Hygrocybe calyptriformis	Pink Waxcap
Hygrocybe spadicea	Date Waxcap
Hypocreopsis rhododendri	Hazel Gloves
Microglossum olivaceum	Olive Earthtongue
Poronia punctata	Nail Fungus
Stipitate hydnoid fungi (species of *Hydnellum*, *Phellodon* and their relatives)	Hedgehogs
Tulostoma niveum	White Stalkball

▲ **In the conservationists' eye: Oldrose Bolete**
Boletus rhodopurpureus.

► **Blackening Chanterelle**
Cantharellus melanoxeros.

Table 3 **Action plans in preparation** (as at June 2010)

Amanita friabilis	Fragile Amanita
Bankera fuligineoalba	Drab Tooth
Boletus immutatus (=*luridiformis* var. *immutatus*)	Constant Bolete
Boletus pseudoregius	The Pretender
Boletus rhodopurpureus (=*purpureus*)	Oldrose Bolete
Boletus torosus	Brawny Bolete
Bovista paludosa	Fen Puffball
Calocybe onychina	Lilac Domecap
Cantharellus friesii	Orange Chanterelle
Cantharellus melanoxeros	Blackening Chanterelle
Chlorocoeha (=*Chlorociboria*) *versiformis*	Flea's Ear
Chrysomyxa pirolata	Wintergreen Rust
Cotylidia pannosa	Woolly Rosette
Entoloma bloxamii	Big Blue Pinkgill
Geastrum berkeleyi	Berkeley's Earthstar
Geastrum corollinum	Weathered Earthstar
Geastrum elegans	Elegant Earthstar
Geastrum minimum	Tiny Earthstar
Geoglossum atropurpureum	Dark-purple Earthtongue
Gomphus clavatus	Pig's Ear
Hericium coralloides	Coral Tooth
Hohenbuehelia culmicola	Marram Oyster
Hygrophorus pudorinus	Rosy Woodwax
Hypocreopsis lichenoides	Willow Gloves
Lyophyllum favrei	Gilded Domecap
Mycena renati	Beautiful Bonnet
Myriostoma coliforme	Pepperpot
Nyssopsora echinata (=*Puccinia athamanticae*)	Spignel Rust
Pholiota astragalina	Conifer Scalycap
Phylloporus pelletieri	Golden Gilled Bolete
Podoscypha multizonata	Zoned Rosette
Psathyrella caput-medusae	Medusa Brittlestem
Puccinia clintonii	Lousewort Rust
Puccinia physospermi	Bladder-seed Rust
Puccinia scorzonerae	Scorzonera Rust
Puccinia septentrionalis	Alpine Rust
Puccinia thesii	Bastard-toadflax Rust
Sarcodontia crocea	Orchard Toothcrust
Sarcosphaera coronaria	Violet Crowncup
Stephanospora caroticolor	Carroty False Truffle
Stropharia hornemannii	Conifer Roundhead
Tephrocybe osmophora	
Tracya hydrocharidis	Frogbit Smut
Tremella moriformis	Mulberry Brain
Tremellodendropsis tuberosa	Ashen Coral
Tricholoma colossus	Giant Knight
Tricholoma robustum (=*T. focale*)	Robust Knight
Tulostoma melanocyclum	Scaly Stalkball
Urocystis colchici	Colchicum Smut
Urocystis primulicola	Bird's-eye Primrose Smut
Uromyces gentianae	Felwort Smut

and smuts, whose 'habitat' is their host species. In their case, we can be more confident. If, as some are, a rust is restricted to a rare plant such as Jacob's-ladder, Moon Carrot or Great Pignut, then, assuredly, it is in trouble! Wisely, the list excludes recently discovered species, and those whose status is more likely to reflect the lack of specialists than lack of fungi. In keeping with other national lists, it is confined to Great Britain, and excludes the whole of Ireland.

Almost certainly, many more than 380 'taxa' deserve to be there. Unfortunately for most species, especially micro-fungi, the data is extremely 'deficient'. And it was for that reason that the list was not approved by the JNCC. Hence, Britain remains one of the few countries in northern Europe without an official Red List for fungi.

Biodiversity Action

Fungi, in legal terms, are held to be plants, and so fall within the Global Strategy for Plant Conservation to 'halt loss of biodiversity'. This is achieved by means of a Biodiversity Action Plan, or BAP. What is a BAP? Briefly, it is the common means by which the nations of the world have decided to try to save our remaining wild places and their wildlife. It was one of the fruits of the famous United Nations Conference on Environment and Development – better known as the Earth Summit – held at Rio de Janeiro, in 1992. The signatory nations, which of course included Britain, agreed to prepare documents that set out the problems, and to formulate plans to deal with them. These became 'biodiversity action plans'. 'Biodiversity' is one of those cumbersome words that came into vogue through the writings of E O Wilson, an American ecologist and green guru whose well-timed book, *The Diversity of Life*, came out just ahead of the conference. It is really just another way of saying 'the variety of life', but capable of supporting a scientific definition. The purpose of biodiversity planning is to hang on to the natural systems of the world, without compromising our own aspirations towards economic growth and social fulfilment. This is, of course, quite impossible.

Britain's response was a document called *Biodiversity: the UK Action Plan*, published in 1994. It summarised our distinctive variety of life and the actions being taken to conserve it. Much of the content was not new. What it did do, however, was to focus attention on a whole gamut of declining habitats and rare species. This was the first time that a detailed national plan had been made for a wide range of animals, invertebrates, plants and fungi. If a relatively rich country like Great Britain could not save its wildlife, then, as the Government was constantly reminded, we had little hope of aspiring less fortunate nations to do likewise.

The big plan promised a shoal of mini 'action plans' for 116 chosen species (selected from a long list of 1,200). For each one, a 'partner' or 'champion' would be found to take the lead. The first BAP listed 27 species of fungi (not counting lichens), each of which was allocated a 'lead partner', which might be a charity such as Plantlife, or a learned society such as the BMS, an institution such as Kew, or some other body with relevant expertise. By 2007, the list had grown to 76 species. Devolution of nature conservation has led to separate lists for Scotland, Wales and Northern Ireland.

The process was slow to gather steam, but, as Vincent Fleming, who managed the process within the Joint Nature Conservation Committee, pointed out, without the BAP 'the claim of fungi on the resources of the statutory conservation agencies' would have been even less (Fleming 2001). Action plans were duly prepared for Devil's Bolete *Boletus satanas*, Sandy Stiltball *Battarrea phalloides*, Nail Fungus *Poronia punctata* and White Stalkball *Tulostoma niveum*, and were published in 1995. More species were added over the following years, including a joint plan for most of the British species of stipitate hydnoid (hedgehog fungi). Recently, yet more species have been added to the list through improvements in recording and monitoring fungi (see Table 3).

The individual plans, which tend to be formulaic, often amount in practice to little more than pleas for more information. Their significance lies in the welcome reminder that fungi, too, are in need of conservation. The BAP has raised the profile of fungi and brought them within the conservation agenda for the first time. They now have, in Fleming's words, 'a priority, momentum and resource commitment... It is up to mycologists', he adds, 'to make the most of the opportunities that have been presented to us.' No doubt they will, but some mycologists are still uncertain about the wisdom of focusing on species. Quite simply, there are too many of them, and it threatens to miss the point. Fungi require a much broader approach. After all, if the processes that support plant growth and soil fertility were to break down, it would not be much comfort to reflect that we managed to save the White Stalkball.

The Satanic and the Sweet: a bolete and a honey fungus

To provide details of the work to date on each of the BAP species would be tedious since, in most cases, they repeat the same kind of action. Field workers, generally amateur mycologists, keep records of where each species has been found, and in what quantity, and try to obtain at least an inkling of their ecology – and all on a minimal amount of funding. In most cases, it is still very much a matter of work in progress. I will therefore restrict this account to two species, one a bolete and the other an agaric, where some interesting results have been obtained – if not those that were necessarily anticipated.

The Devil's Bolete *Boletus satanas* is a charismatic fungus, lurid both in its colours and its reputation as a poisoner – I like the frequency with which it fronts reports and books, most recently on the jacket of the *Collins Fungi Guide* (2012). In folklore, the Devil wore scarlet, and, appropriately enough, when young this bolete has pores of a rich vermilion with a crimson network of veins over its obese, turnip-like trunk. It blushes even redder when bruised. The Devil was also believed to have serious body-odour problems, and this bolete, too, has a putrid smell when over-ripe, reminiscent of carrion, or, in the opinion of another cautious sniffer, of rotting carpets (though one may need to let the fungus swelter indoors for a few hours for the full effect). To cap it all, this can be one of our largest boletes. The bulging hemispheres of its pale caps might remind those with a Gothic imagination of bleached human skulls, half hidden in the grass.

The reason why this uncommon bolete was named after Satan seems to have lain in the imagination of the German mycologist Harald Othmar Lenz, who claimed to have been made ill by its evil 'emanations' when he described the species in 1831. Suitably enough, this is the only British bolete known to be dangerously poisonous. There used to be a mystery about this, for no toxin had been detected in its crimson bulk, and the Devil's Bolete was even said to be gathered as food in parts of eastern Europe. Knowing this, the mycologist at the Natural History Museum, John Ramsbottom, was tempted to test its edibility during a foray at Blenheim Park, Oxfordshire. At home time, the rest of the party waited a long time by the bus before a green-faced Ramsbottom came into view, helped on his way by an anxious fellow mycologist. He had, it seemed, been quickly and abundantly sick. Only recently was the chemical origin of its devilry discovered. *B. satanas* contains quantities of a glycoprotein called bolesatine. Like the toxins in the Deathcap, it inhibits the body's ability to synthesise protein. When fed to mice, the result was liver damage and thrombosis. When eaten accidentally by someone in Ireland recently, the reported symptoms were heavy sweating, increased heart rate, vomiting and 'first degree heart block'. Altogether, its reputation seems justified.

In September 2001, this bolete inspired a cartoon in *The Times* by Peter Brook, comparing Osama bin Laden, in his white turban, with the devilish mushroom. Brook's boletus, *Osama binladena*, wears an evil grin, with a dagger in its teeth. It hangs out with Death Caps *Talebanus terroris*, and its toxins provoke violent reactions as they spread through the body politic. In one corner, Uncle Sam delivers a powerful kick in the boletus. The picture was apparently snapped up by Jeffery Archer, for his collection.

The Devil's Bolete seemed an obvious candidate for the BAP. Although a famous and charismatic species, there were only two recent field records on file, and it was consequently assumed to be in serious decline. Moreover, it was believed to be rare over most of its European range. But in fact there were many more sightings that had not yet been centralised on the fledgling fungal records database. In 1997, Plantlife, as the Devil's Bolete's designated 'lead partner', and English Nature, as

▼ **Not so rare after all: Devil's Bolete** *Boletus satanas.*

the funding body, hired me to investigate its known status and distribution. By a happy coincidence, August and September 1997 proved to be an exceptionally good season for rare boletes in central southern England. Aided by tip-offs from fellow mycologists, I managed to track down the Devil's Bolete in several locations in Oxfordshire and Hampshire, and received reports from many other places, from the Welsh Borders to Kent. The Devil's Bolete, it transpires, is not very rare at all, but a rather characteristic fungus of open woodland, parkland and even open down on chalk and limestone. It likes warm places, especially on banks where multiple fruit bodies nestle among the snaking roots of Beech trees. Like so many fungi, its rarity may be due to shyness of fruiting, not lack of habitat.

Our second species is the Marsh Honey Fungus *Armillaria ectypa*. This smallish, yellow-brown mushroom differs from the better-known honey fungus of gardens and woods in having no stem ring and its habitat of wetland. The most remarkable thing about it is that the Marsh Honey Fungus glows faintly in damp, warm conditions. It may possibly be the cause of some of the sightings of 'will-o'-the-wisps' – mysterious, spooky lights seen in marshy places. But the reason for its inclusion within the BAP list is that it grows within a rare and diminishing habitat: calcareous fen (and, in mainland Europe at least, in *Sphagnum* bogs). It helped, also, that the Marsh Honey Fungus is a recently discovered species. In Britain it was first found at Sunbiggin Tarn, in the Pennines, during a BMS foray in 1995. Since then, it has turned up at Ffrwd Fen, near Pembrey, South Wales, in 2002, on the Garron plateau, Antrim, also in 2002, and in Scotland's Insh Marshes in 2005 – a remarkably neat, if baffling distribution, with just one site in each country. It may also have occurred at Minsmere, the RSPB's famous nature reserve on the coast of Suffolk. Unfortunately, we will probably never know for sure because it grew in a fringe of reeds that was drowned to create pools for birds, and no material was preserved. Bitterns are obviously much higher in the conservation pecking order than small brown fungi, even if they do glow in the dark.

As it happens, all the sites for Marsh Honey Fungus are SSSIs (or the Irish equivalent), and all are of botanical interest. Interestingly, each one has a rare flower growing nearby. At Sunbiggin it is the Bird's-eye Primrose *Primula farinosa*, at Ffrwd Fen the Marsh Pea *Lathyrus palustris*, and at the Insh Marshes the String Sedge *Carex chordorrhiza*, while on the Garron plateau it grows near Ireland's only patch of the rare Marsh

Saxifrage *Saxifraga hirculus*. Yet each of these habitats is different. One is in reeds among lime-rich springs, another a coastal reedbed, another a fen dominated by sedges, and the last one a calcareous flush. Evidently, in Britain at least, the mushroom seems to be fairly adaptable. It is hard to believe it is as rare as the paucity of records suggest.

The Marsh Honey Fungus is about as well protected as any fungus can be. And yet we know almost nothing about it. We do not know what it feeds on. We do not know how it has managed to colonise places so far apart, or how it competes for resources, or why it may fruit in good numbers one year and not the next. The basis for any meaningful 'action' is lacking. All that can be done is to preserve the integrity of its existing sites. There is nothing unusual about that, for the same thing could be said for nearly every rare fungus on the list. Behind the grand-sounding plans, strategies and lists lays a forest of question marks.

The times they are a-changing

Alick Henrici, one of our leading field mycologists, once noted that, with fungi, most years are 'worse than average'. Only one year in about five produces a bumper crop that puts other years in the shade. True enough: in my part of the world there have been two in the past ten – 2004 and 2006. The latter was the best, producing in some places what the French call a *cepage* – a vista of mushrooms carpeting the woodland floor. Even 2004, which began well, was killed in its tracks by early frosts. For the rest, 2003 was too dry, while 2007 and 2008 were too wet. In 2009, another strange season, agarics were at their best in mid-November, by which time many of us had given up (and the low light makes finding them more difficult). The opposite was the case in 2010 – an early fruiting in August and September, and closing for the season in mid-October. While one part of the country may be experiencing a fungal drought, another might be enjoying super-abundance. So it was in 2008. In Wiltshire the season was a washout, but 900km away, in the Grampian region, the birchwoods and pinewoods were burgeoning with fungi.

Are the seasons growing less predictable? In recent years we have experienced some wild swings, from bare dusty soil to puddles everywhere, and no mushrooms in either. On forays in the 1970s you could look forward with confidence to finding enough to sustain one's interest, at least during the peak time. But even then there were sudden shifts from one year to the next, such as the bountiful early autumn of 1976 followed by a very dull season, as though the fungi were exhausted. In the past there were relatively short seasons with a progression of different fungi, starting with species of *Agaricus*, *Amanita*, *Russula* and *Lactarius*, reaching a peak in early October, following onwards to the fag end of the season with troops of Clouded Funnel, Wood Blewit and other late fungi. Nowadays, the season is usually longer and the progression has become blurred. Warmer summers followed by wetter autumns cause many species to fruit earlier than they once did, whilst late-season species are fruiting even later. In mild winters you often find plenty of fungi in the run-up to Christmas. A common mushroom such as the Fly Agaric may appear in June and continue as late as November. In the 1950s, as we know from mycologists' notebooks, the season for fungi lasted about a month. The average has more than doubled now to 75 days. This could be seen as good news, in the sense that the foray season is longer, but your chances of finding lots of fungi at peak times might be less.

▼ Getting earlier: St George's Mushroom *Calocybe gambosa.*

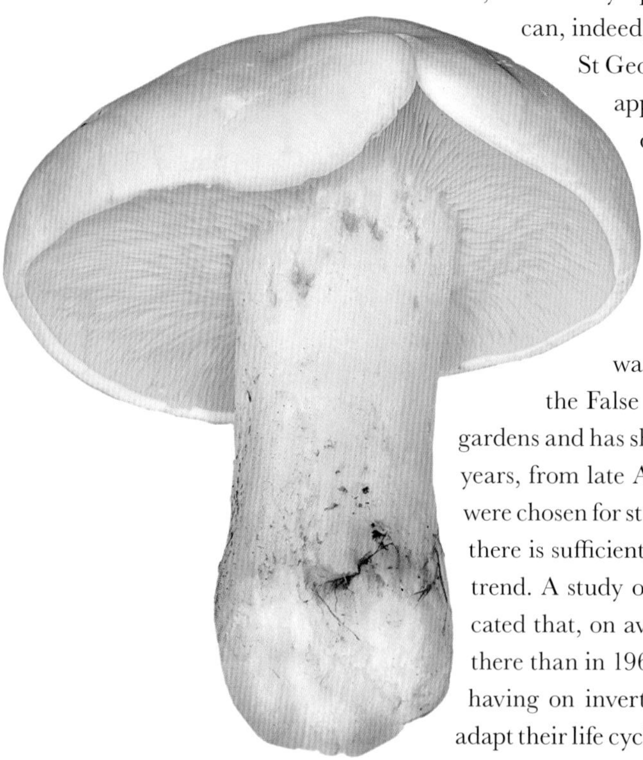

The spring season, too, is starting earlier. St George's Mushroom *Calocybe gambosa* is named after St George's Day, 23rd April, but the saint's day usually came and went without any mushrooms. In the 1970s, it normally appeared around mid-May, yet today you can, indeed, regularly find St George's Mushroom on St George's Day, or even earlier. Morels, too, are appearing earlier. In the 1950s, the average date of first appearance was 13th May, but today it is 3rd April, a shift of 40 days. This impressive time-shift may be due in part to gardens, which tend to be slightly warmer than the surrounding countryside (and where morels also turn up on warm beds of woodchip). But another species, the False Morel *Gyromitra esculenta*, rarely occurs in gardens and has shown an even greater shift over the past 20 years, from late April to as early as February. These fungi were chosen for study because they are easy to recognise and there is sufficient data, but no doubt they indicate a broad trend. A study of spring-fruiting records in Norway indicated that, on average, fungi were fruiting 18 days earlier there than in 1960. One wonders what impact this may be having on invertebrates that depend on fungi. Can they adapt their life cycles accordingly, or will they go hungry?

We know about such things only because of meticulous record keeping by amateur naturalists. Ted Gange and Jim Handley, members of the Salisbury and District Natural History Society, have meticulously documented their encounters with fungi over half a century. Their data – around 52,000 fruiting records of fungi from 1,400 localities – was picked over by a scientific team from Cardiff University, with interesting results. Apart from the increase in the length of the growing season, species that used to fruit only in autumn now sometimes also appear in spring, suggesting increased decay rates in forest soils. The extended season is particularly noticeable in artificial habitats such as compost heaps and woodchip mulch, which are now rotting down at a much faster rate than before. Trees, too, are coming into leaf earlier (though not always; after the long cold winter of 2010, oak in particular was notably late). This may well be due in part to the increased activity by the fungi in their roots.

Fungi have the ability to spread very quickly when conditions are right, and one might expect to see some species moving northwards as the climate warms, in much the same way as well-recorded butterflies and dragonflies. This seems to be happening. *Perenniporia ochroleuca*, a small, thickset, pored bracket first recorded on the Channel Islands in 1999, has since turned up on the mainland coast in England and South Wales. This is a Mediterranean species that seems to be sensitive to frost, and so is likely to take advantage of warmer winters. The same may be true of Yellowing Curtain Crust *Stereum subtomentosum*, a shapeless, yellowish crust-fungus, which is increasing in Britain. Another possible chancer is the bracket fungus *Phellinus wahlbergii*, first found on the rootplate of a fallen oak at Langley Park, Buckinghamshire, in 2007 and subsequently in other places in southern England. A subtropical species, its nearest known station is the Canary Islands. The reported spread of Devil's Fingers *Clathrus archeri*, the smelly squid-fungus from Australia, has also been linked to climate change (although the widespread use of woodchip mulch may have something to do with it). Bearded Amanita *Amanita ovoidea*, another spectacular Mediterranean species, may be a recent colonist, or it may be long-established; it has been restricted to the same small corner of the Isle of Wight for many years.

Milder winters and early springs must mean greater rates of decay in the soil. Unfortunately, it is also good news for fungal scourges such as the Cereal Rust *Puccinia graminis* and various root-rots of trees. The powdery mildew *Microsphaera alphitoides* that is found on oak seedlings and on the foliage of the tree in late summer is much more common than it was. In the past, the mildew rarely produced fruit bodies, but today it is hard to find any without them. The recent increase in so many silvicultural and horticultural 'diseases' caused by fungi (or former fungi such as *Phytophthora*) has complex causes, among which the lack of sufficient controls on plant or timber imports is certainly one. But it is hard not to assume that mild winters allow them to flourish in the wild as never before.

Has the changing climate resulted in the corresponding decrease in some fungi? It is still too early to say. One might guess that some fungi are facing increased competition, and that some alpine species may be suffering from lack of snow (up until 2009, at any rate). Prolonged drought has been blamed for the recent low harvests of truffles in Europe. In only one case so far, and that a non-British species, can climate change be linked directly to an observed decline. This is a little cup fungus called *Lachnellula pini*, which forms orange cups surrounded by a pretty fringe of hair on the bark of Scots Pine. It infects the tree through damage caused by the settling and creeping of snow. Assuming that long-lying snow is essential to its prospects, as its European distribution suggests, one might expect it to be vulnerable to winter warming. We know this much only because *Lachnellula* causes a canker on pines and so has been investigated as a potential pest, not as a species of conservation concern! The truth is that although climate change is a hot topic, its impact on fungi, and the knock-on effect on the British mycota are still not understood. Barring a generous allocation of research funds, we can only wait, watch, and see.

The way forward?

Everyone, nowadays, seems to need a strategy. In autumn 2008, Plantlife published one on fungi on behalf of the Fungus Conservation Forum. With the stimulating title of *Saving the Forgotten Kingdom* (Plantlife 2008), it is thoughtfully and accessibly written, with a minimum of jargon. In the way of conservation strategies, it sets out a framework with five main themes (which it calls 'visions'), followed by a set of targets and an outline of the action needed to achieve each one. For example, the Forum believes that important sites for fungi should be safeguarded by a combination of research, a review of land-management policies and more official protection. In his enthusiastic foreword, Tim Smit, the rock journalist turned Eden Project impre-

sario, notes that, in the case of fungi, the hackneyed phrase 'joined-up thinking' is more appropriate than usual. Fungi, he reminds us, are the 'plumbing systems' that interconnect natural habitats, the out-of-sight threads of matter that keep life on a steady course and protect biodiversity. Kill the fungi, for example by throwing chemical fertiliser all over the meadow, and diversity collapses. This is in no one's interests, except the most shortsighted farmer.

Smit and the Forum hope that a better understanding of the vital role of fungi will eventually bring about a new agrarian revolution, where we will work with the grain of nature instead of confronting it at every turn. Fungi will be transformed from 'the Widow Twankies [to] the Prince Charmings of a new order'. At the same time, we also want to conserve fungi for the same reason that we try to conserve birds and butterflies: because they are beautiful and interesting, because they inspire the human imagination, and because some of them may turn out to be rather useful. Besides which, Britain has international obligations. We are part of an interconnected world and have signed commitments on the protection of wildlife.

Saving the Forgotten Kingdom is an unofficial document, with no force in law or statute. It represents the reflections and discussions of the Fungus Conservation Forum, a loose association of experts, conservation land managers and representatives from wildlife charities that came together once or twice a year to talk fungi. The expertise behind the document was supplied mainly by the British Mycological Society, by professional mycologists at Kew and CABI Bioscience, and by individual field mycologists. The strategy, says Plantlife 'is necessarily ambitious in its scope'. It wants to see results by 2015 at the latest.

It is no criticism of *Saving the Forgotten Kingdom* to point out that it is more of a summary of what is happening already than a manifesto of new and radical ideas. Objective number one is to understand and document fungal diversity, for example by publishing distribution data, producing a Red Data List that we can all stand by, and also publishing checklists of fungi other than the Basidiomycota. This is the kind of thing that we take for granted in other groups, but for fungi the instant stumbling block is lack of knowledge. Mycologists are notorious for disagreeing among themselves about the minutiae, while steadily ignoring practical needs. But the greater cause of our present woeful ignorance is too little money (or, if one prefers, 'resources'), and too few experts. As I have said before (many times, I fear), Britain's professional mycological establishment, always small, is dwindling.

That links us to objective number two, 'conserving fungal diversity', that is, protecting species and their wild habitats. The mechanisms for doing so, namely nature reserves and SSSIs, exist but, in the case of fungi, are not applied. The Forum hopes that important sites for fungi ('Important Fungus Areas') will not only be properly documented and published, but also 'managed in a sympathetic manner'. Identifying such places might be achievable, but the government bodies charged with protecting our wild places have so far shown no enthusiasm for enlarging the present network of SSSIs. Their lack of enthusiasm presumably has a political basis. Perhaps Government feels that there are enough SSSIs already.

Objective three is about sustainability, and ensuring that we do not over-exploit the harvest. The Forum calls for more research into the effects of commercial collecting, and the enforcement of good practice. Although the Forum is clearly worried about the implications of harvesting edible and useful wild fungi, it places its faith in goodwill and the acceptance of guidelines and 'codes of conduct', such as the existing one proposing that we limit our collections to a kilogram or two. No new legislation is proposed.

Objective four addresses education and the importance of persuading everyone that fungi really do matter. 'Society needs to be well informed and able to make wise choices,' urges the Forum. In other words, we need public support for what we do. The public, in this sense, includes landowners and managers, policy-makers and politicians. The only way of achieving the 'embedding' of fungi in our environmental consciousness is to keep plugging away, making the best of media opportunities, hosting high-profile events, and in general banging on about fungi on all possible occasions. One obvious obstacle in the way of this vision is that fungi are nothing like as empathetic or visually exciting as, say, Otters or Swallows. In the media, they seldom merit much more than a late-season nod as part of the backcloth of autumn. Here, as elsewhere, conservationists face an uphill task.

Finally, the strategy addresses 'building capacity'. Although mycology has made some strides in recent times, expertise remains thin on the ground. Without any full-time mycologists on their staff (at least until 2009, when Martyn Ainsworth was employed by Kew with part-funding for three years from Natural England), the agencies are not, the Forum implies, honouring their commitment to safeguarding all biodiversity. 'With no funding available and very little notice', the voluntary bodies have had to provide for themselves. This must change, insists the Forum. The business is in need of radical improvement at every level, not least among field mycologists and conservation bodies. The Forum also suggests some sort of apprenticeship scheme to ensure that there will be younger mycologists to fill the boots of an ageing population. That, presumably, would be the responsibility of universities, but at present mycology (as opposed to applied mycology in the food processing and pharmaceutical industries) is in decline, with fewer and fewer universities offering a course.

And that is where we must leave it. In 2011, the conservation of wild fungi did not lack paper. The amount of reports, plans and strategies would fill a great many filing cabinets. We still lack some of the basic tools of the trade: a creditable Red Data List, for example. We lack nature reserves where the conservation of fungi is a priority. Funding is still modest, irregular and problematic. And we lack the means to do anything about fundamental influences on fungi, such as the slow, insidious increase in soil fertility as a result of air- and water-borne nitrogen pollution. Even so, compared with even ten years ago, we are not doing too badly. More people care about fungi than ever before. They buy books and field guides, contribute to blogs and websites, attend popular forays and even try wild eco-foraging. The National Trust and other bodies are thrilled to learn that attractive mushrooms grow on their lawns and in their gardens, and do their best to conserve them. We have come to agree that fungi, and especially large fungi, are things to cherish.

I hope this book has given you at least an inkling of why this is so, of why mushrooms are exciting and worth bothering about. I hope it has also given you a sense of the fun in fungi: their wild, beautiful and bizarre shapes, their dark and capricious nature, the pleasures of finding, studying and devouring them. They take us back to our foraging roots, show us wild places we might not have noticed, and hint at ways of life beyond our imaginings and experience. They have given me pleasure for nearly 50 years, and will, I hope, for a few more decades to come. Mushies, as someone said, are magic. Let them cast their spell on you just once, and life will never be quite the same again.

References
and further reading

Ainsworth, M 2003 Report on the marsh honey fungus, *Armillaria ectypa*, a UK BAP species. *English Nature Research Reports, No. 540*. English Nature, Peterborough

Ainsworth, M 2005 Identifying important sites for beechwood deadwood fungi. *Field Mycology* 6(2): 41-61

Allison, M 2001 The conservation of fungi on reserves managed by the Royal Society for the Protection of Birds (RSPB). In: D Moore, M Nauta, S Evans, & M Rotheroe (eds) *Fungal Conservation: Issues and Solutions*, 144-155. Cambridge University Press

Anon 2009 Root fungi turn rock into soil. *Planet Earth*, Autumn 2009

Aron, C 2005 *Fungi of Northwest Wales. A mycota of the vice-counties of Merionethshire, Caernarvonshire and Anglesey.* Self-published

Arora, D 1986 *Mushrooms demystified: a comprehensive guide to the fleshy fungi.* Ten Speed Press, Berkeley, California

Arora, D 2001 Wild mushrooms and rural economies. In: D Moore, M Nauta, S Evans, & M Rotheroe (eds) *Fungal Conservation: Issues and Solutions*, 105-110. Cambridge University Press

Arnolds, E 1988 The changing macromycete flora in the Netherlands. *Trans. British Mycological Society* 90: 391-406

Arnolds, E 1989 The influence of increased fertilisation on the macrofungi of a sheep meadow. *Opera Botanica* 100: 7-21

Baker, T 1990 The word 'toadstool' in Britain. *The Mycologist* 4(1): 25-29

Bakker, H C den, & Noordeloos, M E 2005 A revision of European species of *Leccinum* Gray and notes on extralimital species. *Persoonia* 18: 511-587

Bas, C, Kuyper, T W, Noordeloos, M E, & Vellinga, E C 1990 *Flora Agaricina Neerlandica. Vol. 2: Pleurotaceae, Pluteaceae & Tricholomotaceae I.* CRC Press/Balkema, Rotterdam

BBC News 2011 www.bbc.co.uk/news/uk-walews-south-east-12175281. For background. see: wikipedia.org/wiki/Llanishen_Reservoir

Boddy, L, & Coleman, M (eds) 2010 *From Another Kingdom. The amazing world of fungi.* Royal Botanic Garden, Edinburgh

Boertmann, D 1995 *The genus* Hygrocybe. *Fungi of Northern Europe, Volume 1.* Danish Mycological Society

Bowen, H 2000 *The Flora of Dorset.* Pisces Publications, Newbury

Cannon, P F, Hawksworth, D L, & Sherwood-Pike, M A 1985 *The British Ascomycotina. An annotated checklist.* Commonwealth Mycological Institute, Kew

Cannon, P, *et al.* 2001 Microscopic Fungi. In: D Hawksworth (ed) *The Changing Wildife of Great Britain and Ireland*, 114-125. Taylor & Francis, London

Clarke, M C (ed)1980 *A Fungus Flora of Warwickshire.* British Mycological Society

Coppins, A M, Coppins, B, & Quelch, P 2002 Atlantic hazelwoods. Some observations on the ecology of this neglected habitat from a lichenological perspective. *British Wildlife* 14: 17-26

Crawley, M J 2005 *The Flora of Berkshire.* Brambleby Books, Harpenden

Cundall, R D 1998 The meaning of the Latin/Greek names of some larger fungi. *North-west Fungus Group Newsletter* May 1998

Dennis, R W G 1960 *British Cup Fungi and their allies.* Ray Society, London

Dennis, R W G 1986 *Fungi of the Hebrides.* Royal Botanic Gardens, Kew

Dennis, R W G 1995 *Fungi of South East England.* Royal Botanic Gardens, Kew

Dickson, G, & Leonard, A 1996 *Fungi of the New Forest – A Mycota.* British Mycological Society

Evans, S, Henrici, A, & Ing, B 2007 *Red Data List of Threatened British Fungi.* British Mycological Society website, www.britmycolsoc.org

Feest, A 2000 The assessment of the fungal value of sites for conservation. *The Mycologist* 14: 14-15

Findlay, W P K 1967 *Wayside and Woodland Fungi.* Warne, London

Findlay, W P K 1982 *Fungi: Folklore, fiction & fact.* Richmond Publishing

Fleming, L V 2001 Fungi and the UK Biodiversity Action Plan: the process explained. In: D Moore, M Nauta, S Evans, & M Rotheroe (eds) *Fungal Conservation: Issues and Solutions*, 209-218. Cambridge University Press

Fortey, R 2000 Old churchyards as fungal conservation areas. *Field Mycology* 1(4): 121-124

Gilbert, O 2004 *The Lichen Hunters.* Book Guild, Sussex

Griffith, G W, Easton, G L, & Jones, A W 2002 Ecology and diversity of waxcap (Hygrocybe species) fungi. *Botanical Journal of Scotland* 54: 7-22

Griffith, G W, Bratton, J H, & Easton, G 2004 Charismatic megafungi: the conservation of waxcap grasslands. *British Wildlife* 14: 31-43

Hall, I *et al.* 2003 *Edible and Poisonous Mushrooms of the World.* Timber Press, USA

Harding, P 2008 *Collins Mushroom Miscellany.* Collins, London

Harrington, T 2001 Fungi in the Burren. *Field Mycology* 2(1): 30-33

Hay, W D 1887 *An Elementary Text-book of British Fungi.* S Sonnenschein, Lowry, London

Heilmann-Clausen, J, Verbeken, A, & Vesterholt, J 1998 *The genus* Lactarius. Fungi of Northern Europe, Volume 2. Danish Mycological Society

Henrici, A 2005 Notes & Records. *Field Mycology* 6(4): 139

Henrici, A 2008 *Guepenia helvelloides* revisited. Notes & Records. *Field Mycology* 9(1): 28-30

Henrici, A 2009 Notes & Records. *Field Mycology* 10(3): 107

Henrici, A 2010 Notes & Records. *Field Mycology* 11(3): 108-9

Holden, E M (ed) 2003 *List of Recommended English Names for Fungi.* Plantlife International

Holden, E M 2006 Putting fungi on the map: a new name and outlet for the BMS Fungal Records Database. *Field Mycology* 7(4): 133-34

Holden, E M 2006 Fungi. In: P Shaw, & D Thompson (eds) *The Nature of the Cairngorms. Diversity in a changing environment* 145-194. Scottish Natural Heritage

Ing, B 1992 A provisional Red Data List of British Fungi. *Mycologist* 6(3): 124-128

Ing, B 1999 *The Myxomycetes of Britain and Ireland.* An identification handbook. Richmond Publishing, Slough

Ingold, C T 1975 *Guide to Aquatic Hyphomycetes.* Freshwater

Biological Association, Ambleside
Ingram, D, & Robertson, N 1999 *Plant Disease. A natural history.* New Naturalist No. 85 Collins, London
Jordan, M 2004 (2nd ed) *The Encyclopaedia of Fungi of Britain & Europe.* Francis Lincoln, London
Kibby, G 2000 A user-friendly key to the genus *Leccinum* in Great Britain. *Field Mycology* 1(1): 20-29
Kibby, G, Burnham, A, & Henrici, A 2010 Some problems in the genus *Pluteus*. *Field Mycology* 11(3): 93-100
Kibby, G 2011 Editorial. *Field Mycology* 12(1): 2
Kibby, G 2011 *British Boletes with keys to species.* Self-published, Geoffrey Kibby
Knudsen, H, & Vesterholt, J (2nd ed) 2008 *Funga Nordica.* CD set. Nordsvamp
Koestler, A 1968 *Drinkers of Infinity: Essays 1955-1967.* Hutchinson, London
Lannoy, A, & Estades, A 1995 *Monographie des Leccinum d'Europe.* Mycologique Dauphine-Savoie
Lawrynowicz, M 2001 Threats to hypogeous fungi. In: D Moore, M Nauta, S Evans, & M Rotheroe (eds) *Fungal Conservation: Issues and Solutions*, 95-104. Cambridge University Press
Legon, N, & Henrici, A 2005 *Checklist of the British & Irish Basidiomycota.* Royal Botanic Gardens, Kew
Levin, A 2010 The deadly dish that poisoned our lives. *Mail on Sunday*, 5th September 2010
McHugh, R, Mitchel, D, Wright, M, & Anderson, R 2001 The fungi of Irish grasslands and their value for nature conservation. *Biology and Environment: Proc. Royal Irish Academy*, 101B(3): 225-242
Marren, P 1997 *The Devil's Bolete,* Boletus satanus. Unpublished Plantlife Back from the Brink report. Plantlife, London
Marren, P 1998 *The Royal Bolete and the Pretender,* Boletus regius *and* Boletus pseudoregius. Unpublished Plantlife report
Marren, P 2000 *Stipitate Hydnoid Fungi in England.* English Nature Research Report No. 420. English Nature, Peterborough
Marren, P 2006 The 'global fungal weeds': the toadstools of wood-chip beds. *British Wildlife* 18: 98-105
Marren, P, & Dickson, G 2000 British tooth-fungi and their conservation. *British Wildlife* 11: 401-409
Mattock, G 2002 Fungi upon other fungi grow: Britain's parasitic toadstools. *British Wildlife* 14: 117-22
Mattock, G 2006 A quest for British *Amanita ovoidea* fulfilled. *Field Mycology* 7(1): 9-12
Mattock, G, Gange, A C, & Gange, E C 2007 Spring fungi are fruiting earlier. *British Wildlife* 18: 267-272
Merryweather, J 2001 Meet the Glomales – the ecology of mycorrhiza. *British Wildlife* 13: 86-93
Money, N P 2002 *Mr Bloomfield's Orchard: The mysterious world of mushrooms, molds and mycologists.* Oxford University Press
Moore, D, Nauta, M, Evans, S, & Rotheroe, M 2001 *Fungal Conservation: Issues and solutions.* Cambridge University Press
Moore, D *et al.* 2001 Fungal conservation in the 21st century: optimism and pessimism for the future. In: D Moore, M Nauta, S Evans, & M Rotheroe (eds) *Fungal Conservation: Issues and Solutions*, 247-255. Cambridge University Press
Murray, J S 1974 The fungal pathogens of oak. In: M G Morris & F H Perring (eds) *The British Oak*, 235-249. BSBI & Eric Classey, Faringdon
Orton, P D 1986 *British Fungus Flora, 4, Pluteaceae: Pluteus & Volvariella.* Royal Botanic Garden, Edinburgh
Overall, A 2010 Fungi Royale. Some interesting larger fungi of the Royal Parks – Part 1. *Field Mycology* 11(3): 101-04
Pegler, D, Spooner, B, & Young, T W K 1993 *British Truffles. A revision of the hypogeous fungi.* Royal Botanic Gardens, Kew
Pegler, D, Laessoe, T, & Spooner, S 1995 *British puffballs, earthstars and stinkhorns. An account of the British gasteroid fungi.* Royal Botanic Gardens, Kew
Pegler, S, Roberts, P, & Spooner, S 1997 *British Chanterelles and Tooth Fungi.* Royal Botanic Gardens, Kew
Pilz, D, Lorelei, N, Danell, E, & Molina, R 2003 *Ecology and management of commercially harvested chanterelle mushrooms.* US Department of Agriculture, Forest Service, Pacific Northwest Research Station
Plantlife 2001 *Important Fungus Areas. A provisional assessment of the best sites for fungi in the United Kingdom.* Plantlife, London
Plantlife 2003 *Recommended English names for fungi in the UK.* Plantlife, Salisbury
Plantlife 2008 *Saving the Forgotten Kingdom. A Strategy for the Conservation of the UK's Fungi: 2008-2015.* Plantlife International, Salisbury
Ramsbottom, J 1953 *Mushrooms and Toadstools.* Collins New Naturalist, London
Rayner, A 1993 The fundamental importance of fungi in woodlands. *British Wildlife* 4: 205-215
Roberts, P 2009 Wildlife reports: fungi. *British Wildlife* 20: 293-294
Roberts, P 2010 Wildlife reports: fungi. *British Wildlife* 22: 63-64
Rotheroe, M 1995 Saving an historic lawn. *The Mycologist* 9: 106-109
Rotheroe, M 1998 Wild fungi and the controversy over collecting for the pot. *British Wildlife* 9: 349-356
Rotheroe, M 2000 *Vernacular names for fungi.* Unpublished paper for the British Mycological Society
Smith, W G 1867 *British edible and poisonous fungi.* Hardwicke, London
Spooner, B, & Roberts, P 2005 *Fungi.* Collins New Naturalist, London
Thompson, R 2000 *The Somerset Grassland Fungi Project 1997-1999.* Somerset Environmental Records Centre, Taunton
Venturella, G, & La Rocca, S 2001 Strategies for conservation of fungi in the Madonic Park, North Sicily. In: D Moore, M Nauta, S Evans, & M Rotheroe (eds) *Fungal Conservation: Issues and Solutions.* Cambridge University Press
Vesterholt, J 2005 *The genus Hebeloma.* Fungi of Northern Europe Vol. 3. Danish Mycological Society
Wakefield, E 1957 *The Observer's Book of Common Fungi.* Warne, London
Watling, R 1974 Macrofungi in the oak woods of Britain. In: M G Morris, & F H Perring (eds) *The British Oak*, 222-234. BSBI & Eric Classey, Faringdon
Watling, R 1990 On the way towards a Red Data Book on British fungi. *Trans. Botanical Society, Edinburgh* 45: 463-471
Watling, R 1992 *The Fungus Flora of Shetland.* Royal Botanic Garden, Edinburgh
Watling, R 2001 Larger fungi. In: D Hawksworth (ed) *The Changing Wildlife of Great Britain and Ireland* 103-113. Taylor & Francis, London
Watling, R, Eggeling, T, & Turnbull, E 1999 *The Fungus Flora of Orkney.* Royal Botanic Garden, Edinburgh
Watling, R, & Hills, A E (revised ed. 2005) *British Fungus Flora, 1, Boletes and their allies.* Royal Botanic Garden, Edinburgh
Winkler, D 2010 *Cordyceps sinensis* – A precious parasitic fungus infecting Tibet. *Field Mycology* 11(2): 60-67
Wright, J 2007 *Mushrooms. The River Cottage Handbook 1.* Bloomsbury, London

Field guides

Bon, M 1987 *The Mushrooms and Toadstools of Britain and North-west Europe*. Hodder & Stoughton, London

Buczacki, S 1989 *Fungi of Britain and Europe*. Collins New Generation Guide. Collins, London

Buczacki, S, & Shields, C 2012 *Collins Fungi Guide*. HarperCollins, London

Courtecuisse, R, & Duhem, B 1994 *Mushrooms & Toadstools of Britain & Europe*. Collins Field Guide. Collins, London

Lange, M, & Hora, F B 1965 (2nd ed) *Collins Guide to Mushrooms & Toadstools*. Collins, London

Phillips, R 1981 *Mushrooms and other fungi of Great Britain & Europe*. Pan Books, London. (2nd ed 2006 published by Macmillan)

Sterry, P, & Hughes, B 2009 *Collins Complete Guide to British Mushrooms & Toadstools*. HarperCollins, London

Websites

Association of British Fungus Groups: www.abfg.org

British Mycological Society: www.britmycolsoc.org.uk

CABI Bioscience: www.cabi.org

Cybertruffle: www.cybertruffle.org.uk. David Minter's international site with its own cyber-library and links galore

Fungi Online: www.mykoweb.com

Fungi Perfecti: www.fungi.com

www.boletales.com. Comprehensive and beautiful website by Boris Assyov of Bulgaria, Europe's top bolete expert

Learning more

There are two nationwide organisations devoted to the study of fungi. The first is the **British Mycological Society (BMS)**, founded in 1896 and now the largest mycological society in the world. Its activities range from cutting-edge experimental science to field study and conservation. For more information, see www.britmycolsoc.org.uk.

The **Association of British Fungus Groups (ABFG)** was founded in 1996 'to support amateur enthusiasts at all stages of the "learning curve" in their foraying and other activities concerned with fungi'. For more information, see www.abfg.org.

The many local and county fungus groups are affiliated with one or other of these bodies.

Photographic credits

Rae Allen/Wikimedia Commons 128; Irene Andersson/Wikimedia Commons 177; Archenzo/Wikimedia Commons 1, 86, 191; AYArktos/Wikimedia Commons 208; Jill Butler 14; George Chernilevsky/Wikimedia Commons 106-107, 164; Dino Chiapetta/Wikimedia Commons 241; Sandy Coppins 154-155; Adrian Davis 12; Bob Gibbons 2-3, 8, 20, 24, 37, 39, 44, 50, 54-55, 58, 64, 66, 69,73, 75, 77, 80(t,b), 81(t), 82, 92, 100, 102-103, 103(inset), 108, 114-115, 120, 130-131, 137, 140, 142, 145(t), 146-147, 148, 159, 160, 165, 180-181, 182, 196, 201, 203(b), 234; Bryan Edwards 29(b); Dave Genney/SNH 109, 119, 126(b), 186, 207, 249, 250(b); Fornax/Wikimedia Commons 84; Jean-Paul Grandmont/Wikimedia Commons 34; Hans Hillewaert/Wikimedia Commons 32(t); Liz Holden 246(l); Barry Hughes/Nature Photographers 31, 33, 40, 51(r), 53, 56, 60, 70, 74, 79(b), 87, 93, 97, 104, 124, 126(t), 144(m), 145(m,br) 153, 157(t,b), 158, 163, 165(inset), 178, 200(b), 203(t), 209(t,b), 213, 243, 250(t); Ilmari Karonen/Wikimedia Commons 212; H Krisp/Wikimedia Commons 62(b); Marco/Wikimedia Commons 162; Peter Marren 13, 46, 51(l), 68(t), 72, 85, 105, 144-145(b), 169(t), 170, 255; Ben Mitchell/Wildeep/Wikimedia Commons 25(b), 26; Dan Molter/Wikimedia Commons 169(b); Ron Pastorino/Wikimedia Commons 71; George Peterken 185; Alan Rockefeller/Wikimedia Commons 217; Royal Botanical Gardens, Kew 171; L Shyamal/Wikimedia Commons 227; Fred Stevens 240; Paul Sterry/Nature Photographers 17, 25(t), 29(t), 30, 32(b), 35(t,b), 38, 42, 43(t,b), 48, 52(t,b), 61, 68(b), 76, 78(t,m,b), 79(t), 81(b), 91, 94, 99, 112-113, 123, 125, 133, 134, 135, 138, 139, 144(t), 155(t), 175(inset), 199, 200(t), 202, 205, 210, 211, 244, 245, 258; Timnit/Wikimedia Commons 116; Tomomarusan/Wikimedia Commons 229; Tripsis/Wikimedia Commons 226; Roy Watling 27; Wikimedia Commons 175(main), 184; Rosemary Winnall/Wikimedia Commons 62(t); John Wright 220; Mark Wright/Northern Ireland Environment Agency 246(r).

Index

Page numbers in *italics* refer to photographs.

Agaric, Fly *8*, 30, *48*, 49, 51, 52, 69, 107, 132, *165*, 206, 216
Agaricus 74, 109
arvensis 51, 53, 123
bernardii 168
bisporus 136, *197*
blazei 136
campestris 51, 74, *74*, 85, 132, 197, *198*
devoniensis 115
endoxanthus 128
moelleri 214
oreades 130
placomyces 214
rufotegulis 136
silvicola 51
subrufescens 136
xanthodermus 51, *84*, 85, 214
Agrocybe 73
praecox 121
rivulosa 134
Ainsworth List 152-154
Ainsworth, Martyn 153, 154, 237, 247, 262
Alder, fungi of 108
aldercaps 72
Aleuria aurantia 51, *62*, *80*
algae 39-40
Amanita 68
caesarea 49
ceciliae 138
citrina 51, 165
crocea 191
friabilis 246, 251
fulva 51
inopinata *138*, 139, *139*
muscaria 30, *48*, 51, 107, 132, *165*, 206
nivalis 117
ovoidea 191, *191*, 259
pantherina 51, 110, *203*, 204
phalloides 51, *205*, 206
rubescens 51, 204
simulans 174
vaginata 51
verna 208
virosa 207, *207*
Amanita 68
Bearded 191, *191*, 259
Fragile 246, 251
Amorphotheca resinae 26
Amylocystis lapponica 246
Angel, Heather 12
Angelico 216
Anthracobia 125
Antrodia albobrunnea 246
Armillaria 69
ectypa 173, 246, 250, 256
gallica 122
mellea 51, 69, *102-103*, 126, *126*, 202, 215
Arnolds, Eef 146, 148, 149, 150, 231, 238
Arrhenia 74
Arthroderma curreyi 26
Ascobolus stercorarius 111
Ascocoryne 79
Ascomycota 64, 65, 79-81
Association of British Fungus Groups (ABFG) 57, 185, 236, 237, 248
Asterophora 71
lycoperdoides 37
parasitica 36, *37*
Aurantiporus alborubescens 152, 153
fissilis 152
Auricularia auricula-judae 51, 52, *53*

Baeospora myosura 26
Bankera 157
fuligineoalba 158, 251
Basidiomycota 64, 65, 66-79
Battarrea 76
phalloides 238, *240*, 250, 253
Bayfield, Neil 13
Bedgebury Pinetum, Kent 191
Beech, fungi of 106, 152-154
Bell, Funeral 204
Berkeley, Rev Miles Joseph 46, *47*, 180
Berne Convention 246, 247
besoms 81
Biodiversity Action Plan (BAP) 238, 252-257
birch, fungi of 107
Bird's Nest, Common 51
Fluted 135
Yellow 29, *29*
Bisporella 80
citrina 80, *80*
Blewit 70
Field 51, 53, 70, 132
Blue-leg 51, 53
Blusher (The) 51, 69, 204
Boertmann, David 146-147, 148, 149
Bog Beacon 51, 80
Bolbitius 73
titubans 73
Bolete, Alder 108
Aspen *97*, 98
Bedgebury 191
Bovine 30, *65*, 165
Brawny 251
Brown Birch 98
Constant 251
Cow 213
Deceiving 83
Devil's 16, *17*, 110, 254-256, *255*
Dusky 194
Ghost 96
Golden Gilled 246, 251
Iodine 192
Larch 168
Lurid 110, 214
Oldrose *85*, 192, *250*, 251
Orange Oak 97, 98
Parasitic 30, *30*
Peppery 30
Red Cracking 163
Royal 16, 238, 241-242, *241*, 250
Ruby 192
Saffron 96
Slate 96, 138
Sulphur 132
Wood 30
Yellow-cracking 96
boletes 66
identification 91
naming 96
Boletopsis grisea 246
leucomelaena 173, 178
perplexa 173, 178, 250
Boletus chrysenteron 163
depilatus 174
dupainii 246
edulis 51, 67, *91*
immutatus 251
impolitus 192
legaliae 192
luridus 214
pseudoregius 16, 242, 251
queletii 83
regius 16, 238, 241-242, *241*, 250
rhodopurpureus *85*, 192, *250*, 251
ripariellus 162, 163
satanas 16, *17*, 54, 110, 253, 254-256, *255*
satanoides 192
scaber 96
splendidus 192
subappendiculatus 174
testaceoscaber 96
torosus 251
Bolton, James 54, 193-194
Bon, Marcel 88
Bonnet, Beautiful 251
Burgundydrop *71*
bonnets 71
Bootleg, Golden 213
Botanical Society of the British Isles 235
Botrydina 118
Bovista 76
paludosa 173, 246, 251
Bracket, Artist's 107
Aspen 173
Beeswax 152
Brownflesh 152
Clustered 152
Greasy 152
Lacquered 202
Pink 152
Purplepore 36
Red-belted *20*
Robust 161
Southern 107
Brain, Mulberry 251
Yellow 36, 78, *78*
brains 78
Branson, Andrew 19
Brefeldia maxima 43
Bridgeoporus nobilissimus 151
British Lichen Society 41
British Mycological Society (BMS) 57, 165, 171, 173, 176, 184, 185, 223, 224, 235, 236, 237, 248, 249, 261
Brittlegill, Blackening 36
Crab 86
Gilded *56*
Greasy Green 215
Naked 187
Ochre 165
brittlegills 68
Brittlestem, Medusa 251
brittlestems 73
Brownie, Blueleg 136
brownies 72
Bu 227, *227*, 228
Buchwaldoboletus lignicola 30
sphaerocephalus 132
Buczacki, Stefan 88, 89
Buglossoporus pulvinus 239, 250
Bulgar 79
Bulgaria inquinans 79
Bull, Henry Graves 183

CABI Bioscience 236, 238, 261
Callistosporium luteo-olivaceum 174
Calocera 78
pallidospathulata 168
Calocybe constricta 34
gambosa 51, 53, 131, 258, *258*
onychina 251
Calvatia 76
gigantea 51, 76, 92, 109, 199
Camarops polysperma 152
candlesnuff 79
Candlesnuff, Beechmast 107
Cantharellus 75
amethysteus 191
aurora 111
cibarius 51, 75, *202*, 230, 231
friesii 251
lutescens 111
melanoxeros 246, *250*, 251
cap, identification 84
Cap, Conifercone 26
Cucumber 85
Liberty 72, 136, 216-219
Caterpillarclub, Scarlet *32*, 80, 227
caterpillarclubs 80
Cauliflower, Wood 75
cavaliers 70
Cave Artist 152
cemetery, Abney Park 139
Darlington West 139
Eastleigh 138
Kensal Green 138
North Watford 139
Cep 51, 67, 91, *91*, 221
Ceratomyxa fruticulosa *43*
Ceriporiopsis aneirina 173
gilvescens 152
herbicola 174
pannocincta 152
Chalciporus piperatus 30
Chamaemyces 68
Champignon 51
Fairy Ring 121, 122, 129, 130, 131, 213
Chanterelle 51, 75, 169, *202*, 221, 230-232
Blackening 246, *250*, 251
False *203*, 204
Golden 111
Orange 251
chanterelles 75
CHEG method, indicator species 143-144
Chicken of the Woods 51, 106, *106-107*, 200, 214
Chlorociboria

aeruginascens 24, *120*
Chlorocoeha (=*Chlorociboria*)
versiformis 251
Chlorophyllum rhacodes 51, 215
Choke 31, *31*
Christensen, Morten 152
Chroogomphus 67
roseus 30
Chrysomyxa pirolata 251
churchyards, fungi of 137-139
Highmoor Cross 138
Rotherfield Greys 138
Savernake Forest 137, 138
Clark, Malcolm 194
Clathrus 76
archeri 51, 59, 92, 135, *135*, 259
Clavaria 51
argillacea 116
zollingeri 137, *137*, 144
Clavicorona pyxidata 163, *163*
Clavulina 75
Clavulinopsis 75
corniculata 138
fusiformis *75*
umbrinella 138
climate change, and fungi 257-260
Clitocybe 70
clavipes 214
dealbata 55
geotropa 131
nebularis 37, *70*
phaeophthalma 86
rivulosa 132
Clitopilus prunulus 51, 211
Clover, Charles 224
Club Foot 214
Club, Moor 116
clubs 75
cobwebs 78
Cockleshell, Bear 152
Fox 152, *153*
cockleshells 74
Code of Conduct, for picking 223-224
Collybia 25, 71
cookei 37
dryophila 165
multijuga 128
peronata 54
tuberosa 37
conecaps 72
Conocybe 72, 109, 113
watlingii 12
conservation, and picking 222, 223, 227-231, 232-233
of fungi 235-263
Cooke, M C 163, 183, 184, *184*
Cooke, Rod 217
Coprinopsis 73
atramentaria 51, 214
cinerea 125
nivea 111
ochraceolanta 162
picacea *73*, 74, 190
plicatilis *94*
tectispora 174
Coprinus 73
comatus 51, *51*, 54, 74, 122
micaceus *61*
Coral Spot 51
Coral, Ashen 251
Candelabra 163, *163*
Ivory 138
Meadow 138
Upright 135
Violet, 137, *137*
Beige 138
corals 75
Cordyceps 80, 202
militaris *32*, 80, 227
sinensis 227, *227*, 228
Coriolopsis gallica 152
Cortinarius 72
arcuatorum 174
calochrous 110
camphoratus 86, *87*
caperatus 199
cinnabarinus 63
cinnamomeus 28
cisticola 110
diosmus 174
flexipes *72*
ionochlorus 246
mucosus 186
obtusus 86
odorifer 111
orellanus 210
phaeopygmaeus 173
poppyzon 63, 174
praestans 210
purpurascens 62
rubellus 209, *209*
speciosis-simus 209
violaceus 13
vulpinus 86
Cotylidia 77
pannosa 179, 251
Courtecuisse, R 89
Cramp Balls 31, 51
Craterellus 75
cornucopioides 51, 54, *58*, 75
Crep, Jelly 59
Crepidotus cinnabarinus 173
mollis 59
Crepidotus, Flabby 59
Crowncup, Violet 246, 251
crowncups 80
Crucibulum 76
laeve 51
Crust, Cobalt 93
Fruity 152
Glue 36, 156
Hairy Curtain 36, 166
Mothball 152
Wrinkled *78*
Yellowing Curtain 259
crusts 77
Cudonia 80
Cup, Bay 123
Cellar 128
cups 80
Cyathus 76
stercoreus 115
striatus 135, *135*
Cystoderma 68
amianthinum 38
Cystolepiota 68
Cytidia salicina 173, 177, *177*
Daedalea 77
Daldinia concentrica 31, 51, 52, *52*
Dapperling, Plantpot 128, *128*
Redspored 125
dapperlings 68
Datronia 77
Dawyck Botanic Garden, Scotland 187
Dead Man's Fingers 51, 52, 79
deadwood, fungi 152, 153, 154
Deathcap 51, 69, *205*, 206, 207, 208, *208*, 255
False 51, 55, 165
Deceiver, (The) 51, 199
Deceiver, Amethyst *182*
deceivers 70
Dennis, Richard 194
Denny Wood, New Forest 154
Denticollis fragilis 174
Dermoloma magicum 122
Destroying Angel 51, 207, *207*, 208
Devil's Fingers 51, 91-92
Dickson, Gordon 17, 18
Diderma niveum 119
Disciotis 80
Disco, Common Grey 80
Lemon 80, *80*
Nut 26
Snowy 80
discos 80
diseases, plant, and fungi 103-105
DNA 94, 95, 134, 159
Dobson, Frank 188
Domecap, Clustered
Gilded 246, 251
Lilac 251
Doody, Samuel 176
drug laws, and fungi 218-219
Dryad's Saddle 51
Duhem, Bernard 89
dunes, fungi of 115-117
Dung Cannon 112
dung, fungi of 109, 111-114, 123
Dutch elm disease 166, 167, 169
Dyeball 116, *116*

Ear, Flea's 251
Jew's 51, 52, *53*
Pig's *162*, 163, 246, 251
ears 81
Earth Summit 252
Earthball, Common 30
earthballs 76
earthfans 77, *77*
Earthstar, Arched *76*
Beaked 138
Berkeley's 173, 180, 251
Collared 181
Elegant 251
Field 180
Pepperpot 174-176, *175*
Rosy *181*
Striated 138
Tiny 251
earthstars 76, 180-181
Earthtongue, Dark-purple 246, 251
Olive 250
earthtongues 80, 142-144
Eden Project 133, 134
Efibulobasidium rolleyi 122
Eggerling, Tom 195
Elaphomyces 79
Elf Cap, Scarlet *80*
Elfcup, Green *24*, *120*
elfcups 80
Elm, fungi of 169-170
Emmet, Ernest 18
Encoelia fimbriata 156
English Nature 223
Entoloma 71, 137, 150
bloxamii 246, 251
clypeatum 123
sinuatum 210, *210*
Entoloma, Leaden 210
Livid 210
Entomophthora dipterigena 32
muscae 32, *32*
Epichloë typhina 31, *31*
Epipogium aphyllum 29, *29*
Esher Common, Surrey 188
Essex Field Club 184
Eutypa spinosa 152
Evans, Nicholas 210
Evans, Shelly 18, 122, 176, 249
Exidia 78
glandulosa 51, 52, 78
Exobasidium 36, 79
vaccinii *79*
fairy bonnets 116
fairy clubs 51
fairy ring 23, 51, 129-132
Falsebolete, Black 173, 178, 179, 246
Fibrecap, Deadly 209, *209*
fibrecaps 72
field guides 88-91
Field Mycology and Conservation Committee 236
Fieldcap, Spring 121
Yellow 73
fieldcaps 73
Filobasidiella lutea 170
fingers 79
Fingers, Devil's 59, 135, *135*, 259
Fistulina hepatica 51, 106, 242
Flammulaster carpophilus 26
limulatus 152
muricatus 152
Flammulina velutipes 202
Flemming, Vincent 238, 253
Fomes fomentarius 46, *46*, 107
foray, fungus 183-195
Forestry Commission 222, 223, 232-233
Formitopsis pinicola *20*
Fortey, Richard 137, 174
Fulgio septica 43, 202
fungi, and climate change 257-260
and insects 31
and the law 218-219
bird's-nest 76

bracket 77
classification 64-81
collecting 262
common species 165-166
crust 36, 77
deadwood 152, 153, 154
declines 169-172
distribution change 259
edible 197-204
European legal protection 247-252
future conservation 260-263
gasteroid 91
groups 183-185
habitats 262
hallucinogenic 216-219
hedgehog 16-17, 75, 157-159, 250
inkcaps 73
jelly 36, 78
jelly rots 78
jellybabies 80
jellydiscs 79
mycorrhizal 110, 157
new species 172-174
of heaths 115-117
of old grassland 141-144
of sand dunes 115-117
parasitic 34-38, 169
picking 185-186, 221-233
piggyback 36-37
poisonous 204-215
rare species 161-164
saddle 81
stomach 76, 91
threatened species 246
tooth *13*, *140*
UK legal protection 238-247
Fungus Conservation Forum 57, 236, 260
Fungus, Beefsteak 106, 242
Bootlace 51
Brain 75
Bulbous Honey 122
Candied Red Jelly 168
Candlesnuff 51, *44*, 54, 79, *79*, 124, 166
Cannonball 112
Cauliflower 51
Dog-turd 116
Honey 51, 55, 69, *102-103*, 126, *126*, 202, 215
Hoof 46, *46*, 107
Marsh Honey 173, 246, 250, 256-257
Mule-dung 116
Nail *112-113*, 113, 194, 250, 253
Orange Peel *62*, 51, 80
Porcelain 200, *201*
Stinky Squid 59
Turban 212
Winter 202
Funnel, Clouded 37, *70*
Ivory 132
Tawny 118
Trooping 131
funnels 70

Galerina 116
marginata 204
galls, fungal 36
Gange, Ted 259
Ganoderma applanatum 107
australe 107
lucidum 202
pfeifferi 152, 153
gasteroid 76
Gasteromycetes 91
Gastrosporium simplex 124
Geastrum 76
berkeleyi 173, 180, 251
campestre 180
corollinum 251
elegans 251
fornicatum *76*
minimum 251
pectinatum 138
rufescens *181*
striatum 138
triplex 181
Geoglossum 80, *142*
atropurpureum 246, 251
Gibbons, Bob 247
Gilbert, Oliver 41
gills, and identification 84
Gleophyllum 77
Gloeohypochnicium analogum 152
Glomales 29
Gloves, Hazel 36, 154-156, *155*, 250
Willow 156, 251
Gomphidius 67
Gomphus clavatus *162*, 163, 246, 251
Gould, Stephen J 47
Grampian Fungus Group 173
grassland, fungi of 108-111, 141-150
Green, Ted 14-15, *14*, 19, 88, 224, 241
Griffith, Gareth 149
Grifola frondosa 106, 200
Grisette 51
Mountain 117
Orange 191
Snakeskin 138
Tawny 51
Guepinia helvelloides 168, *168*
Gymnopilus 72
dilepis 136
junonius 219
Gymnosporangium 36, 107
Gypsy (The) 199
Gyrodon lividus 108
Gyromitra 212
Gyromitra 81
esculenta 212, *212*, 258

habitats, and identification 87
bonfires 125
buildings 127-128
churchyards 137-139
compost heaps 124
dead wood 166
flowerbeds 123
garden 121-127
grassland 131-132
heaths 115-117
indicator species, woods 150-156
lawns 121-123
micro 101
mountains 117-119
natural 101-119
old grassland 141-150
sandy 180-181
woodchip mulch 124, 132-137
woodland 102-108
Handkea utriformis *114*
Handley, Jim 259
Hapalopilus croceus 246
odorus 246
Harper, Martin 18
Hawksworth, David 188
Hay, W Delisle 54
Haymaker 121
Hazel woods, fungi 155
Hebeloma 72
aminophilum 33
crustliniforme 95
radicosum 33
sordescens 110
vinosophyllum 33
Hedgehog, Devil's 158
Wood 51, 75
hedgehogs 16-17, 75, 156-159, 250
Heilmann-Clausen, Jacob 152
Helvella 81
lacunosa 135
Hemimycena 71
Hen of the Woods 106, 200
Henrici, Alick 18, 162, 249, 257
Hericium 75
cirrhatum 152
coralloides 54, *55*, 152, 245, *245*, 251
erinaceus 151, 152, *234*, 239, *244*, 244-245, 246, 247, 250
Heterobasidion annosum 104
Hills, Alan 18, 174
Hohenbuehelia 34, 74
auriscalpium 152
culmicola 115, 246, 251
leightonii 164
mastrucata 152
Holden, Liz 57, 58, 179, 184, *186*
Holden, Margaret 124
Hora, F Bayard 88, 212
Horn of Plenty 51, 54, *58*, 75
Hydnellum 75, 157, 250
aurantiacum 158
caeruleum 158, *159*
concrescens *157*, 158
diabolus 158
gracilipes 159
peckii 158, *158*
scrobiculatum 159
spongiosipes 158
Hydnum 75
repandum 51, 75
Hygrocybe 69
aurantiosplendens 138
calyptriformis 137, 148, *148*, 246, 250
chlorophana 147
coccinea *69*, *92*, *144*
conica =nigrescens *145*
conica 147
conicoides 115
flavipes 138
glutinipes 149
helobia 150
insipida *145*
irrigata 138
miniata 63
nigrescens 62
pratensis 149
psittacina *62*, 149, 219
punicea 138
quieta 147
reidii 147
russocariacea 86, *145*, 147
salicis-herbaceae 118
spadicea *144*, 150, 250
splendidissima *145*
virginea *146-147*, 149
Hygrophoropsis aurantiaca *203*, 204
Hygrophorus 69, 149
camarophyllus 118
hypothejus 190
pudorinus 251
purpurascens 246
speciosus 189
Hymenochaete 77
corrugata 36, 156
tabacina 156
Hymenogaster 78
Hymenoscyphus 80
Hypholoma 72
fasciculare 51, 72, *160*, *165*, 166
Hypocreopsis lichenoides 156, 251
rhododendri 36, 154-156, *155*, 250
Hypomyces 200
Hypopitys monotropa 29, *29*
Hypoxylon 80, 124

indicator species, CHEG method 143-144
woodland fungi 150-156
Ing, Bruce 42-43, 239, *249*
Ingold, Terence 11
Inkcap, Common 51, 214
Glistening *61*
Magpie *73*, 74, 190
Pleated *94*
Shaggy 51, *51*, 54, 74, 121, 122
Snowy 111
inkcaps 73
Inocybe 72, 193
corydalina 86
erubescens 208, *209*
patouillardii 208
Inonotus 77
cuticularis 152
*nodulosus*152
radiatus 108
International Mycological Institute 189
International Union for the Conservation of Nature (IUCN) 247
Inverey, Braemar, Scotland 186-187

jelly rots 78
jellybabies 80
jellydiscs 79
Jordan, Michael 56, 89, 198, 216, 237

Kew Gardens 180, 184, 189
Kibby, Geoffrey 90, 162
King Alfred's Cakes 31, 51, 52, *52*
Kings Wood, Bedford 192-193
Knight, Giant 107, 246, 251
  Poplar 138
  Robust 251
  Soapy *86*
  Sulphur 110
  Yellow 213, *213*, 228
knights 58, 69
Koestler, Arthur 217
Kuehneromyces mutabilis 204

Laccaria 70
  amethystina 182
  laccata 51, 199
Lachnellula pini 260
Lachnum virgineum 80
Lacrymaria glareosa 215
  lacrymabunda 51, 122, 215
Lactarius 51, 67
  acris 194
  camphoratus 85
  chrysorrheus 63, *68*
  deliciosus 87
  deterrimus 87
  glyciosmus 85
  nanus 118
  picinus 174
  quietus 164, 165, 199
  repraesentaneus 13
  rufus 87, 165
  salicis-herbaceae 118
  salicis-reticulae 118
  salmonicolor 87
  torminosus 214, *200*, 202
Laessoe, Thomas 231
Laetiporus sulphureus 51, 106, *106-107*, 200, 214
Lamproderma cribrarioides 119
Lange, Morten 88, *88*
Large, E C 56, 57
Laricifomes officinalis 48, 246
Lawson, Peter 240
Lawyer's Wig 51, *51*, 54, 74
leaf-spots 103
Leccinum 67
  albostipitatum 98
  aurantiacum 97, 98
  carpini 192
  changes in taxonomy 96-98
  crocipodium 96
  cyaneobasileucum 98
  duriusculum 96, 138
  holopus 96
  molle 97
  oxydabile 97
  quercinum 97, 98
  scabrum 98
Legg, Alan 139, 177
Lentinellus 74
  laurocerasi 162
  ursinus 152
  vulpinus 152, *153*
Lentinus 74
Lenzites betulinus 36
Leotia 80
Lepiota 68
  ignivolvata 190
  naucina 59
Lepista 70
  flaccida 118
  glaucocana 86
  irina 86
  luscina 131
  nuda 51
  panaeola 131
  saeva 51, 53, 132
Leratiomyces ceres 133, 134
  squamosus var. *thraustus* 134
Leucoagaricus 68
Leucocoprinus birnbaumii 128, *128*
Leucopaxillus 70
  compactus 246
  tricolor 174
Lichenomphalia alpina 118
  umbellifera 40, 41
lichens 38-41, 81
Llanerchaeron Mansion 144
Llanishen Reservoir 144
Lodge (The), Sandy, RSPB 189
Loreleia postii 128
Lucas, Alan 247
Lycoperdon 50, 51, 76
  perlatum 50
  pratense 132
Lyophyllum decastes 137
  favrei 246, 251

Macrocystidia cucumis 86
Macrolepiota 68
  procera 51, *82*, 199, *199*
Man on Horseback 213, 228
Marasmiellus ramealis 25
Marasmius 25, 71
  oreades 51, 121, 129, 130
  pseudocaricis 162
  rotula 25
Massee, G E 184
Mattock, Graham 19, 191
Mazegill, Birch 36
  Dyer's 30
  Spongy 152
  Toothed 152
mazegills 77
McCarthy, Michael 58
Melanogaster intermedius 173
Melanoleuca 70
Melanophyllum 68
  haematospermum 125
Melanotus 74
Meripilus giganteus 104, *104*
Merryweather, James 19
Mickleham Common, Surrey 188-189
Microbotryum violaceum 35
  olivaceum 144, 250
Micromphale 25, 71
  brassicolens 86
  foetidum 59
Microsphaera alphitiodes 103, 260
Mildew, Oak 103
Milkcap, Coconut 85
  Curry 85
  False Saffron 87
  Oakbug *164*, 165, 199
  Rufous 87, 165
  Saffron 87
  Woolly *200*, 202, 214
  Yellow *68*
  Yellowdrop *68*
milkcaps 51, 67
Miller (The) 51, 211
Minter, David 90
Mitchel, David 184
Mitrophora 81
Mitrula 80
  paludosa 51, 80
Molisia cinerea 80
Moore, David 236
Morchella 81
  elata 81, 135
  esculenta 51, 81, 135
Morel 51, 135
  Black *81*, 135
  Common 81
  False 212, *212*, 258
  Landscape 135
  Urban 135
morels, false 81
  true 81
Mosscap, Orange *125*
Mottlegill, Brown 121
mottlegills 73
mountains, fungi of 117-119
Mucilago crustacea 42
Mucor 112
Mushroom, Bernard's 168
  Brain 212
  Caesar's 49
  Cultivated 136, 197
  Field 51, 53, 74, *74*, 85, 132, 169, 197, *198*, 214
  Fly 52
  Fool's 208
  Horse 53, 123
  Inky 214
  Magic 72, 216-219, *217*
  Oyster *34*, 54, 124, *196*, 197
  Paddystraw 198, 208
  Parasol 51
  Pot Plant 128
  St George's 51, 53, 131, 258, *258*
  White Sanctity 226
  Wood 51
  Yellow Houseplant 128
mushrooms, true 74
Mutinus 76
Mycena 25, 71, 116
  belliae 26
  haematopus 71
  leptocephala 86
  pterigena 26
  renati 251
  seynesii 26
Mycetozoa 42
Mycoacia nothofagi 152, 153
Mycocalia 76
mycorrhizal fungi 27-30, 104, 106, 110, 117, 157, 232
mycotas 193-195
Myriostoma coliforme 174, *175*, 246, 251
myxomycetes 41-42

naming, of species and identification 94-99
Naucoria 72, 108
Navel, Heath 39, *40*
navels 39, 71
Nectria 80
  cinnabarina 51, 80, 104
  coccinea 104
Neobulgaria 79
Neolentinus lepideus 26, 59
Neottia nidus-avis 29
New Forest 113, 154, 192, 222, 232-233, 241
Newborough Forest, Anglesey 191
Nidularia 76
Nyssopsora echinata (=*Puccinia athamanticae*) 251

oaks, fungi of 106
Old Man of the Woods 51, 139
Omphalina 71, 125
  ericetorum 41
  pyxidata 168
Onygena corvina 26
  equina 26, *26*
Ophiostoma novo-ulmi 166
Orchid, Bird's-nest 29
  Ghost 29, *29*
Orton, Dennis 172
Orton, Peter 179
Ossicaulis lignatilis 152, 153
Otidea 81
Oudemansiella mucida 200, *201*
Outen, Alan 18, 184, 193
Ovenden, Denys 89
Overall, Andy 184
Oxyporus latemarginatus 152
Oyster, Branching 170, *170*
  Marram 246, 251
  Mealy 152
  Orange 152
  Spatula 152
  Woolly 152
oysterlings 74
oysters 74

Palmer, Irene 139
Panaeolina 73
  foenisecii 121
Panaeolus 73, 109, 113
Panellus 74
Panthercap 51, 69, 110, *203*, 204
Parachute, Cabbage 86
  Collared *25*
  Twig *25*
parachutes 71
parasitic fungi 34-37
Parasol *82*, 199, *199*
  Shaggy 51, 215
Parasola plicatilis 121
parasols 68
Paurocotylis pila 168

Paxillus 67, 108, 174
  involutus *27*, 28, 88, 211, *211*
Peach, Wrinkled *169*, 170
Peltigera 40
Peniophora 36, 77, 164
Penny Bun 51, 67, *91*
Pepperpot 246
Perenniporia ochroleuca 259
Peziza 80
  badia 123
  cerea 128
Phaeolepiota aurea 213
Phaeolus 77
  schweinitzii 30
Phallus 76
  hadriani 115
  impudicus 50, 51 *52*, 63, 76, 166
Phellinus 77
  cavicola 152, 153
  robustus 161
  tremulae 173
  wahlbergii 259
Phellodon *13*, 75, 157, 250
  confluens 158
  melaleucus 158
  niger 158
Phillips, Roger 15, 57, 88
Phlebia 78
  radiata *78*
  tremellosa 78
Phlebiella 78
Phleogena faginea 152, 153
Pholiota 73
  astragalina 251
  aurivella *64*
  highlandensis 125
  squarrosoides 174
Phycomyces 112
Phylloporus pelletieri 246, 251
Phyllotopsis nidulans 152
Phytophthora 103-104, 260
  quercina 104
  ramorum 104
Piggyback, Powdery 36-37, *37*
  Silky 36
piggybacks 69, 71
Pilobolus crystallinus 112
pinewoods, fungi of 107
Pinkgill, Big Blue 246, 251
  Livid 210, *210*, 211
  Shield 123
pinkgills 71
Pinwheel, Stinking 59
Piptoporus betulinus 107, *108*, 242
  quercinus 151, 239, 242-244, *243*, 250

Pisolithus arhizus 116, *116*
Plantlife 236, 255, 260
Pleurotus 74
  cornucopiae 170, *170*
  nebrodensis 226, *226*
  ostreatus *34*, 51, 54, 124, *196*, 197
Pliny 49
Plot, Robert 129
Plums and Custard 51, *51*, 136
Pluteus 71, 99, 153, 170
  cervinus 99, 219
  petasatus 86
  taxonomy 99
  violarius 163
Pocket Plum 81
Podoscypha multizonata *178*, 179, 246, 251
Poisoner, Lead 210
Poisonpie 95
  Rooting 32, 33, *33*
poisonpies 72
Polypore, Birch 107, *108*, 242
  Giant 104, *104*
  Noble 151
  Oak 151, 239, 242-244, *243*, 250
polypores 77
Polyporus 77
  squamosus 51, 200, *200*
Pope, Colin 191
Porecrust, Frothy 152
  Green 152
  Pink 152
  Silvery 152
porecrusts 93, *93*
Poronia erici 114
  punctata *112-113*, 113, 194, 250, 253
Porphyrellus porphyrosporus 194
Povey, Chris 176
Powdercap, Earthy 38
  Golden 152
  Toothed 152
powdercaps 68
Pretender (The) 16, 242, 251
Prunus armeniaca 63
Psathyrella 73, 113, 125
  ammophila 62
  caput-medusae 251
  hirta 111
Pseudoboletus parasiticus 30
Pseudomerulius aureus 93, *93*
Psilocybe 72, 113
  ceres 134
  cyanescens 136
  mexicana 216
  semilanceata 72, 136, 216, *217*, 219
Pterula 75
Puccinia antirrhini 167
  clintonii 251
  distincta 167
  graminis 259
  lagenophorae 167
  malvacearum 167
  pelargonii-zonalis 167
  physospermi 251
  poarum *78*
  polemonii 176
  scorzonerae 251
  septentrionalis 251
  thesii 251
  urticata 35, *35*
Puffball, Common *50*
  Fen 173, 246, 251
  Giant 51, 60, 76, 92, 109, 199
  Meadow 132
  Mosaic *114*
  White Stalk 118
puffballs 51, 76
Purge, Miller's 210
Pycnoporellus alboluteus 246
Pyromena 125

Queletia mirabilis 240

Ramaria 75
  stricta 135
Ramariopsis 75
  kunzei 138
Ramsbottom, John 254
rarity 161-164
Rea, Carleton 163, 184
Red Data List 247-249, 261, 263
Redhead 128
Redleaf, Cowberry *79*
redleafs 79
Reid, Derek 15, 139, 178
Revett, Jonathan 135
rhizomorphs 69
Rhizopogon 78
Rhodotus palmatus *169*, 170
Rhytisma acerinum 36, 103, *103*
Rickenella 125
  fibula *125*
Rigidiporus ulmarius 170, *171*
Roberts, Peter 19
Rollrim, Brown *27*, 28, 88, 211, *211*
rollrims 67
Root Rot 104
Rosegill, Piggyback 37
  Silky 152, 170
  Stubble 123, *123*, 168
rosegills, 69
Rosette, Roothole 173, 179
Roothole 179
  Woolly 179, 251
  Zoned *178*, 179, 246, 250
rosettes 77
Rot, Dry 51, 127, 128
Rotheroe, Maurice 115, 142-143, 161, 223, 231
Roundhead, Conifer 251
  Redlead 133-134, *133*
roundheads 73
Roydon Woods, Hampshire 187
Russula 68
  adusta 86
  amoena 86
  aurea *56*
  cavipes 86
  densifolia 86
  emetica *60*, 87, 214
  fageticola 87
  fellea 86
  font-queri 173
  fusconigra 173
  heterphylla 215
  illota 13
  mairei 87
  nigricans 36
  nobilis *68*, 87, *100*
  ochroleuca 165
  pseudointegra 86
  torulosa 191
  vesca 58
  vinosobrunnea 173, 187
Rust, Alpine 251
  Bastard-toadflax 251
  Bladder-seed 251
  Cereal 259
  Cineraria 167
  Coltsfoot *78*
  Daisy 167
  Hollyhock 167
  Lousewort 251
  Nettle 35, *35*
  Pelargonium 167
  Scorzonera 251
  Snapdragon 167
  Spignel 251
  Wintergreen 251
Rustgill, Spectacular 219
rustgills 72
rusts 35-36, 78, 107
Rusty Ladders 177

Saddle, Dryad's 200, *200*
  Elfin 135
Salmon Salad 168, *168*
Sarcodon 157
  fuligineoviolaceus 246
  imbricatum 157
  regalis 164
  scabrosus 157, 158
  squamosus *157*, 158
Sarcodontia crocea 251
Sarcoscypha 80
  austriaca *80*
  globosum 246
Sarcosphaera coronaria 246, 251
Savernake Forest, Wiltshire 187, 190
Saving the Forgotten Kingdom 236, 260-263
Sawgill, Scaly 26
Scalycap, Bonfire 125
  Conifer 251
  Golden *64*
scalycaps 73
Scarlet Splash 173, 177, *177*
Schafer, Derek 184
Schaffer, Julius 212
Schizophyllum commune 168
Scleroderma 76
  citrinum 30
Scolt Head Island 114
Scottish Wild Mushroom Forum 224
Scytinostroma portentosum 152
Serpula lacrymans 51, 127
Shank, Velvet 202
Shanklet, Lentil 37
  Splitpea 37
shanks 71
Shield, Deer *99*, 219
shields 71, 99
Shooting Star 112
Shorten, Dave 15, 185
Sickener (The) *60*, 87, 214
  Beechwood *68*, 87, *100*
Simocybe 73
Simpson, Gordon 177
Skeletocutis 77
  carneogrisea 36

odora 246
Skullcap, Autumn 204
Slapton Ley, Devon 188
slime moulds 41-43, 172
Slippery Jack 51, 215
Smart, Jane *12*
smell, and identification 85
Smit, Tim 260
Smith, Worthington 183, *185*
Smut, Anther 35, *35*
Bird's-eye Primrose 251
Colchicum 251
Felwort 251
Frogbit 251
smuts 35, 36, 78
Sowerby, James *175*, *198*
Sparassis 75
crispa 51, 75
Spathularia 80
Sphaerobolus stellatus 112
Spike, Rosy 30
spikes 67
spindles 75
Golden *75*
Splitgill 168
Spongipellis delectans 152
pachyodon 152
Spooner, Brian 18, 75, 188, 213, 219
spores, and identification 84
Spot, Coral 80, 104
spots 80
Squamanita 37-38, 68
paradoxa 37, 38, *38*
pearsonii 37
stagshorns 78
Stainer, Yellow 51, *84*, 85, 214
Staley, James 236
Stalkball, Feather 26
Fenugreek 152
Horn 26, *26*
Scaly 251
White 118, *119*, *246*, 250, 253
Winter 125
stalkballs (stiltballs) 76
Stemonitis fusca 43
Stephanospora caroticolor 251
Stephensia 124
Stephensia bombycina 124
Stereopsis 77
vitellina 173, 179
Stereum 77
hirsutum 36, 166
subtomentosum 261
Sterry, Paul 89, 138, 180
Stiltball, Sandy 238, 240-241, *240*, 250, 253
stiltballs (stalkballs) 76
Stinkhorn 50, 51, *52*, 76, 166, 200
stipe, and identification 85
stipitate hydnoid fungi 156, 250
Storey, Malcolm 15, 18, 177
Strangler, Powdercap 37, *38*
stranglers 68
Strobilomyces strobilaceus 51, 139
Stropharia 73
aurantiaca 133, 134
hornemannii 251
Sudden Oak Death 104
Suillus 67
bovinus 30, *65*, 165
grevillei 168
luteus 51, 215
placidus 191
sibricus ssp. *helveticus* 246

Taphrina 36, 81
alni 81, *81*, 108
amentorum 108
johansonii 81
pruni 81
Tapinella 67
Tarcrust, Spiral 152
Thick 152
Tarspot, Sycamore 36, 103, *103*
tarspot 36
taxonomy 94, 95, 146, 159
Tee-Hillman, Mrs 233
Teloschistes chrysophthalmus 39
Tephrocybe osmophora 251
Terana caerulea 93
Thelephora 77
penicillata 77
Toadstool, Corpse 33
Powdercap 37
Tomey, Keith 114
Tongue, Alder 81, *81*
Aspen 81
tongues 81
Tooth, Bearded 151, 152, *234*, 239, *244*, 244-245, 246, 247, 250
Bitter 158
Black 158, 159
Blue *157*, 157
Coral 54, *55*, 152, 245, *245*, 251
Devil's 158, *158*
Drab 158, 251
Fused 158
Grey 158, 159
Orange 158
Scaly *157*, 158
Tiered 152
Velvet 158
Zoned 158, 159, *159*
Toothcrust, Fragrant 152
Orchard 251
tooths 75, 156
Torrendia pulchella 246
Toughshank, Russet 165
toughshanks 71
Tracya hydrocharidis 251
Train Wrecker 59
Trametes 77
versicolor 36, 51, 124, *124*, 166, 202
Tremella 78
aurantia 36
mesenterica 36, 78, *78*
moriformis 251
versicolor 164
Tremellodendropsis tuberosa 251
Trichaptum abietinum 36
Tricholoma 29, 58, 69
aurantium 86
colossus 107, 246, 251
equestre 213, *213*, 228
hemisulphureum 110
leucocephalum 33
magnivelare 228, 229
matsutake 228-230, *229*
populinum 138
robustum (=*T. focale*) 251
saponaceum 86, *86*
sulphureum 110
rutilans 51, *51*, 136
Truffle, Bohemian 116
Carroty False 251
hunting 171
Périgord 202
Piedmont 202
Red 202
Steppe 124
Summer 51, 123, 124, 171, 202
Winter 202
truffleclubs 80
truffles 79
false 78
Tubaria 73
dispersa 26
tenuis 59
Tuber 79
aestivum 51, 123, 171, 202
brumale 202
magnatum 202
melanosporum 202
rufum 202
Tuft, Sulphur 51, 72, *160*, *165*, 166
tufts 72
Tulostoma 76
brumale 125
melanocyclum 251
Tulostoma niveum 118, *119*, 246, *249*, 250, 253
Turkeytail 36, 51, 124, *124*, 166, 202
Turnbull, Evelyn 195
twiglets 73

Urediniomycetes 78
Urocystis colchici 251
primulicola 251
Uromyces gentianae 251
Ustilaginomycetes 78
Ustilago marina 169

Volvariella 69
bombycina 152, 170
caesiotincta 189
gloiocephala 58, 123, *123*, 168
surrecta 37
volvacea 198

Wallace, Tom 115
Wasson, Gordon 216
Watling, Roy 12-13, *12*, 186, 194, 210, 223
Waxcap, Ballerina 137, 148, *148*
Blackening *145*, 149
Cedarwood *145*, 147
Crimson 138
Date 144, 150, 250
Dune 115
Glutinous 149
Golden 147
Honey 147
Meadow 149
Mountain 118
Oily 147
Orange 138
Parrot *62*, 149, 219
Pink 137, 148, *148*, 149, 246, 250
Scarlet *69*, *92*, 144
Slimy 138
Snowy *146-147*, 149, 150
Spangle *145*
Splendid *145*
Vermilion 63
Yellow Foot 138
waxcaps 69, 92, 142-150
Webcap, Deadly 209, *209*, 210
Fool's 210
Goatcheese *87*
Goliath 210
Orange 186
Pelargonium *72*
webcaps 72
Webster, Professor John 11, *11*
Weeping Widow 51, 60, 122, 215
White, Gilbert 129, 130, 132
Wilkinson, John 89
Willow, Dwarf, fungi of 117
Windsor Great Park 154, 161, 224, 241
Winterslow, Wiltshire 203
Witches' Butter 51, 78
Witches' Broom 32
Withering, William 130
Woman-on-a-motorbike 59
woodchip, fungi of 132-137
woodland habitats 102-108
woods, fungi of 150-156
Woodtuft, Sheathed 204
woodwarts 80
Woodwax, Arched 118
Rosy 251
Sandy 189, 190
woodwaxes 69
Woolhope Naturalists' Field Club 180, 183, *185*
Woollyfoot, Wood 54
Wright, John 199, 200, 215, *220*

Xerocomus 67
armeniacus 63
rubellus 192
silwoodensis 174
Xylaria 79
carpophila 107
hypoxylon 44, 51, 54, 79, *79*, 124, 166
polymorpha 51, 52, 79

Yorkshire Naturalists' Union 184, 194